FIRE

By the same author

AIRCRASH DETECTIVE

STEPHEN BARLAY

FIRE

An International Report

Illustrated

HAMISH HAMILTON
LONDON

First published in Great Britain 1972
by Hamish Hamilton Ltd
90 Great Russell Street London WC1

Copyright © 1972 by Stephen Barlay

SBN 241 02101 4

TO NICHOLAS AND ROBIN

Printed in Great Britain
by Ebenezer Baylis & Son Limited
The Trinity Press, Worcester, and London

CONTENTS

The illustrations appear between pages 152 and 153.

A spectre is haunting humanity
—the spectre of fire. All the powers of the world have
entered into an unholy alliance of silence to sacrifice thirty
thousand lives and fifteen thousand million dollars each year
to the flames. Despite the annual volume of words, the horror
of the ever-mounting losses is still economically acceptable.
Or else something would be done about it. Perhaps the
orphans and the widows, the jobless and the bankrupt ought
to be asked.
Raising a single fire is a crime. Governmental nonchalance
in preventing the slaughter and the squandering, ministerial
acquiescence of public ignorance, are not yet criminal
negligence.

CHAPTER ONE

THE DEADLY TRIANGLE

IT WAS not the sight that seared itself into the mind of a
Chicago baker, not the strident cacophony of fire, the crackle
of sparks, the hiss of flames or the roar of the victorious holocaust, but the thuds, the thuds that came with sickening
regularity as the children jumped from the windows of the
school, one after another, to their deaths on the pavement.

The causes of the fire and of its rapid progress are unknown.
The case is closed. Except to the baker and the others who still
wake up at nights hearing the thuds that ended the lives of their
children on that first December afternoon in 1958.

It is presumed that the fire began at about 2.35, some twenty
minutes before the classes were to be dismissed. There were
about 1,200 boys and girls, between the ages of eight and fifteen,
at the Our Lady of Angels Catholic School in Chicago's
Italian quarter. Some parents, too early to collect their children,
began gathering outside.

The first priests, nuns and children in the building knew
about the fire was when smoke began to seep into the class-
rooms under the doors. There was no automatic fire detection
equipment. A nun ran to the phone and called the fire department. The officer who took the call remembered: 'She was
screaming and incoherent. She was too hysterical to tell me
where the fire was.'

A salesman saw the smoke from his car. He stopped and ran
from shop to shop, door to door, in a frantic search for a telephone. His call was delayed for twelve minutes. The nearest
station was a mile and a half away and it took the first engine a
minute and a half to get to the U-shaped school where a
massacre was already under way. Now at last a general alarm
was put out.

On the Iowa Street side, children lined the pavement. They had been led to safety by nuns. Still more were arriving out: in the dense smoke a nun led children crawling to the stairs, and she rolled them down to make the evacuation faster. From the top floor windows children shouted jokes and hurled books at their friends in the street. Then suddenly the flames caught up with them. They began to climb out on the window-sills.

The situation on the other side was even more desperate. Children there had already begun to jump. The first ladder ran up . . . but only to a height of twenty-four feet. The children screamed and burned another six feet higher up. More fire engines arrived and firemen ran up to save the burning group. There was no time to bring them down. The men threw the children into safety nets and the arms of parents. Some men's arms were broken as they caught the falling bodies. A nun leaned out of another window and dropped children twenty feet on to a tin roof from where they bounced off into the street.

Fire-fighters forced their way in. In one room, twenty-four children sat at their desks. They had been killed by the smoke and then burnt before they had had a chance to escape. Some dead children had hardly been burnt at all. Three nuns, now dead, had covered and tried to protect them with their own bodies.

On top of a ladder, a fireman hesitated. A child in a window, between him and a colleague, refused to jump. If only the child would move so that the other fireman could catch him . . . Encouragement did not help and there was no time for persuasion. The fireman directed a powerful jet of water at the child sweeping him into the arms of the second fireman.

Ten-year-old Ronnie Sarno called to his nine-year-old sister to jump with him. 'Do you want to come?' 'Don't jump, Ron!' He did, and died. She was saved.

A man below screamed at his wife: 'Why didn't you keep her home today?'

Gas exploded and the ceiling collapsed. Last rites were administered in the street as ambulances began to run a taxi service mainly to the mortuary. The search for the dead went on all night. Parents waited in vain all night. Fire Commissioner Quinn suspected it had been a 'touch-off'. His reasons were several cases of arson in schools and a synagogue at the time, and also the rapidity of the spread in a building which had been considered 'safe'. But this was not the first safe school to be gutted in minutes. There had been dozens in America and elsewhere with a toll of hundreds of lives. Ultimately, no indication of arson was discovered. With a few injured dying in hospitals, the number of victims grew to ninety-three.

A nine-year-old boy, dead on the pavement, had left his note to go with the Christmas present unfinished: 'I, Joseph, promise to do my best, to do my duty to God and my country, to be square, and to . . .' Did his country do its duty to him?

Two days after the fire, policemen could not decide whether they should let a man injure himself or prevent him banging his head and fists against the charred door, shouting and begging, 'Come on out, son! I'm here, waiting for you.'

Melodramatic, some people may say, for despite the tales of horror, bravery and stupidity—the story of Fire—it is all 'such an ancient curse'. Fire is older than man. We were virtually born with it. We are used to it. The familiar sight of most fires we encounter is friendly—awe-inspiring at its worst. Fire is warmth. Fire is light. Fire is dinner. Fire is under our control: we can kindle it and put it out at will. Disaster is the inevitable exception, we like to believe. And it will always happen to the other guy. More so than the road accident.

Is it then really so completely unavoidable that the loss of lives must continue to mount at an ever increasing pace and that fire must snatch away an ever greater disproportionate share from the wealth nations sweat for? Fire-prone industrial plants like oil refineries have answered 'no' and then proceeded to prove their point. Authorities have also answered 'no' and then proceeded to do very little about it.

In 1969, Lord Stonham, then Britain's Minister of State at the Home Office, told fire brigade officers that the country could not go on ignoring the 'incineration' of some seven hundred people a year (now around a thousand) and that the extent of property losses could not be tolerated. He then spoke about a quarter of a million pounds going up in smoke every day of the year. (Since then the loss is more than a third of a million a day.) 'No one knows the total real cost to the country. But if we add on the loss of production, the time men and

women are out of work, the cost of hospital treatment, the loss of
export orders and of goodwill, the total loss assumes the proportions of an annual national disaster.' (The real cost to Britain is
estimated to be three times the value of the direct loss or a
million a day even if you take into account that, as with the cost
of crime, a part of the loss is a 'mere redistribution of wealth' by
one firm taking over the market of another.)

Lord Stonham found it 'even more disturbing . . . that these
suicidal losses increase regularly each year'. He called for a
sense of personal responsibility, more fire education and publicity, and better fire prevention to 'stop fires starting instead of
risking lives putting them out'.

So what was then done about it? As a major effort to achieve
a break-through, the Home Office was to publish the casualty
figures quarterly instead of annually to make people more aware
of the problem. Yet this constant show of fetishistic respect for
education is doomed to certain failure; partly because people
cannot be forced to learn (except in schools where the Australians, for instance, have developed some remarkable in-
novations); partly because fire is not really news worth reading
(except in cases of disaster); and partly because it is ordinary
human weakness not to associate the tragedies among the steady
flow of staccato reports (Munich family burnt to death when
child played with matches—Seattle do-it-yourself man loses
family in fire—Cardiff factory gutted—Fifteen thousand acres
in flames after Riviera picnic) with the staggering statistics that
win alarming headlines monthly, quarterly, yearly, but have
lost their novelty value long, long ago.

In 1896, Americans were told by the press they had turned
their country into a 'national ash heap'. The damage was then a
hundred million dollars. In 1969 the loss was 2,415 million. But
that did not make any householder unplug his television set
before going to bed. In ten years, from January 1961, some
45,000 Americans were killed in Vietnam. In 1969 alone,
12,200 were killed at home in fires. In 1970, sixty Americans
were killed in battle each week—while fire claimed a weekly
toll of 240 lives. But the latter did not result in any protest
march. And the fact that Britain's fire losses almost match the
increase of productivity, or that Germany and Switzerland lose
a much smaller proportion of their national product than

Britain does, has not yet sent any export manager scurrying to the chairman of the board and begging him on his knees to do more about fire precautions.

'They fail to see the significance of the figures,' fire authorities round the world told the author. In other words we, the stupid public, have only ourselves to blame that fire education has failed to have the required effect on us.

When one asks people in the fire business from New York to Melbourne, from London to New Delhi and Cologne and Paris and Stockholm and San Francisco, to pinpoint the three most common universal causes of fire, they all tend to quote Percy Bugbee, retired general manager of the American National Fire Protection Association, who forged a now proverbial answer naming the notorious triplets as *men, women and children*. That makes, once again, the 'stupid public' the whipping boy even though the categories of 'men' and 'women' inevitably include fire experts, authorities and masses of people who have something to do with fire. (In the United States, almost three million people, about one and a half per cent of the population, are directly or indirectly engaged in the business, profession and administration of fire protection.)

Fire authorities can quote lamentable and ridiculous examples of public lunacy. It is easy to share their irony about the staff of the Waqf, a Moslem religious trust that looks after Jerusalem's holy places, including the Aqsa Mosque, victim of arson in 1969. For according to the final report of a thorough Israeli investigation, when a Fire Prevention officer had warned the Waqf two years before the fire that their fire-fighting equipment was ancient and unsuitable, they rejected further expert advice saying: 'Allah is mighty, there is nothing to fear, God is great, and he will preserve the place for us!'

It is equally easy, however, to sneer at the authorities whose follies are just as deplorable today as the eighteenth-century Russians' who, as reported by Captain John Perry in his book on *The State of Russia*, complained bitterly about the enormity and frequency of fires in the country and about the blind conservatism of the population that refused to build with bricks rather than wood. What they did not mention but Perry discovered was that brick prices were grossly inflated by a prohibitively excessive taxation. If those Arabs' hopes are over-optimistic, many people's trust in officials—epitomized by the Hungarian peasant saying that 'if God grants you office, he'll also provide you with brains to match it'—is plain wishful thinking.

When so many signs of all-round apathy are highlighted by devastating infernos, would it not be logical and timely to revise our entire thinking about prevention, relegate that hitherto fruitless exercise of preaching and education to the status of a secondary aide for the betterment of humanity, and accept stupidity concerning fires as a fact, as a natural state of the human mind? Then authorities could begin to legislate counting on stupidity, harnessing ignorance and devising foolproof systems based on negligence.

What legislation does exist is full of loopholes, ambiguities, confusion, incongruity, and openings for free evaluation and interpretation by unqualified members of local government. That is why factories are compelled to buy firefighting equipment but are not urged to train staff in their use; why the installation of sprinklers is encouraged by incentives like grants, tax and insurance premium concessions but deterred by subsequently increased rates and water rates in many countries; why the maintenance of fire defence is the owner's responsibility; why hotels, hospitals and old people's homes are left insufficiently prepared or totally unprotected; why the fire hazard to our glorious space-age in the 1970's is fought with the swinging methods of the seventeenth century, when to this day some American unpaid volunteer brigades collect protection fees, issue 'paid-up' tags and let late-paying clients' premises burn to the ground.

'No one can afford to have a fire, however well insured a business is,' wrote N. C. Strother-Smith, director of the Fire Protection Association in *The Times* of June 2, 1969, and he could have added that however well insured a home is, nothing can compensate for the damage and disruption a blaze creates. Yet he found that 'the outstanding feature of nearly all fires is the total unpreparedness of the firm involved. In the face of the relentless and increasing toll that fire is wresting from the country's economy, it is surprising that neither the Government nor industry as a whole seems to be prepared to take effective steps toward controlling the waste'.

Against more determined action and nation-wide legislation there appear to be two main arguments: one is the defence of individual liberty, the other is claimed to be a simple lack of funds.

As for individual liberty, misguided champions of this honourable cause tell us that there is already too much legislation and government control; that anybody should have the right to gamble with his own belongings (which should include the right of letting his own property burn); that the majority of the population do not want new fire laws; and that policing is no substitute for persuasion. They seem to forget that, however regrettable, the ever-increasing volume of legislation is also due to the unprecedented growth of the population and is part and parcel of the sort of society we have chosen to live in; that when a man gambles with his home the neighbours, too, are likely to suffer, and when a factory burns out many people lose their jobs and income for indefinite periods, thus ultimately affecting the·whole nation's economy; that the majority of drivers in the Western world do not want and refuse to wear car safety belts but understand and accept the laws designed to protect them from themselves; and that as far as fire is concerned, we have proved ourselves to be no better than notorious criminals who cannot be convinced, only convicted.

'Lack of funds' as an excuse for lack of better legislation shows up certain politicians, governments and various other authorities as unashamed liars. For they lie either when they make alarmist statements, read the words 'national disaster' into the cool figures of fire statistics, whine that their countries' economy cannot absorb the tremendous blows any longer and that we must not accept the fire losses as an inevitable punishment from Allah—or they lie when they claim that it is too expensive to combat the fire hazard more effectively.

To cover up for the lack of centralized action, a great deal of the nagging is left to the insurance companies, and most of the responsibility burdens the shaky shoulders of local authorities. (American elected officials are expected to put up a fight for better equipment but in so doing they either endanger their own re-election or accept that, for example, there is no standardization in fire protection or fire brigade equipment and shrug their shoulders when one village brigade cannot help out another fighting a big fire only because their equipment does not fit the different hydrants. This has recently happened at London's Heathrow airport, too.)

Finally, the entire mess is glossed over by the well-meaning efforts at education. Despite that, just as aviation is the most overrated, fire remains the most underrated menace to our lives. People who may make lengthy inquiries about the safety of the airline that flies them to their annual holidays, will never question the fire protection of that latest glorious resort or the means of escape in that new hotel that scrapes ever-blue skies according to the travel agents. (Actually, it is at least eleven times more likely that you will be in a fire at a hotel than in your home.) Miners' unions have a tradition of fighting for greater safety below the ground, but a call for a strike because of insufficient fire protection in a plant or an industry has yet to be heard. Parents who will pay a great deal of attention to the cleanliness of others whose children their own offspring choose to play with, will let them stay the weekend with the friend whose do-it-yourself grandfather supplied that lovely rambling old house with electricity fifty years ago. We console ourselves by claiming that fire is such an old hazard, and experts seem to know such a lot about it . . . Well, they do. But they still rely mostly on experience when it comes to telling what caused a particular fire. Investigators resort almost to guessing when they do not know the answer for sure (after all, it is in the nature of fires to destroy most of the evidence), and prefer not to commit themselves on the cause of more than half of the big fires, when they can have no more than an intelligent guess but there is still likely to be a big public enquiry.

There is a rude shock in store for the reporter who wants to write about the intriguing and magic ways of fire investigators. For the magic is missing. Most of the modern, sophisticated, determined and ingenious scientific and technological methods aviation investigators use are also missing. What is left is often no more than a report of a supposed cause supplied by witnesses after an investigation that tends to be lengthier and more thorough in cases of financial loss than those of deaths.

All this supports those fire specialists who regard it as a miracle that so many people escape from fires and only so *few* are being killed as yet. Approaching the twenty-first century, we

shall need to rely less on the supernatural if we try to break up
the eternal deadly triangle of the fire symbol

which is firmly held together by the technologically most
advanced glue: a mixture of stupidity, false economy and
lackadaisical legislation.

CHAPTER TWO

NO CALL FOR ACTION

THE 25th was a cold and wet day in February 1969. The ante-room of the large open floor of the architect's office, near New York's Rockefeller Centre, bore the wet marks of melting snow round the lift doors where men and women, back from lunch, took off their galoshes and put them away in the large built-in closet. The architect was away. In his private office at the far end of this third floor, his deputy discussed some plans with four visitors. The time was about a quarter past four in the afternoon.

The open floor, where eleven employees worked, was divided to some extent by light tackboards placed in a chequered pattern. Notes, drawings, unfinished plans were stuck to these all over, almost to the ceiling. The boards were connected by one-inch strips of timber from which huge rolls of flimsy tracing paper hung down to desks and drawing boards.

It was probably at 4.20 that a small, flickering flame was noticed immediately above a desk near the closet and the first window facing north. An architect, whose desk it was, usually put down his pipe on an ashtray just where now a seemingly playful little flame ran up the loose roll of tracing paper.

Facing that window, on the far side of the street, a gynaecologist conducted an examination. He saw some smoke seep through that third floor window but it was not enough to divert his attention for long from his patient. Then he heard faint screams. He looked up once again and saw flames behind that window. Being an enthusiastic beginner at his newly-found hobby, photography, he immediately thought about his camera. What he did not think about was calling the fire brigade. He left his patient, ran through some rooms to get the camera and although—as he later told investigator Chief Fire Marshal Vincent Canty—he 'had to figure out the right

settings, exposure and what-not', he managed to get a remarkable sequence of pictures, covering the progress of the fire from
window to window.

In the architect's office, one employee first tried to beat out
the flames with a cushion. He failed. The others who watched
him then decided that there was nothing to be done and warned
the five people in the boss's private office. The visitors began to
gather up their papers. The employees put their desks in order.
Mrs. Jean Golding, the book-keeper, tidied up, packed away
her books, checked the petty-cash and locked the filing cabinets.
Somebody pushed off a telephone—there was a set on every
desk—but picked it up without making a call. Then all the
sixteen people began to dress without panic. Men put on their
rubber overshoes—remember, it was a cold wet day.

Then they all tried to get into the lift.

The fire department received the first much-delayed alarm
call at 4.34, from an onlooker in a building on the other side of
the street.

The superintendent of the building where the fire was, first

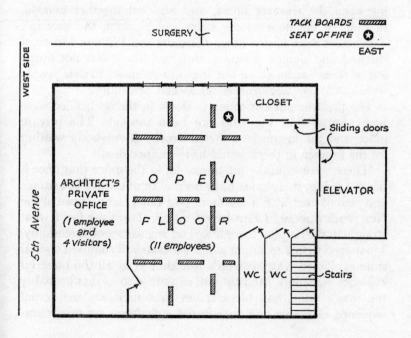

heard screams coming down to the lobby. He saw on the call-
board that 'the elevator must have been locked at the third
floor' so he ran up the stairs. He tried the door but he could not
open it. Very little smoke was coming through. He had a bunch
of keys with him but none of these seemed to fit. (He does not
remember whether he could turn any of the keys at the first
attempt.) He ran down again, put through an emergency call,
and returned to the third floor with a patrolman. Once again
they failed with the keys, so they put their shoulders to the door.
Behind them, people from the upper floors were quietly moving
down the stairs. The staircase and the outside of the door to the
architect's office suffered no damage.

At last, the two men managed to force the obviously blocked
door slightly open. Tremendous heat and smoke hit them in the
face through the gap. One of them closed his eyes, reached down
and grabbed. They pulled a horribly burnt unconscious woman
(Mrs. Golding) through the gap.

That was when the firemen arrived. They drove the fire
back a little and broke down the door. They had to climb over
fifteen bodies 'stacked inside the elevator, piled up in and holding open the elevator doors, and huddled together outside,
in front of the door to the stairs and blocking the way in'.
The bodies were passed down the stairs and William Moore, a
stunned and shaken fireman, muttered 'there was not much
left of them' as he came out into 5th Avenue. Eleven people
were dead, five were rushed to special care units.

The fire was put out quickly. Doors in the open floor were
badly burnt—but they did not burn through. The private
office and the lavatories were undamaged. Anybody waiting
for the firemen in there would have escaped death.

'There were so many inflammables in the office that once a
fire got going, there must have been a lot of thick black smoke
and vicious heat within minutes,' said Chief Canty, head of the
New York Bureau of Fire Investigation. 'From the fire I went
straight to the hospital to see if we had any witnesses. Eventually,
I managed to talk to a man whose shocked and confused mental
state explained why his words wouldn't fit at all the material
evidence we found. Medical staff explained to us that probably
the man's mind had blocked out subconsciously the actual
sequence of events and substituted a fictitious set of circum-

stances with which he could live. Another patient I met remembered only the futile attempts to get into the elevator all together. Doctors prevented me from talking to another two survivors because the conversation would have driven them right back to the initial shock from which their mental recovery was questionable in any case. Mrs. Golding was severely burnt, like the others. But she insisted on talking to me, even though I wanted to excuse her. She could only whisper, just about able to press air through what had been saved of her trachea. She told me about the lengthy preparations to leave the office and about the struggle at the elevator door where they were overcome by smoke, and then burnt. We checked out what she said and what we found confirmed that the fire had started right where that man usually kept his damn' pipe. Other possible causes like electrical appliances, hot plates, wiring were eliminated.

'She couldn't tell me anything about why nobody called us in the first place. It's just one of those mysterious, unaccountable ways people behave in a fire. There is a stress situation, some negative panic that leads to resistance to action, like when people aboard a blazing ship refuse to get into the lifeboats. When the aircraft carrier *Constellation* was burning here in the harbour, people came up on deck screaming for help but refusing to step on a gang plank a crane had lifted to them. They rather returned into the ship. They thought they'd be okay. They weren't. But they wouldn't believe us.

'Anyway, the elevator was working even after the fire. It would have taken fifteen seconds for those steel doors to close and the first lot would have been safe. The door to the stairs was probably ignored completely. People just don't seem to think of stairs. They use them only if the elevators stop which just doesn't happen. Except perhaps in a complete blackout. What would New York do without elevators? So no one even tried to open the door.'

In this office, as in many homes and factories, fire and smoke played the role of the executioner. But it was the delay that sentenced the victims to death. What the Australian Fire Protection Association uses as its slogan, 'A little fire is quickly trodden out, Which being suffered, rivers cannot quench' (Shakespeare, *Henry VI*, Part III), ought to influence our entire thinking about fires. Yet this most notorious killer crops up in every stage of tragedies: delays in discovering the fire, delays in calling the firemen, delays in firemen asking for reinforcements.

'It will never be possible to prevent all fires, but they ought, at least, to be detected early,' said D. I. Lawson, director of the Boreham Wood Fire Research Station, in his paper presented at the second Australian National Conference on Fire in 1968. 'An analysis of 1,200 large fires showed that over half had become large when they were discovered; the other half were caused by bad building design in the main, though about one third of these had become large because of a failure to summon the public fire brigade after discovery.'

A significant indicator is that when all fires are grouped together, statisticians find that most outbreaks are discovered *between four and eight p.m.* But when the large fires are considered separately, the peak discovery time is the night: most large fires, those which by then cannot be prevented from becoming large ones, are discovered *in the four hours after nine o'clock in the evening*—at a time when most factories are already deserted and when people at home have already gone to bed. The implication is that when a fire is discovered early, and fire-fighters are summoned without delay, usually it can be 'quickly trodden out', but if it has time to build up and spread without discovery, it becomes large enough to call the attention even of passers-by.

Usually the damage measures a fire: if the direct loss exceeds ten thousand pounds, the fire is regarded as a 'large' one. One in about every hundred large fires becomes a real holocaust and these few account for more than half the total direct fire losses of a country. 'A study of these fires', according to M. J. O'Dogherty, writing in *The Times* of June 2, 1969, 'shows that the two principal features associated with them were delay in discovery, and absence of means of controlling their spread.' It is also known that most large fires burned for at least an hour before discovery, and it is estimated that if only those fires which were first noticed by passers-by had been prevented from becoming large ones, Britain's annual fire loss could be reduced by about twenty per cent.

The early period in the life of any fire is the most likely to imperil human lives and it determines ultimately how big a fighting force will have to be summoned. As fires usually become large—or comparatively large—when the flames reach the ceiling, it is vital that they should be discovered before then.

The argument presented even by such a brief summary obviously favours the use of automatic fire detectors. There are various systems in general use—mostly they detect heat and smoke although a new one watches for the infra-red radiation from fires. They are all designed to discover potential disasters at the earliest possible stage. The choice among them is influenced by several factors such as the characteristics of the building to be protected, the nature of combustible materials involved, activities and 'natural' heat changes in the premises, shape of roof construction and environmental conditions. A great deal of research is continually being carried out to determine which system is the most suitable for particular types of buildings when cost effectiveness is also considered in order to avoid uneconomical over-protection.

Automatic fire detectors can raise the alarm in various ways, determined largely by the demands of special circumstances and the protected values. There are audible warning devices that can be heard within the premises or in a certain area, others also give visual signals on control panels or can be connected directly to the fire brigade. (From unmanned stations these direct alarms are automatically transmitted to a central control room.)

The required sensitivity of the system to be chosen depends on the extent of the hazard and on the assets it is supposed to guard. Britain's National Trust, for instance, looks after numerous buildings, each of unique historical importance, packed with art treasures worth millions of pounds, which cannot be insured against total loss because they are irreplaceable. The Trust has therefore begun to install extra-sensitive radio-active devices at an initial cost of £30,000. Smoke detectors are hidden behind plasterwork at Blickling Hall, Norfolk, the Jacobean mansion built in 1616-24, so that they should not ruin the décor of the sixty rooms in Sir Henry Hobart's home which was 'to satisfy the most romantic conception of an English country house'. The detectors there are so sensitive that they set off the alarm if a match is lit or there is a burning cigarette anywhere in the building, and a siren on the roof can be heard four miles away.

In other buildings, three people smoking in the same room could set the bells ringing. At Sudbury, Derbyshire, while such protective gadgets were being installed, somebody lit a bonfire nearby. The smoke was detected immediately and a false alarm was set off.

The expense of false alarms is, in fact, the greatest argument against automatic fire detectors. It has been estimated that these devices, together with their communication lines, are responsible for something like ten false calls for every real one. But although this figure emphasises how urgently a more reliable generation of detectors is needed (experiments with a laser beam detector at Boreham Wood are promising), these protective systems are responsible for only a fraction of the undue hazard and waste of money caused collectively by all false alarms.

In England and Wales, fire brigades attended 188,045 fires (plus almost 60,000 chimney fires) in 1968. They also answered almost 90,000 false alarms. More than half of these were 'jokes' and malicious alarms (arsonists like to keep the local brigade busy elsewhere); 36,000 false calls were made with good intent by mistaken people; and only 5,000 false alarms were caused by faulty apparatus.

New York alone had almost 130,000 fires in the same year. The ratio between real and false alarms was almost one to one but detectors were responsible for only an insignificant proportion. In Boston, firemen answered more than 15,000 false alarms. In Houston, out of 3,097 alarm box calls, only 163 reported real fires. If you consider that a run by an American fire brigade may cost anything from five hundred dollars upwards, this favourite kids' game becomes rather expensive. Local authorities on Chicago's South Side would have saved a great deal of money and anxiety had they installed fire detectors in DuSable High School before that single spring day in 1969 when the alarm handle at the school was pulled twenty-six times and the firemen had to respond to each false call (*Newsweek*, July 28, 1969).

The false alarms by automatic detectors are, however, numerous enough to create a bad reputation for the device. (When sprinklers—to be dealt with elsewhere—are attached to them, this ultimate means of fire protection also causes some water damage.) Rather typical was the British factory in which the automatic fire detection was nicknamed Matilda because like Hilaire Belloc's little darling, 'Matilda told such Dreadful Lies, It made one Gasp and Stretch one's Eyes' and it regularly 'summoned the Immediate Aid of London's Noble Fire Brigade'. So every time this automatic Matilda 'shouted "Fire !" They only answered "Little Liar !" '

The manager of a West London manufacturer gave no names to his over-zealous detector system that initiated many false alarms whenever it spotted ordinary kitchen processes or exhaust fumes from fork lift trucks. Instead of getting the automatic device adjusted, this public-spirited manager introduced a new procedure : the factory guard on duty in the gatehouse, a fair distance from most parts of the plant, had to walk to the threatened area, check the cause of any alarm signal, and call the brigade only if he really found a fire. This routine was followed when, at five past nine one evening in September 1968, the smoke detector system alerted the guard with a signal of fire in 'zone No. 6' (second floor) of the factory. The guard went dutifully to ascertain that a fire was indeed in progress, and then telephoned the fire brigade. According to the findings of the Chelsea fire prevention branch the net delay was at least fifteen minutes. Almost complete destruction, as in Matilda's house, was inevitable. The roof and two floors collapsed, the floor below was burnt out, and tremendous damage was caused by the rupture of two tanks that had contained 24,000 gallons of water.

Factory guards and particularly night-watchmen are yet another frequent cause of delays in calling the fire brigade because in practically all countries where there is no large volume of unemployment, employers tend to turn the filling of these jobs into charitable acts. In the Soviet Union, this practice is almost part of the social security system. In several American, German, French and Swedish big towns firemen and other specialists complain bitterly that the type of people employed are, much too often, thoroughly unsuitable for such responsible jobs. In Cologne, an officer of the fire brigade said : 'Usually these watchmen get a torch and some vague instructions about making their rounds. As firms employ old people whom they regard as unsuitable for 'better' jobs—the low pay keeps away more able applicants in any case—they hardly ever train them in the use of fire-fighting equipment, often fail to give them access to a telephone, and even if they trust them with a phone, they instruct the watchmen to phone first a manager rather than call the fire brigade on their own initiative.'

J. B. Firth, as director of Britain's Home Office Forensic Science Laboratory, went on record as saying that 'many fires have been discovered by outsiders (often too late) when watchmen have been on the premises' because, he added in the *Institution of Fire Engineers' Quarterly*, 'all too frequently men who are feeble, not only physically but mentally, are employed as watchmen'. They are used simply as 'sitters in'. He mentioned a fire at a factory where 'the watchman was deaf, did not know how to use a telephone, and had to run to the nearest Police Station to raise the alarm'. Luckily, unlike many of his colleagues, this man had two legs to run on.

Several American experts echoed in interviews what a fire specialist of the Münchener Rückversicherungs-Gesellschaft (Munich Reinsurance Company) summed up when he stated that 'insurance companies have been driven to regard night-watchmen as a liability rather than an asset'.

For this malpractice nobody can blame the watchmen themselves, most of whom are full of goodwill restricted only by their own limitations. It is the people who choose and assign them who are responsible and who thus contribute yet another chapter to the saga of human lunacy aggravated by delayed reports of fire.

Many people still drive miles and miles to experience the awesome fascination commanded by fires. The sight of flames, however, makes them overwrought and seems to deprive them of their logic. The result is a total loss of initiative and they fail to think of simple acts like calling the firemen. A small selection of case histories speaks for itself.

When, in 1969, Britain's Maltings concert hall, the new home of the Aldeburgh Festival at Snape, Suffolk, caught fire, the rows of 850 seats were already empty. The flames spread fast and shot through the roof of the largely wooden building at about eleven o'clock in the evening. Sightseers gathered from all directions and stared at the blaze. Howard Griffiths, chief fire officer for Suffolk, told the county fire authority: 'The astounding thing was that people were watching and even taking photographs before we were called.' The delay was almost half an hour. As a result the building and its contents were completely destroyed. The irony was that the next performance would have begun with Benjamin Britten's overture 'the Consecration of the House'.

A holidaymaker returned from the French Riviera with this account: 'We witnessed with several villagers the outbreak of yet another of those devastating bush fires. When I suggested calling the fire brigade, local men merely referred to the wind—it was blowing, and driving the flames, away from their village.'

One morning in Hemel Hempstead, Hertfordshire, somebody saw a glow in the sky and called the firemen to the Rowans, where most of the flats were occupied by old people, many of them over seventy years of age. Station Officer Ronald Percival found that the fire had started about three quarters of an hour earlier, when, at dawn, a pensioner lit a candle to save on electricity. It set fire to the curtain and she tried to put out the flames herself. When the heat began to crack windows, a neighbour woke up and went to help the old woman, who warned her: 'Don't you dare call the fire brigade or I'll never speak to you again.' As the smoke spread into other flats a dozen more neighbours came to join the vain efforts. Some were convinced there was something shameful about having a fire. Others thought that they would have to pay for calling the firemen. The *Daily Telegraph* reported: 'After about half an hour a man went to the nearest telephone box, but on his way slipped and broke his spectacles. When he got to the box the light was out.' Therefore he tried to call the fire brigade by pressing buttons A and B on the coin box.

It happened as recently as 1969.

The North Berkshire Coroner recorded a verdict of Accidental Death on Mrs. Marie Higginson, aged twenty-two, in May 1970. She died from carbon monoxide poisoning and shock caused by smoke from a small smouldering fire in her room at Spring Terrace, Abingdon. Secondary causes of death were a large dose of aspirin and of a tranquillizer drug. And yet for all that, she could still be alive. The agony of her dying moments was heard by two women who sat through it in the flat below hers.

One of the women lived there, the other was a visitor. Their husbands were out when they heard thuds and screams from the flat above. This was at about nine in the evening on March 14. One of them called out asking if everything was all right, but there was no answer. Then came sobbing followed by groans. Instead of calling the police, they locked themselves in because, they said, 'we did not know what had happened and we were a bit frightened'. The crying went on for some time. Then all was quiet. The husbands returned at about 10.40. They tried to get into the flat above, failed, and then called the police and the fire brigade. It was too late.

In Sydney, while the five-storey department store, Buckinghams', was being demolished in 1968, a vast amount of rubbish accumulated. Large bonfires were built and the flames soon bit into stacked bare timber all around. Men on the premises 'tried to do something about it' but after a while one of them went to the Brighton Hotel on the other side of the street saying, 'I have got a small fire that has got a little bit out of hand.' The bit by which that small fire got out of hand radiated such a tremendous heat by the time the firemen were called that their engines had to retreat even from the far side of the road, and three floors of the hotel opposite were severely burned. When, finally, the wall of the main frontage toppled into the street, firemen had to run for their lives.

Telephone vandalism, the wrecking of kiosks and breaking into cash boxes, is a serious problem particularly in American, but also in European, towns. It is a frequent cause of delayed fire calls because sometimes entire areas of twenty minutes walking distance are left without a single public telephone at night. At least, however, it is easily recognized as a criminal act, while lack of foresight and proper fire drill neatly escape the charge of criminal negligence even though they may show clear non-compliance with the law and cause even more frequent delays. Three big British fires, which became notorious in many respects, are good examples of this delay hazard.

One was the Queen Victoria Street fire in London, in 1902. The top three floors of the five-storey building were occupied by the General Electric Company. Fire broke out in a waste-paper basket. The offices had internal fire hydrants and a private brigade. Formerly there had been a standing order there to call the London Brigade as soon as fire had been reported. But shortly before this fire, new regulations came into force, the standing order was cancelled, and on the printed list of action to be taken the alarm call was crossed out. It was a passer-by who alerted the brigade at 5.10 in the afternoon although in the building the fire had already been discovered at five o'clock. Later a hall porter claimed that he had sent a boy round to the Watling Street fire station, but that was never confirmed. Nine people who were completely trapped on the top floor were killed. The jury at the inquest concluded that 'the call was a very late one, and in our opinion contributed to the lamentable loss of life'.

The beginning of the Eastwood Mills, Keighley, disaster was like a tragi-comedy. Although highly inflammable Botany wool yarns were produced there by worsted spinners, there was no automatic alarm or sprinkler system, and no fire drill procedure was laid down, let alone practised. In 1956, regardless of all these factors, a man stood on a ladder and used his blowlamp without a care in the world. When the flame started a fire, he tried to beat it out with his cap. When he failed, he descended, put down his blowlamp, went up to the engine house on the first floor where he failed to find the engineer. Then he ran to the first floor workroom where he poured a few buckets of water on the floor hoping to control the spread of the flames.

The engineer was in the boiler house, below the engine house, when he heard shouts for help. He, too, went up, then into the workroom, then together with the plumber back down to the ground floor carrying an extinguisher. By this time they found the fire out of control. So now the engineer had to go to the warehouse, some fifty feet away, from where he telephoned the office asking them to call the fire brigade. The delay was at least ten minutes. Eight people lost their lives.

In Liverpool, the Henderson department store fire was reported after about four minutes' delay because first the general manager's attention was drawn to a crackling noise above the ceiling, and then he had to call the switchboard operator who

in turn telephoned the brigade. Then the operator rang back
to ask the manager if she should sound the alarm—this delayed
the start of any evacuation by a further minute. When the
brigade arrived in two minutes, business was still as usual on
the ground floor. Total cost: eleven lives.

Department stores all over the world are still curiously
reluctant to sound a general alarm. The manager of a large and
well-known store in New York refused to allow his name to be
printed but 'off the record' he admitted that he was 'less afraid
of facing a small or even potentially somewhat dangerous fire
than of coping with even a hint of possible panic'. He agreed that
all large fires began as small ones but argued that 'we still
don't know how people react when faced with the tiniest threat
from the mysterious phenomenon we call fire'.

CHAPTER THREE

PANIC IN THE NIGHT

A YOUNG man called Neil Armstrong coolly dodged the flames when his house caught fire one night and saved the lives of all his family. Later he became famous as the first man to set foot on the moon.

Another young man called Johannes B. was in the room on the third floor of the Munich workshop where a small fire began to spread. He ran out of the room without a word to anyone, swept down the stairs passing scores of people, dodged the traffic recklessly as he crossed the road and was a mile away by the time, a few minutes later, somebody called the Munich fire brigade. In keeping with many cases mentioned in this book, his full name has been omitted to save him from undue embarrassment because after the blaze, when he was located by a German fire investigator, he could offer no explanation of his action.

We do not understand the motives of these two men's different reactions—why one chose flight and the other fight—any more than we can solve the enigmatic behaviour of the passer-by who dives into an inferno to save a stranger or of the parents who stand almost paralysed screaming for help but doing nothing for their children who burn to death almost in front of their eyes. To call one brave and the others cowards would be an unjustifiable over-simplification. For, on this basis, everyone who returns to a conflagration for any, sometimes the most trivial, reason ought to be classed as brave. Indeed, onlookers and reporters praised without hesitation the bravery of cashier girls who escaped from blazing office canteens and supermarkets (just to mention two recent cases), and then returned to save the contents of their tills from the roaring flames. By the same token one ought to admire the London councillor of Tower Hamlets who escaped hurriedly down-stairs from his burning house but told a policeman in an excess of modesty that he would first have to return to the second floor bedroom for his trousers as he could not possibly appear before by-standers without them; and we would have to acknowledge the 'calmness' of the two women at a plastics warehouse in Leicestershire, of the superintendent and pupil at the Grade School in Caraway, Arkansas, and of thousands of others who have returned into burning buildings, sometimes trying to run against the fleeing flood of people, merely to collect handbags and other trifling belongings. Yet knowing that the councillor was found dead in his bedroom, that the women lost their way and died in dense smoke, that the pupil and the superintendent, like thousands and thousands of others, died as victims of this widespread and extremely hazardous folly, we recognise that they probably acted with the impulse of momentary lunacy, one of the many forms of irrational behaviour induced by atavistic fear and total incomprehension of fire.

Bravery in fire can be due to many factors like the overriding compulsion brought on by devotion, determination and senti-ment, or the strength of experience acquired in earlier, perhaps seemingly insurmountable, deadly encounters. (When Neil Armstrong was chosen for the first mission into the unknown, it was probably taken into consideration that he was obsessively determined to get to the moon and had already remained calm in emergencies like fire, misbehaving experimental rocket planes, an out-of-control Gemini 8 spacecraft, and in the crippled war-plane which he coaxed on to the deck of a carrier with inches to spare during the Korean war.) But bravery in fire is ultimately just as irrational as the most contagious fire madness: panic.

The word itself is derived from Pan, the name of the Greek half-man-half-goat rural god. Reputedly, he could induce lustful frenzy in the subjects of his amorous advances, and had the power of causing panic—wild groundless fear, affecting large bodies of men and causing them to behave like frightened beasts.

According to the legend, Pan played a vital role in the Battle of Marathon, where the Athenians triumphed against all odds. The Persian army of fifty thousand men, led by Darius the

Great in 490 B.C., greatly outnumbered the tiny Greek force, which naturally sought reinforcements but in vain. Pheidippides, the finest Greek runner, was sent to Sparta for help, but the Spartans did not want to leave their city and excused themselves by arranging a religious feast. The luckless, weary Pheidippides then met Pan who offered his support. When Darius, fully reassured by all his overwhelming military might, delayed his attack, the handful of Greeks charged the invaders with unexpected ferocity. Confusion appeared in the Persian front ranks and it spread fear in all the lines. Retreat quickly turned into a self-destroying stampede and it was this, rather than the Greeks, that annihilated the Persians.

The victors chose to thank Pan for the irrational behaviour of the enemy. From their point of view it was irrelevant that Darius was unprepared for such an attack, that his army contained many slaves who were driven to battle under the lash of whips and had no will to stand and fight, and that the surprise had eliminated the deadly Persian tactical overture of battle, a hail of arrows to decimate their opponents. From our point of view, however, unpreparedness is vitally relevant when we are confronted by the disruptive force fire has inherited from Pan.

In 1942, after the Cocoanut Grove night club disaster, a Boston, Massachusetts, official curtly stated that 'nobody could have foreseen such an event'. Even if one ignored the internationally notorious cases, he and others like him ought to have been forewarned by the precedents that have made furious fires and uncontrollable panic almost as American as apple-pie.

It is only necessary to mention a few. There was the Chicago Iroquois theatre which burned down in 1903—panic helped to kill 602 and injure 250 people partly because most of the exits were locked and shuttered. The dance hall at Ville Platte, Louisiana, which occupied the second floor of a wooden building, had only one stairway which collapsed in 1919 under the rush of panic-stricken dancers, twenty-five of whom lost their lives. Seventy-seven bodies were piled up on the single small stairway of the school in Camden, South Carolina in 1923. Windows were barred and exits were blocked, the Christmas decorations had no fire resistance, wax candles were used and a kerosene lamp was there to be knocked over and to explode when confusion began at the Rural School, Babbs Switch, Oklahoma where thirty-six people were burned to death in 1924. Five years later, twenty-two people died and some fifty were seriously burnt in a Detroit night club where inflammable draperies transmitted flames in a flash, the ventilation system created a furnace on the second floor, the fire exit was locked and windows were completely concealed by wallboards. The gory list could go on and on, right up to April 1940, when more than two hundred was the toll taken by the Natchez, Missouri, fire at a dance hall with shuttered and nailed doors and windows, and to November 1942, only a fortnight before the Cocoanut Grove inferno, when an East Boston night club fire claimed six lives and caused the urgent inspection of all places of assembly.

The Cocoanut Grove, a popular night club run by a gangster in prohibition days but later 'frequented by the better class people of Boston', was no exception. The fire inspector was there on November 20, eight days before the fire, and found that the conditions were 'good', exits were 'adequate', and decorations including the fake palm trees and half-coconut lamp fittings were not inflammable. (He later claimed that he had tried in vain to ignite the fake foliage with a match.)

Afterwards, there were lengthy inquiries and thorough analyses by experts. All these have undoubtedly been mixed with the personal recollections of a survivor who had made a statement to the authorities at the time but could bring herself only now to talk about the emotional torture of that night and the ensuing twenty-eight years.

She is a petite, plumpish woman, forty-six years of age, with anaemic white skin and soft features. The Los Angeles fire officer who persuaded her to talk, described her as a 'real gentle soul'. She married her husband twenty years ago 'partly because he was the first young man who accepted my strange behaviour without some gruelling interrogation'. She wished to be quoted only as Mrs. L. F.

'Saturday nights were always very crowded at the Grove, and a special rush was expected on that November 28, after the Boston College-Holy Cross football game. I was a freshman at college then, very interested in football, and especially excited about my date that night because a young naval officer was my escort who had been badly wounded at Pearl Harbor and who, after hospital and a short leave home, was to return to his ship within a couple of days. He reserved a table at the Grove and we sat in the almost brand-new Broadway Cocktail Lounge, near the bar. I can't remember the time, but it was at about a quarter past ten when he lit a cigarette and I suddenly thought I had some optical illusion: behind that little flame I saw a girl run towards us and her hair seemed to be on fire. Then she collapsed. I think she didn't even scream. But the flames were there. No optical illusion. By then my escort saw her, too. He stood up and told me quietly "let's get out of here". Then he began to say something about my coat. What I vividly remember is that I had a sudden, warm, wonderful feeling of having a hero as a date. With him there I couldn't be in danger. I thought.'

The fire began in the basement Melody Lounge. A prankster stood on a chair and unscrewed a light bulb to make the atmosphere 'more romantic' and create more privacy for his necking session at the expense of the already dim lighting. A waiter told a student, helping out on weekends, to screw the bulb back in. The room was too dark, so the boy held a match next to the coconut fitting while he manoeuvred the bulb with the other hand. After a moment the highly inflammable palm caught fire. Flames skimmed over the cloth-covered walls and ceilings. At first, people just stared without comprehension. Then everything seemed to ignite all at once. Somebody cried 'fire!' Everyone round the bar and at the tables rushed for the single exit—the narrow stairs up to the foyer. A few went through the door to the kitchen where some died in the smoke near the locked exits, some escaped through a small window, and some fought for the refuge of the large walk-in refrigerators in which about three people survived. 'Inside the icebox there wasn't much air—we couldn't let in a crowd', said a survivor. The scene there was like those at the entrances of bomb-proof shelters in an atomic war of all too realistic science fiction.

Many people in the Melody Lounge never even reached the stairs. By the time the firemen found them, they had been incinerated. On the stairs the flow of escape was quite fast at first. Just at the top of the stairs there was a door to the street. It was locked to prevent guests leaving without paying the bill.

People stopped to try and open it and held back the tide for a few seconds. Then they were swept away. In the lobby, some guests stopped to pick up their coats while waiters tried to make the first escapees pay. Some rushed straight for the single revolving door, the main entrance, which soon jammed with people inside it. At that moment perhaps it could have been broken down. But the steady pressure on those up front made women stumble. About two hundred people just piled up on top of them within seconds. They were only a few feet away from Piedmont Street.

Noxious fumes and flames overtook the refugees from the Melody Lounge. On the main floor (at street level) a yellowish ball of flame seemed to roll through the air near the ceiling. It was followed by a dense cloud of black smoke that blotted out the lights. Round the dance floor and the stage where the show was about to begin, patrons who did not react fast enough never even had a chance to leave their tables. The toxic gas killed them and their cremated bodies sat there until rescuers touched them—then they just crumbled.

In the Broadway Cocktail Lounge the flames and fumes arrived at the burning girl's heels. Mrs. L. F. thinks somebody screamed: 'It might have been me but I'm not sure who gave that piercing shriek I cannot forget and still hear in nightmares. But I do remember quite clearly my young escort. He stood up, took my hand, but suddenly began trembling as he shouted "keep calm! keep calm"! It might have been the moment when the shock for which he had just been treated, returned to him. He began to drag me towards the Broadway entrance at the far side of the room, but then just let me go as he knocked down a man, and then another, who appeared in his path. That was the last time I saw him alive.

'By now, everybody was screaming. Our rush to the door, where we had entered, came to a halt. For there were swing-doors that opened inwards. A few people got through, but the next few were crushed against the handles and our efforts to get there created a constant pressure that pinned the doors shut. I heard later that about a hundred people were found there piled up neatly almost to the ceiling.

'From there on my memories are very hazy. At the hospital somebody told me that I must have fainted and firemen who broke in through thick glass block-windows pulled me out. I think I got through to the main dining room and it is possible that a waiter led me to safety with another few people through a half-opened hidden back door. A dancer thought that she saw me standing on a roof near the dressing rooms upstairs together with two mink-clad naked girls from the chorus line, but she was not sure whether I jumped down with her or waited for the firemen's rescue ladders.'

From that point, she was so profoundly shaken by constant sobbing that it was impossible to record her words. Yet she insisted on continuing 'and get it out for once'. Certain fragments she remembers clearly. She cannot forget the smell of fumes which she must have inhaled prodigiously. Only a couple of years ago, when the electric toaster broke down and burnt a slice of bread, she fainted instantly.

'Why we all began clawing, fighting, and tearing clothes off each other I don't know. Panic, I suppose.'

In her home, all floors are parquet or tiles with nothing to cover them. She cannot walk on anything soft and still feels sick if she steps on deep-pile carpet. 'I ran on bellies and women's breasts towards the door. I tried to climb that hill of bodies and I slipped. The heel of my shoe sank softly into someone's neck.'

For twenty-eight years she has never been to a cinema, theatre, restaurant or any other public place. She never returned to school but studied by correspondence courses. She used to be a regular churchgoer. 'My faith hasn't remained strong enough to give me reassurance in a crowded hall. I was sick of explaining myself to small suburban communities. Luckily, my husband doesn't mind living in apartments downtown where nobody asks questions why you don't go to church.'

The seating capacity of the three lounges in the Cocoanut Grove was licensed for about five hundred customers. That Saturday night, almost a thousand people were there. More than half of them died in twelve minutes. A full 'bombing raid' emergency was declared and the injured arrived at hospitals at eleven-second intervals.

In the wake of the disaster came a great deal of legal wrangling and whitewashing, and the call for heads to roll was inevitable. What mattered most was the lesson the fire taught us

once again. But were people ready to learn? The bitter answer
came only a fortnight later when at a barn dance in a hostel at
St. John's, Newfoundland, ninety-nine panic-stricken people,
mainly servicemen, died in a fire—and this answer has been
repeated all over the world many times with sickening regularity
ever since.

Back in 1942, the Boston findings were rather typical of the
international situation. Compliance with already existing
Building Codes could have prevented the disaster. Great loss of
lives was caused by the jammed revolving door but the Code
did require swinging doors next to it. The Cocoanut Grove
safety requirements could have been carried out without constructional changes or great expense. Robert Moulton of the
Fire Protection Association wrote in his analysis: 'Following the
fire there has been a wave of public demand throughout the
United States and Canada for legislation to assure fire safety
in places of public assembly. The majority of building codes
throughout the country are antiquated and incomplete. Fire
prevention legislation generally leaves much to be desired.
However, there is a real danger in attempting to remedy the
conditions such as were responsible for the Cocoanut Grove
tragedy by the enactment of laws. This is too apt to result in
satisfying the public demand by passing a law and then leaving
the law to gather dust on the statute books without any continuing or effective effort to put it into practice.' He also referred to the likely resistance to retroactive legislation and
suggested therefore charging 'a competent enforcing authority'
with responsibility for satisfying the existing requirements.

The National Fire Protection Association then proposed a
legal format for states which had not yet drawn up such laws.
But that exposed once again a peculiar American problem
which exists to a lesser extent in Britain and other Western
countries, too. It is the freedom of the local authority and it is
apt to create vastly differing local standards. The *Christian
Science Monitor*, for instance, was quick to point out after the
Boston fire that 'the chaotic conditions of Boston's building
laws, incompetent enforcement, political influence and careless
management' played an important role in bringing about the
disaster.

The case became well known everywhere in the world. It

was discussed again and again, and the lessons it taught us were absolutely clear. Yet in November 1970, after a painfully similar dance hall holocaust had killed 146 young people including two of the managers, the only surviving manager's first stunned reaction was: 'Who would have ever imagined such a fire?' And what made it even worse was that a local government official repeated the question soon afterwards. But was it really all that unimaginable?

The tragedy is still the subject of a judicial inquiry, but information provided by the Centre National de Prévention et de Protection (and published in the *FPA Journal* in April 1971) reveals a great deal about the circumstances. The 'Cinq-Sept' dance hall at Saint Laurent-du-Pont occupied a large, single-storey, rectangular building that could accommodate about six hundred people. The section where the dance floor was had no windows. One turnstile controlled the entrance and another, operated by a pedal at the cashier's feet, made sure that nobody would leave without paying the bill. There were four other exits which, complying with the regulations, opened outwards. But they were locked. They were also half as wide as required by the law. There was a balcony served by only two very narrow spiral staircases. Much of the décor and furnishing was highly inflammable. There was a hydrant outlet—but it was not connected to the water supply. Three extinguishers were supposed to render all fire protection. There was no emergency lighting. There was no telephone—the nearest kiosk was one kilometre away. In the one year of operation, there had been no fire drill at the 'Cinq-Sept'. Construction of the dance hall was started before the necessary permit could be obtained from the Préfecture of the Département. After the permit had been issued, several constructional modifications were carried out (turnstiles, balcony, etc.) without permission and resulting in many of the above dangerous features. The 'authorization to open' was issued to the owners without any official visit to the premises to check if the building conformed with the construction permit.

If all this sounds familiar or even repetitious, it only worsens the horror that was to come. At about 1.30 in the morning of November 1, a chair caught fire, perhaps from a cigarette. A waiter tried to smother the flames with first a coat and then a table. Then, suddenly, there was a bright yellow flash. Furniture, foam plastic cushions on the seats and even the walls, sprayed with foam plastics to give the impression of a white grotto, seemed to have burst into flames all at once. Burning drops of plastic rained from the ceiling. The band tried to play on, but panic and a stampede were inevitable. The exit turnstile jammed and was too high to climb. A few people scaled the entrance turnstile. A few more were led to safety by a barman who managed to open a door. Others piled up at the only known exit, fell unconscious to the dance floor or managed to locate locked doors on which they hammered in vain until felled by the fumes. It was over in five minutes. The fire brigade arrived twenty minutes after the last cries had been heard.

After each such case, legislation is re-examined, but the question remains: could it happen again? The answer must be that yes, it can and probably will happen again. It was only in 1971 that Britain's Home Secretary was asked to extend fire regulations to cover functions in barns and marquees, not because the authorities foresaw the hazard, but because it occurred to the South-East Cheshire magistrate 'that we may have a disaster on the scale of the fire in the French ballroom last year unless there is tighter control'.

Even if there were certain failures in fire precautions and even if decorations were highly combustible, most – if not all – lives could have been saved in many great holocausts by the provision of adequate means of escape and the prevention of panic. 'Fire experience all too clearly shows,' concluded Robert Moulton in his Boston analysis, 'that the fear of being burned to death or suffocated, the rush of smoke and hot gases, and the sight of spreading flame completely alter the pattern of logical human behaviour. Under such conditions people do not behave like thinking human beings. A mad rush to escape in any possible way without regard to others is characteristic of mob psychology in such cases. Human nature being what it is, we cannot expect people to act otherwise, no matter how much instruction and training they may have had.'

Experience also shows that strict enforcement of 'anti-human-nature' legislation can solve the problem. When the path of escape is clearly marked, when no obstruction causes bottlenecks or makes even the weakest stumble and fall, when adequate doors ensure a steady flow towards safety, panic is usually averted no matter how perilously close the hot breath of fire. It is, however, a very sad state of affairs that although we have had plenty of experience since the days of Darius, we still know very little about the human mechanics of panic.

The *Fire Service News* of British Columbia, Canada (1968) considered the causes of death by fire and showed the very low level of human tolerance to conditions normally created by fire. Carbon monoxide is the greatest killer and a concentration of 1.28 per cent in the air is enough to cause unconsciousness after a couple of inhalations and death in up to three minutes. Mixed with other usual gas by-products of fire, the effect is multiplied, dulling the brain and killing at an increased rate. The reduction of oxygen in the air diminishes muscular skill and control, and causes quick fatigue and faulty judgment. Tests in Germany showed (*Fire International*, October 1967) that forty-two ounces of smouldering textile alone could produce 0.4 per cent carbon monoxide in the air of a largish living room—a concentration that would give less than ten minutes' evacuation time.

The fast-increasing temperature also creates panic long before burns and pain result. The Canadian study admitted 'the wonder is not that people die in fires but that so many are able to escape that fate' and recognized our limited knowledge of panic, saying that 'the shock of discovery of fire, the involvement of children in other rooms for example, all induce a mental strain hard to visualise'.

The initial shock gains sometimes a strange expression in so-called *negative panic*, a stunned condition with inability to act rationally. In a London restaurant fire (reported in the *Evening News*, September 5, 1969), diners continued with their meal and one of them later remarked that 'it was a bit uncomfortable really. The smoke and the sirens of fire engines . . . but the food was too good to leave'. Truly stiff upper lip, one might say, but it is more likely that this behaviour was akin to negative panic, manifesting itself also in burning airliners whose passengers show a marked inability to escape and are often seen wandering dazed against the rush for exits to pick up a forgotten bottle of duty-free liquor. Some passengers in such a state refuse to leave an aircraft in an emergency without an overcoat because it is too cold outside. They have to be pushed to jump because they want to wait for stairs to arrive. Often they stop to light cigarettes outside in a pool of fuel before running for safety.

There is often an initial confusion in the very thought of fires which prepares the ground for panic in actual outbreaks. The heart-warming, comforting images of flames conflict with menacing associations. The sacred and profane, sad and joyous, solemn and ecstatic, sane and insane connotations struggle for supremacy. Our language is full of them. 'Fire in the belly' is complimentary. 'Seeing red' is a symbol of destruction. Red fire stands for hearth as well as murder, blood and sexual passion. And they all belong to the subconscious and the mysterious which made bomber pilots and victims describe burning cities equally as sights of 'awe-inspiring magnificence'. In the minds of pyromaniacs and other insane arsonists this mental struggle is won by the destructive elements before the fire is lit. In the minds of threatened people, the conflict is settled when fear becomes the dominant factor. Apart from the fire itself, many other sometimes trivial events can help make fear supreme. Blocked escape routes, as we saw, are perhaps the most important of these.

At the traditional oyster roast in a church at Baltimore, Maryland, some flames appeared following a minor explosion in 1956. Perhaps it was most unfortunate that there was no immediate rush for the door. Three men climbed a ladder to put out the fire. When 'one squirted something', a witness said, 'everybody yelled hooray, like it was a big joke.' The three men's failure to fight the fire suddenly became obvious. There were a thousand people trapped but the stampede began even before the flames grew to menacing proportions. A cruelly fought battle for the exit knew no mercy. Those who fell were trampled on. Eleven people, including two children, died. Most of the two hundred injured were victims of the panic rather than the conflagration.

A Cologne boarding-house fire raged on the first floor. It spread fast to the old staircase blocking the way both up and down. Two people climbed out on the window-sill. On the second floor, where there was not yet any immediate danger, people waited patiently at the windows to be evacuated by the fire brigade that had just arrived. Now, these also climbed out of the window. The first ladder was already approaching the more exposed two below when a flame blew out and a woman on the first floor panicked: she jumped to the street and got away with minor injuries. On the second floor there was still no sign of the fire. But two people up there, having seen the desperate leap, were immediately overwhelmed by panic and they also jumped. One was killed, the other suffered several broken bones.

In the same way as panic can be brought about by apparently innocuous events, it can also be averted by almost unnoticeable reassurances like a well lit emergency exit sign that is read by hardly anybody but noted subconsciously by most people in a cinema audience. The presence of a policeman or somebody who can retain by training or experience a sense of calmness and clarity of mind can also prevent panic. Newspapers report many cases of fire when a helpless—panicky?—crowd of on-lookers was suddenly mobilized for life-saving heroism by a determined move or authoritative command from a spectator or fireman.

In 1965, 200 firemen fought the blaze at a postal sorting office in London's Upper Street, Islington. Before they got there, one postman died and many more had to leap to safety. Arthur Giles who worked in the office held a roll-call and found that about seventy postmen and sorters were missing. He knew they must have been trapped upstairs, in the canteen, where they were having their break. He ran up the stairs but the smoke was already too dense. So he stopped after two flights up 'and stayed there shouting at the top of my voice', he said afterwards. 'I knew the men trapped upstairs could not see a hand in front of them. I was hoping they would follow the sound of my voice.' He kept shouting 'down this way!' The men heard him and although it took them time to get their bearings in the dark cloud of smoke, 'eventually they came stumbling down like blind mice'. That one man's voice forestalled panic not only by giving guidance and promising safety within reach, but also by giving the trapped men a definite line of action to take in place of a possible mad rush to self-destruction.

No legislation can, of course, count on the presence of a calm, experienced man or on the help of a born hero, especially now that psychologists at least know that heroism, the old choice between flight and fight, depends on distinct physiological processes just as much as on psychological ones. Recent research has discovered more and more of the inner mechanism of the body. When we experience emotion of any kind, we are aware 'of some changes in the tear glands, salivary glands, sweat glands, heart beat and stomach', said A. J. W. Taylor, lecturer in psychology, Victoria University, at the twenty-fourth annual conference of New Zealand fire engineers. 'All our reactions, whether joyous, mildly disturbing or frantic have their inner physical changes . . . When we face external threats our inner resources are marshalled to concentrate upon essentials such as flight or fight.' Once, it was thought that only external behaviour showed the difference between emotional states. Now it appears that the purely physiological reactions may be typical for each individual, and physical processes inducing fear or attack may be distinguished.

'Group behaviour can be quite different from a sum of the behaviour of its individual members' and a great deal of research has gone into this phenomenon. The evidence is, however, inconclusive, and it was only quite recently that Britain's Loughborough University has been assigned to study the behaviour of people in fire. That such research had not been carried out much earlier is only one example of incomplete fire investigations and the reluctance to employ scientific assistance in the quest for causes of fire and death.

Group behaviour, in fact, can lead to premature or even unnecessary panic. Loneliness can do the same to us. Overwhelmed by a hostile environment, even 'brave' men experience isolation and helplessness that may result in negative or positive panic. There is an element of panic in claustrophobia. The spaceman's loneliness can invite panic even when his computer tells him that all is well. Young soldiers have panicked when putting on gas masks for the first time. Novices at skin-diving are put to a hard test until experience teaches them that their silent environment is not hostile. The man alone with delayed information about the fire around him hardly ever gets a second chance to learn from experience how to combat Pan's curse on us.

CHAPTER FOUR

DEATH OF A SALESMAN

THE DEATH of a salesman came swiftly and painlessly. His body and surroundings were untouched by flames but the unmistakable signs were there to show that he had been aware of the blaze around him and that he had experienced the agony of fear.

That Saturday evening in June 1969 was a comparatively quiet one at the C Division of the London Fire Brigade. There were several fires in the division's East End area but none of them was big enough to require the presence of a professional investigator from the Fire Prevention Branch. In these cases, investigation is left to the officer in charge at the scene who would put in a standard report giving the 'supposed cause' for statistical and administrative purposes.

Stanley Walter Sewell, Assistant Divisional Officer, was the man on duty in the Prevention Branch. He spent the evening in the small, rather derelict office trying to catch up with ever-mounting paperwork. Then he returned home, within the fire station where the flat goes with the job, and although he remained 'on call', he hoped to put up his feet and watch television. At half-past ten in the evening there seemed to be a good chance that he could sleep that night.

At '2246 hours' the switchboard recorded a call to a small textile warehouse at Nos. 8–10 in a little side-street of the East End. Four pumps were to attend to it within a couple of minutes. Such small, 'routine fires' were of no concern to Sewell. But then there was a second call from a passer-by reporting fire at No. 6 of the same street. With two fires side by side, and eight pumps attending, the prevention branch had to be alerted. Sewell was on his way within minutes. In his car, he heard a 'persons reported' message on the crackling radio. This could have meant one or more people trapped, injured or killed by the fire.

A fireman directed him first to No. 6 where he had to get through the blaze in the ground floor warehouse to the back where a flimsy partition still prevented the flames from entering the office area. There was black smoke but no fire in there. A thin door, undamaged, led to a lavatory with a wash-basin. That is where Sewell found the salesman. He carefully noted the details while the fire-fighting went on outside and above.

The man, an Indian later identified by papers in his pockets, sat there with a wet handkerchief in one hand and a small key-sized torch in the other. The lavatory seat and cover under him were in the closed position and his clothes were in perfect order. The key to the main door was in his pocket. These clues indicated to Sewell that the man had not been suddenly overcome by smoke while he was in the lavatory but had probably tried to escape in there from the flames.

'An experiment I had once read about came back to me there,' Sewell said. 'Scientists put a few white mice in a cave and began to pump smoke into it. The smoke was not dense enough to keep the daylight from the mice which could have run through the smoke and away easily. Yet the mice retreated from the danger and huddled together at the far end of the cave, kind of waiting for death with the approaching smoke. They repeated the test several times and the reaction was always the same. Like most of us would revert to the animal instinct in such situations, this man must have retreated as far away from the fire as he could. Loneliness is a great inducer of panic. Our logic disappears fast. Most people are not trained for such situations. Some heroes are created by the moment, but most people react to crises with panic.'

Sewell's job was to find out what had happened. His first question was: how is it that two buildings burn at the same time? It might have been an unlikely coincidence or the two fires might have had the same origin or there might have been two seats of fires, indicating arson. As he began his investigation, a process of elimination, he had the great advantage of being on the scene while the fire was still burning. Every moment of further destruction and the inevitable damage caused by fire-fighting would obliterate more and more evidence.

As Sewell came out of No. 6 he made a mental note that although there was fire in the ground floor warehouse, the staircase area was still almost completely intact and the stairs, where the flames would naturally spread upwards, were undamaged right up to the first floor. No. 6, like the house next door, was a three-storey building and the fire seemed to be fiercest from its first floor upwards. Firemen told him that the stairs from the first floor up had been burnt out and they had to use ladders to climb further up from there. Could the fire have started on the first floor in No. 6? How would it spread to Nos. 8–10?

In Nos. 8–10, the severest destruction appeared to be at the back of the ground floor area—on the other side of the wall from the last refuge of the man in No. 6. Could the fire have started there? If so, how would it spread to No. 6?

'When I see a fire, I look for the spots where it is burning most fiercely,' explained Sewell. 'But I must be careful not to confuse the seat of the fire, the origin, with the seat of its development which may be far more destructive. If you drop a burning match in a metal waste-paper basket, this will be the seat of the fire. But there the flames would probably burn out. On the other hand, if the flames reached something above, that spot may well become the seat of development and the gate to disaster. Or if a faulty lighting fixture over-heats and drops on inflammable materials like oily rags, the fire will develop on the ground but the rags will not be the cause.'

Having registered his first impressions, Sewell then returned to the entrance and sought out the first firemen on the scene. How did they enter? Was the door open? Was there any sign of forced entry? In other words, could there have been a burglar or arsonist in the premises when the fire began? No, the door was locked, it had to be broken down. Any sign of forced entry on the windows? No. These were clues to eliminate arson. But if it was not arson, and if there was only one origin of the two fires, how did the fire spread from one building to the other? There was no apparent way for the flames. When later he examined the walls, especially between the two single-storey sections, Sewell found no holes, no cracks or gaps, not even cables, pipes or fireplaces that would run—and tunnel the fire— from one house to the other.

Sewell marked three suspicious spots where the fire seemed

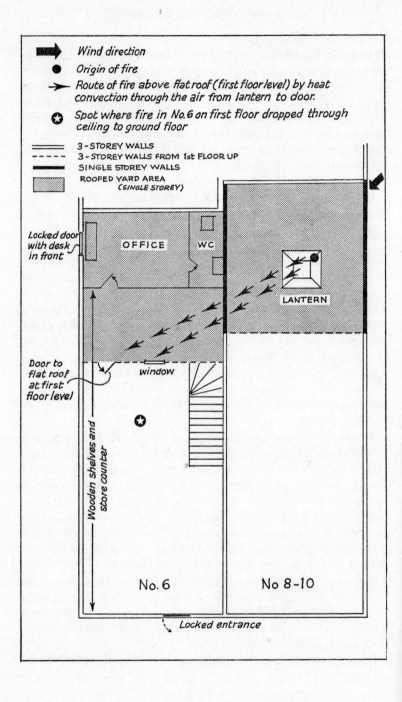

to be at its fiercest: one on the ground floor of No. 6 above
which there was a hole burnt into the ceiling; another on the
first floor above, near that hole; and a third at the back of the
ground floor in No. 8. He then made a rough sketch of the
premises. Both were three-storey buildings with basements,
brick load-bearing walls, partly enclosed timber staircases, and
roofs partly of tiles on battens and partly of zinc sheets on timber
boards. At ground level, all the houses around had small, enclosed back-yards. These two buildings were no exceptions, but
their yards had been roofed over to create two single-storey
extensions projecting at the rear. Both these extensions had
glazed lantern lights fitted to the ceiling. In No. 6, the far end
of this single-storey extension was used as the office.

Both ground floors had been used as wholesale warehouses.
In No. 6, shelves and a long store counter ran on the left-hand
side from the street front to the office partition. The fire had
caused great damage in the stock of domestic supplies like
cosmetics, dress jewellery, clothing and various products in
aerosol containers. Cardboard packages were stacked on racks
to the ceiling. In Nos. 8–10, domestic textiles were stored
similarly in huge quantities.

As the fire retreated from the powerful water jets, Sewell
began a long, painstaking visual examination. There was no
smell of accelerants—that again argued against arson. He
looked over each piece of timber. How much of it had burnt?
Which side of it was charred more deeply? He relied on his
great experience to tell him if the damage had been caused by
heat or direct flames. Noting smoke-discoloration on structures
and goods away from the flames, he could see which side was
more affected; and that told him whether the smoke had risen
to a particular spot from below or was driven there sideways by
draught.

'I used the simple clues and principles of fire investigation
which can be interpreted and coordinated by experience,' he
said. 'And it is mainly by experience that the cause of the fire
hits you in the eye so to speak. When you look at a door or
window frame, you know that fire is most likely to burn upwards, so you look for the lowest point: did the fire start there
or did it spread to there from somewhere else? From the depth
of charring you can tell more or less how long that piece of

timber burned. If you scratch it, you see the depth. Occasionally I'd use a knife to measure the depth.

'When rubble is burnt on the floor, even if the roof came down on it, I can clear it away a little and see, for instance, that the floor is damaged but is not burnt through. So the flames couldn't have got there from below, could they?

'Electrical installations, wiring, fittings and appliances cause a lot of fires and are tricky to investigate. But there are many clues you can go on. I had a case where lamp fittings had fallen on a bench which was badly burnt until it collapsed. Among the charred bits of wood I found an electric iron which had obviously dropped from the burning bench. The area appeared to be the seat of the fire, but what started it: the lamp or the iron? The iron had all the signs of having been exposed to flames and smoke from the outside. I then opened the iron and inside there was no trace of over-heating or malfunctioning that could start the fire. But the wires that had fallen from the lamp showed such clues: the discolouring is completely different if it comes from outside flames or inside over-heating by, say, shorting.

'Anyway, I spent the night in Nos. 6 and 8–10, looking for clues, photographing the remains step by step as the firemen gained ground. It was towards dawn that the police found relatives who came at once. I talked to the dead man's sons and got some useful information. They told me that their father suffered from a mild form of asthma for which he had been treated. Otherwise he was healthy, forty-five years old, and his sight and hearing were perfect. How is it then, it occurred to me, that he did not notice the fire in time to escape?

'The sons also told me that he was a very meticulous man who often worked on his books at night. That night he did the same getting ready for a stock-check on Monday. This point raised a question of arson once again, but later the books were found in perfect order—he had no reason to start a fire or commit suicide. Another useful piece of information I got was that whenever he worked at night, he would lock the front door and make sure that the protective shutters on the windows were all right because this was a deserted area at night with plenty of burglaries in the vicinity.

'I received the post mortem report, too: inhalation of fire

fumes was the cause of death. The CO_2 content of the air in the burning building was given to me as 69 per cent, far more than a man could tolerate even if it was just beginning to seep into the office area.

'In No. 6, the ground floor did not show signs of the fire's possible origin. If it had started there, it would have spread along the stocks burning through the partition at one end, which it didn't do, and up the stairs which again was not the case. I was back to square one and started all over again in several spots. The hole in the ceiling looked like one that had burnt through downwards. It was quite possible that the fire burned on the first floor for quite a while when at last it dropped down. But up there, once again, no trace of the seat of the fire.

'In Nos. 8–10, on the ground floor, there was a likely point of origin: at the far end, the roofed-over single-storey section must have been quite a furnace. It was so bad that the plaster had come completely off the walls—a more severe damage than elsewhere, also showing the duration of burning time there. The glazed lantern light was totally destroyed and the roof was burnt through: that's where the fire vented itself.

'This was an important clue: once the fire got up through there, the single-storey projections, surrounded by three-storey walls, would act like a flue. I checked it with the Met. Office: yes, the wind blew that evening in a direction that could carry heat between the three-storey walls from Nos. 8–10 to No. 6, but not strong enough to carry large burning pieces. In theory, I found the origin and the way it spread.

'Fire spreads in three ways: by direct burn or flames, by radiation which is the way a bar in an electric heater works, and by convection when the heat is carried by the air. Flames or radiated heat from that hole at the lantern could not have affected No. 6. But in this enclosure, a kind of chimney, the heat would create a lot of currents and turbulence and with the aid of the wind, the heat by convection could silently and stealthily reach No. 6 right above the head of the man working in the office.

'This heat would not be enough to burn through the wall. But if there were openings . . . Practical proof of my theory was on the first floor in No. 6. The door and window opening on to the flat roof were severely burnt. Yes, the fire could have entered through them. The pattern of the damage inside confirmed this. The window was adjacent to the timber stairs and the staircase from the first floor up was burnt out. Stocks were destroyed in the path of the fire right to the hole, where it dropped to the ground floor. Below that was the worst burnt part of the No. 6 warehouse.

'So what could have happened to the victim? As he worked, he would know nothing about the blaze for a long time. There was no window in the partition, so he could not see flames. Probably the smell was his first warning—and it is quite possible that he had swallowed a fair amount of carbon-dioxide before he realized that something was wrong. Even a small quantity of that gas is capable of slowing down the logic, decision-making power and movement of a man. He would open the door and the flames would hit him in the face.

'He might have made an attempt to escape. The light from the flames would be blotted out by dense smoke.

'Even though he knew the store well, he might have tried to use the small torchlight which he was still clutching when we found him. After an unsuccessful attempt, his logic would deteriorate even more. Panic would urge him to escape as far from the flames as possible. That would explain why he did not even try to move his desk and break down the locked door behind it—through there he would have been out of the building and safe. Instead, he retreated to the toilet. With a wet handkerchief he tried to defend himself. Probably he had only seconds left and died without pain. The intensifying heat and smoke in the office then discoloured everything although the flames never got through.'

The burnt-out lantern in Nos. 8–10 left behind no tangible evidence that in fact it did cause the fire. After Sewell's careful process of elimination, the fanlight remained the most likely 'supposed cause'. Yet when he wrote his report, he was obliged to add a rider: in Nos. 8–10 there had been customers in the store; although smoking had not been permitted there and the employee who had locked up at three in the afternoon saw no sign of fire, 'a lighted cigarette, put down or discarded amongst stocks' of textiles 'remains a possibility' as a cause of this fire.

This rider destroys, of course, all the effect of Stanley Sewell's logic, reasoning and painstaking investigation. But sentences like this accompany more than half of the fire reports all over the world and they tacitly admit that fire investigation is a rather primitive art which still cannot do much to turn the tide of losses.

CHAPTER FIVE

TRIAL BY ERROR

'SMOKING' AND 'children playing with matches' usually gain prominent places in the casual lists of fire statistics. Yet everybody in the fire world knows—and privately admits—that these statistics are exaggerated. Arson as a cause of fires usually gets away with a modest ten per cent. Yet it is well-known to the specialists that the real proportion of incendiary fires must be at least twice as large. 'Must be', because in the absence of sufficient evidence many suspicious cases remain in the 'cause unknown' category. There are plenty of excuses for the investigators, but the fact remains that the staggering number of inexact reports and intelligent guesses not only leaves individual mysteries often unsolved, but also hinders better prevention by statistical hazard-spotting.

Many fire investigators argue that no further development in this detective work will ever be possible. Percy Bugbee, the American fire protection specialist of international renown, admits that in the United States 'fire investigation has not been accorded the importance that it deserves'. This polite understatement, which recognizes the advancement potential in this work if more attention were focused on it, is equally true about practically any other country.

The limitations of better investigation begin with the training, choice and number of specialists charged with this duty. Most of them are experienced fire-fighters although many have only police background, and practically all of them are expected to learn as they go. Fires are strictly chemical reactions. Most fire investigators lack the knowledge of chemistry that is vital for the clear understanding of fires, and this is why most 'experienced fire investigators are liable to err', according to Paul L. Kirk, Professor of Criminalistics at the University of California.

He recognized that the vast amount of relevant publications are of a highly technical nature which are understandable to the trained chemist but beyond the comprehension of the average investigator. As chemists are rarely called in for fire investigations—and their lack of 'detective' training would make them poor investigators—he wrote an excellent simplified handbook for the fire specialist. Before that, there were only two such books: one was a useful collection of old case histories published in 1945, the other was very long and rather more demanding. It is not untypical of the situation that when this author interviewed an admittedly small sample, some seventy investigators all over the world, more than half of them had never heard of Kirk's *Fire Investigation*,* only six claimed to have seen it, and one said he had read it.

It would be almost impossible to paint a universal picture of fire investigators because their background and circumstances vary greatly from country to country and even from town to town.

In New York, the job is done by ninety-one fire marshals and eleven supervisory personnel under the command of Chief Fire Marshal Vincent Canty. Their number suggests a very large department—but only until we take into consideration that New York alone has about fifty thousand building fires a year, more than a whole country of the size of France or Germany. This fine body of dedicated men with an impressive investigation record has its headquarters near Wall Street, in the Municipal Building, where a spring-loaded half-door like those in the bars of Westerns leads to their large, over-heated open floor. They work there in their shirt-sleeves and so display a variety of guns stuck into shoulder-holsters or just under belts near their spines. Once the department belonged to the police but now weapons are discretionary: they have to buy their guns if they want them. Apparently they all do. It is perhaps understandable because they still do everything a policeman would do, except carry out actual physical arrest, and because in America even ordinary fire-fighters are regularly abused, pelted and even shot at by people they try to help.

New York fire marshals come from the fire service, bringing all their experience to the Bureau of Fire Investigation, and

* John Wiley & Sons Inc., New York, 1969.

then they have the exceptional benefits of a specialist training course. Unfortunately, this course reflects the general belief that investigation cannot be taught and therefore much of the emphasis is on report writing, administration and police-type instructions. For report writing they even get a glossary to explain that an ARTICLE is 'A thing of a particular class or kind', and if the trainee investigator is still in doubt, to enlighten him that a THING is 'An object of value. Personal belongings. Product of work or activity. A material substance of a particular kind. An inanimate object as distinguished from a living being.'

They are taught a great deal about giving descriptions, the circumstances that justify 'the use of deadly physical force' (shooting), and legal expressions like 'dying declaration' which, for instance, will not be valid unless it meets certain requirements including '(a) The declarant must be dying. (b) The declarant must know that he is dying. (c) The declarant must have given up all hopes of recovery. (d) The declarant must die'.

For testifying, an investigator should wear a tie and relax by taking 'a few deep breaths'. For 'courtroom conduct and demeanour' the trainee gets plenty of rules and useful hints. He must plan his 'suitable attire (neat and conservative)'. When he takes the oath, he should speak firmly and clearly, and 'keep revolver out of sight (if possible)'.

On the witness stand, he can rely on twenty-five listed pieces of advice. No. 1 is 'sit upright'. No. 2 urges 'keep feet flat on floor'. No. 5 warns 'avoid doodling with key, pencil or paper. It is important for the officer on the witness stand to exercise dignity, courtesy and courage'. No. 7 calls for patience, and No. 12 rules that 'there should never be any demonstration of bias towards the defendant' because, it is later explained, it is wrong to 'give the impression that you are seeking conviction'.

'Tell the truth' is No. 16.

In most American states it is the fire marshals' duty to investigate fires. They may come under all sorts of government departments like the state treasury, they may be appointed by the state governor or officials such as the insurance commissioner, or they may be elected officials serving as ex-officio fire marshals. The appointment may be indefinite, but in several states the marshal serves only for a definite, inhibitive term of

four years. In many states like California, investigators are, in
fact, police officers with all the police powers, including arrest.
They tend to be arson-orientated—their office is often called
the arson section or a name to that effect—and this deprives
the investigation of non-maliciously caused fires of some of its
importance. The average Los Angeles investigator gets 1,107
dollars (detective sergeant rate) plus a great deal of overtime
worth at least a hundred dollars a month, but they do shiftwork
and fatigue is a constant problem.

A very large part of the United States is served only by
volunteer firemen. If the full-time departments do not always
bother to conduct an investigation, volunteers sometimes call in
experts but mostly just forget about this complicated task.
'No one can expect them to do this job,' said John Stuerwald,
Assistant Manager of the Fraud and Arson Bureau of the
American Insurance Association, in New York. 'We work for
insurance companies and our agents up and down the country
must have police and fire experience as well as investigation
training, knowledge of accounting, psychology, chemical and
electrical engineering. The guy who wants to pick up a buck as
a volunteer can't have the experience, so perhaps he'd better
leave investigations alone.'

The essentially police-trained investigators are also an
acute problem in the United States and yet very little has been
done about it. It was as long as ten years ago that Battalion
Chief C. W. Stickney, Chief Investigator of Portland, Oregon,
wrote about them in the journal of Arson Investigators:
'When such an inexperienced person is required to investigate
"undetermined" or "suspicious" fires, he will probably spend
but a few moments at this wet, cold and unfamiliar fire scene
conducting what might be called a "tip-toe" investigation.
However, he may not hesitate to close the case by rendering a
final, unsubstantiated opinion as to the cause. It is a sad picture
to watch some such unequipped person tip-toeing into the
muck of the fire scene, with trousers held knee-high as he peers
credulously about the burned timbers . . . he will usually be
quickly discouraged and focus his attention on other areas—
probably looking for some loose-lipped Lesbian with a homosexual twitch, on the popular assumption that all incendiary
fires are caused by sex-crazed pyromaniacs . . .'

He also complained—and this is also still perfectly valid—that after a million-dollar robbery the FBI sends swarms of agents to chase the villains, but after an equally damaging fire only one or two men can be spared for the job.

While in America all fires are regarded as accidental until proven otherwise, in Germany it is the other way round: having a fire amounts to breaking the law that guards public safety, and so, automatically, all fire investigations must be done by the police. Local police who attend all fires with the firemen get only very elementary and fragmentary instruction about fire investigation and their main job really is to spot suspicious cases. The firemen's experience is cut out from the beginning apart from the advice he may render. If a local police station feels that a particular case is suspicious or demands more expert knowledge, it must call in the local specialists from the criminal police. These specialists are detectives assigned to arson investigation after a three-week course, and they participate in an experience exchange with colleagues from other towns for three weeks in every second year. If they need answers to some specific technical problems or require scientific assistance, they can turn to forensic and other experts at the criminological institute.

Most cases never get beyond the local police. If the specialists were consulted in every case, they would not have the time even to register the fire. Take, for instance, Cologne, a town with a great deal of industry and a population approaching the million mark. The police fire department there has only three officers and one of these, with less than four years of service, is regarded as just about ready for real investigation work. Kriminal Hauptmeister Boge, who has engineering and police training, and has been in this section for fourteen years, knows only too well that 'there is a chronic lack of time. It depends on luck how long a case may take: it may be an hour, it may be weeks. A recent not very big furniture storehouse fire took three weeks to investigate'. These men work from 7.30 in the morning till 5.30 in the afternoon, and then may be on night call, in and out of bed. 'Wives get used to the night-calls, but our constantly dirty and foul-smelling clothes are always a source of irritation.'

In other parts of Germany the situation is just the same—a

small number of specialists are supposed to investigate a large number of fires, and in Munich, for instance, more than a quarter of the fires remain of unknown origin. But these German detectives at least settle in their jobs and tend to regard fire investigation as a career. In Britain, where the police are called in by the fire brigade in cases of fatal fires or suspected arson, any detective may do the job because there is no specialist section. In Australia, police have arson squads. But former arson detectives complained in Melbourne: 'It takes a lot of time to learn the ropes but two or three years later, when you're beginning to master it all, you're suddenly transferred to some other duties and a new man can begin struggling.'

In Britain, as in Australia, most fires are investigated by the fire-fighters themselves, and the officer in charge at the scene must write a report. Firemen's training is still based on the *Manual of Firemanship* which was published in 1945, and was reprinted with some patching up many times. The *Manual* consists of nine volumes, some 2,500 pages, of which two and a half pages deal with The Cause Of The Fire, and a single further page is all there is about arson. It is widely recognized that revision of this miniature investigation section is overdue, but it is accepted that 'these things take time'. A short confidential guide for British police, *The Investigation of Fires*, was due for a complete rewrite more than ten years ago. It still is.

When British and Australian firemen handle a difficult case, they can enlist the help of professional investigators, who participate automatically if the fire is large or causes injuries. But once again, comparatively few such specialists are available —it is a matter of funds, availability of the right men and their training—and even these have to divide their limited time between duties of investigation and prevention work, which includes never-ending jobs like inspection of premises.

A revealing feature of fire investigation backwardness is that it relies to a tremendous extent on the least reliable element: the witness. An experienced German investigator said in Fankfurt-am-Main that 'there is only one sure way of telling how a fire began—and that's by asking the man who saw it'. He said this with a derisory smile to underline the exaggeration, the fruit of frustration, but he made it quite clear that there was a strong element of truth in this sweeping statement.

An important research project has recently been carried out for the British Home Office and many of its findings are now under consideration. One of these is a startling statistical table that shows the type of evidence which led to the 'supposed causes' of fires. The researchers examined 5,018 case histories where causes had been established. More than one-third of these results were based merely on the reports made by witnesses who had actually seen the fire start. Other witness statements were the sole basis of a further thirteen per cent of the successful investigations. In addition to that, in more than a quarter of the cases the investigators' examination of the physical evidence at the scene of fire was supported by valuable contributions from witnesses. Therefore, *in almost half of the five thousand cases, witnesses were the sole source of the final findings—and in all, three-quarters of the 'supposed cause' reports were fully or partially dependent on what witnesses remembered.*

From interviews, it now emerges that the situation may be even worse in several countries. In France, Belgium, Holland and Italy, fire investigators may base some sixty per cent of their findings on witness evidence.

It has long been accepted that the 'absolute witness' does not exist. An American defence attorney proved this in court when he cross-examined an eyewitness in a murder case. The witness could only testify he had seen the defendant take aim with his gun, observed the flash and the fall of the victim, and he remembered the bang. He did not see the bullet leave the barrel, travel through the air and hit the victim's body. The witness had to admit that the defendant might have fired a blank at the same time as another gunman shot and killed the victim.

Most fire witnesses can give a far from perfect recollection of events. Aircrash witnesses usually claim to have seen a 'ball of fire in the sky' even if later it is clearly proved that the fire started only on impact. Few people are accurate observers, and in the excitement caused by what they see they not only fall victim to optical illusions, but also tend to confuse time and sequence of events. They relate what they sincerely believe to be true recollection but subconsciously they fill in gaps of memory with their imagination.

Although the colour of flames and smoke, especially in the

early stages of an inferno, can be a most useful clue for investigators as to the cause and intensity of the fire, witnesses make
the most confusing statements about their observation. In a
Marseilles hotel fire arson was suspected because the owner had
already been involved in gang warfare. Statements by the staff
revealed that there had been some gasoline in the store room,
but firemen knew that the flames reached that part of the
building only after their arrival. Investigators were therefore
anxious to find out if gasoline or other hydrocarbon liquids, the
most usual accelerants applied by arsonists, had been burning
at the beginning. They interviewed more than a dozen witnesses
who all remembered 'quite clearly' the colours in question.
Three stated that the flames were dark, brownish yellow and
there was 'a lot of black smoke'—an indication of always
suspect hydrocarbons. Others saw the flames were red, yellow,
white, 'sort of greyish' and even blue. The smoke colours they
remembered also ranged from white to black. Some of these
statements could be explained by the vantage points occupied
by the witnesses: those who stared into moonlight were bound
to see lighter colours than those who observed flames and smoke
with the dark background of a high unlit building. (Ultimately,
the cause remained unknown although arson was still strongly
suspected.)

To bring out the optimum performance from a witness
investigators need all the well-tried interrogation techniques
together with the methods of verifying statements (vantage
point, time, etc.), but paradoxically, unlike policemen, fire
officers receive no such formal training.*

The most disappointing part of fire investigation is, however,
that the physical evidence at the scene of the average case—the
overwhelming majority of fires—gets very little investigating
time and attention. The Home Office research project, already
mentioned, led to startling results in this respect, too.

It studied 3,055 fires after which the examination of the
physical evidence was vital to reach the final causal verdict. Of
these there were only six cases on which investigators spent more
than twenty hours each. Five of the six were accepted, however,
as unsolved mysteries.

* Instead of locally organized sporadic lectures, Britain's Fire Service Technical
College has now included the subject in its regular curriculum.

Only 157 fires seemed to have warranted more than two but fewer than twenty hours each—and half of them resulted still in 'cause unknown' reports.

The remaining 2,892 fires, ninety-five per cent of the sample, were subjected to less than two hours of investigation per case—and 319 of these, eleven per cent, were passed as 'cause unknown' without any further ado.

If all these are added up, the result shows that although admittedly, the sample includes small and insignificant fires, *four-fifths of the mystery verdicts are reached by less than two hours of investigation.* According to several specialists, this 'less than two hours' could mean no more than a ten-minute glance-round by the officer in charge of putting out the fire.

The effort expressed in man-hours would not matter if investigators were aided by some powerful magic or a scientific ready reckoner to simplify their job and make them infallible. This, however, is not the case. Without checking every single investigation it is impossible to reach exact figures, but many experts confidentially estimate that in the United States, Australia and Europe, half of the alleged 'supposed causes' come from experienced assessment and intelligent guesswork rather than tangible evidence.

Increased investigation investment is hindered not only by lack of funds, but also by prevailing attitudes. 'What a fire investigator most needs is luck,' said a Frankfurt detective, and this view was apparently supported by a British loss adjuster, writing in the *Institution of Fire Engineers Quarterly*, December 1965, who referred to the insurers' fire investigator as finding physical evidence only 'if he was lucky'. F. E. Woolhead, Staff Fire Control Officer of the Ford Motor Company, claimed that 'the investigation of apparently minor fires with the object of preventing possible future major incidents may not be as exciting, or as well appreciated, as similar work following a serious fire; but it can be far more satisfying to those of us whose responsibilities include protecting our plants from the consequences that disastrous fires can bring'.*

Investigators all over the world can explain away why this kind of satisfaction is often sought in a few minutes and mostly

* Paper presented to the Merseyside Branch, Industrial Fire Protection Association, April 17, 1968.

in less than two hours. They claim that if you are experienced, the cause of an outbreak and of the fire development 'just hits you in the eye'. A fairly high-ranking British government official admitted off the record that 'you cannot ignore the value of the loss or even the value of the property involved. Most fires are just not worth the trouble of going into long investigations. You look at it, jump to conclusions if you like, and accept the cause that seems to be most obvious. It's different, of course, if the damage is large or there is loss of life or suspected arson'. To the argument that this kind of average investigation prevents statistical hazard-spotting his answer was that 'statistics are always inaccurate and no set of figures can save lives'.

Another widespread view that 'the evidence is usually destroyed by the fire' seems to find support in the fact that the bigger the fire the more investigation follows it and yet the more unlikely it becomes to discover the supposed cause: in the British research project the biggest fires were shown to have received the most man-hours of investigation and yet this category contained the highest proportion of cause unknown (five-sixths) reports. While the strong element of truth in this view and the difficulties it implies are obvious, it overlooks the question: what kind of investigation is being done at all? If fire investigation is in its infancy, this view commits infanticide because it ignores the fact that until fingerprinting was discovered, judges would have laughed at any prosecution attempt to prove without witnesses that the suspected murderer had ever visited the victim's room. It is also oblivious of now so pitifully ridiculous stories like the one about the British military court of inquiry which was convinced at the end of World War I that the fragmentary burnt remains of an aircrash were insufficient for the investigation of the accident and that the cause must have been in the realm of the 'what goes up must come down' principle.

The beginning of all scientific and technological advances depends on attitudes: refusal to acknowledge the existence of the impossible and determination to succeed against all odds. It may well turn out that fire investigation is an exception. But officials, who never fail to pay solemn lip-service to the importance of this work, know perfectly well that regular fire investigation, introduced during World War II from the fear of sabotage, has already produced considerable advancement of the technique and has led to much more conscious and effective fire prevention than anybody would have ventured to predict.

It is almost impossible to measure good fire prevention, the outcome of careful investigation, because it is at its best when the results are negative—it is impossible to claim credit for fires that did not happen. A slow-down in the rate of increase of fire damage can be an indication of success. Perhaps the most convincing direct evidence was produced in Buenos Aires where the fire brigade (Direccion Bomberos) is part of the federal police but enjoys full independence. Its prevention section is the only Argentinian government body that has the right to control adherence to the fire regulations in dwellings and industry. An investigation section was set up in the late 1950's and within a few years its work resulted at least temporarily in an actual decrease in the number of large fires. Since then, the rate of increase in overall fire losses has also been checked to some extent.

In all it appears that apart from better techniques, training and facilities, fire investigation needs the spirit of what a German detective once summed up as, 'Never let go, sir: that is the only rule. I like to keep touch of 'em once I've got 'em'.

The technique of fire investigation is widely varied and utilizes a vast amount of fire-fighting experience. Without attempting for a moment to give a full description of it, some examples might help towards the appreciation of its undeniably enormous scope.

The main object of fire-fighting is to break up the deadly triangle—heat, fuel and oxygen—which produced the fire, by cooling the fuel, and all materials present, below ignition temperature and, if possible, by excluding air supply. The main objective of fire investigation is to reconstruct conditions where and how the first fire triangle was formed, and how the fire spread from there. It is for this purpose that the preservation of evidence is vital. Apart from pilfering and careless handling of the remains, like dumping them in the most completely burnt-out area, which the investigator always suspects as a likely spot of the outbreak, the fire brigade itself can destroy many clues not only by their actual work, but also by their traditional helpful intention to leave everything 'shipshape'.

A basic concern of the investigator is to differentiate between incendiary, spontaneous and accidental fires. It has often been admitted in trade journals and at specialist gatherings, but never to the general public, that a fairly significant section of the investigators not only suspect incendiarism in all fires as all investigators are supposed to do, but go to the scene with a strong preconceived idea that it must have been arson and all they try to do is to prove this theory. Many others have different pet causes like smoking, faulty wiring or even the old, though now less widespread, excuse, spontaneous combustion.

Spontaneous fires are, in fact, a category by themselves among accidental cases because they are caused by a chemical reaction without the presence of sparks, flames or any other outside heat. The conditions in which these destructive reactions may occur are, however, so well known that lack of prevention qualifies them for the heading of negligence-caused fires—an important division of accidental outbreaks. Spontaneous combustion may begin in places like stores of chemicals or holds of cargo boats, but they are found mostly in hay-stacks. The investigators can rely on many clues in spotting spontaneity as opposed to maliciously started fires.

The worst rural danger period is between five to ten weeks after stacking when the hay is only partially cured. A fire outside this period arouses immediate suspicion. Spontaneous combustion begins *inside* the stack, unlike the incendiary fire, and vents itself by burning a chimney to the exterior. An important observation investigators make is when firemen spread apart a burning stack: if it was spontaneous combustion, the hay not yet on fire would immediately burst into flames. Finally, an important tell-tale sign is that hay in which the fire has been spontaneous has a very dark colour and laboratory examination reveals a higher than usual acidity content. With so many weapons in the armoury of the investigator, the wide acknowledgement of the fact that many incendiary hay-stack fires are regularly attributed to spontaneous origin is a scathing comment on the investigating zeal.

We shall deal with arson elsewhere; but it applies to incendiary fires as well as to all others that the investigator's first major task is to locate the seat of the fire, where an explanation of how and when it all began may await him. This is chiefly

3

done by a two-way process of constant probing: the physical evidence—all the remains of a fire, not forgetting the unaffected areas—is examined to trace the pattern of the fire leading to a suspected point or area of origin, from where the supposed pattern is re-checked backwards to see if the theory can be substantiated. This entire process is tested step by step in the light of other available evidence like the statements of witnesses, fire brigade, people familiar with the building, and also against the investigator's knowledge of general fire behaviour. This latter is, in fact, so constantly and prominently in the minds of fire detectives that many have come to talk about Fire as if it was a person. 'Fire plays many tricks on you,' they say, 'Fire can walk along narrow ledges, Fire can jump a couple of floors up, it is nothing for Fire to be in and out of windows, and Fire can run up an elevator shaft leaving hardly any traces in no time.'

In tracing the pattern, the investigator looks for the lowest point of fire damage where usually, but by no means invariably, the seat of the fire is 'because Fire, as a rule of thumb, likes to go upwards'. In special circumstances, for instance just under ceilings where hot gases accumulate, there may be a considerable lateral spread before the upward trend continues and the fire can vent itself. Downward burns are also possible, particularly if accelerant liquids are present, because these penetrate and seep through the gaps, and as a principle, investigators take great pains to avoid confusing such lower yet secondary seats of fire with the origin. (In homes or department stores, for instance, where curtains may be the first to catch fire, wind or draught may play the flames over a limited floor area where holes may be burnt. Investigators tend to regard such holes near windows as red herrings.)

Because of the upward trend, the basic fire pattern is an upward conical shape, rising and spreading at the open end and pointing at the seat of the fire at the other. This 'pointing arrows' theory, when it is applied to the whole blaze, creates a much more complicated fire pattern. It may show, for instance, how fire spread into an adjoining room through a rat hole in the wall. It may also call attention to destroyed but nevertheless important features such as some obstruction in the way of the flames or the presence of highly inflammable materials that caused fast lateral spread. To recognize these ever-present arrows, investigators compare the extent of burns on the top and bottom of shelves, burnt edges of structural woodwork like doors, the ruins of furniture, and on both sides of partitions. Sometimes, if possible, they even reconstruct the scene from the remains for clarification of the pattern which has been obliterated not only by the fire but also by fire-fighting, rescue or possibly cleaning up.

The most suspect areas of possible origin are those that have been burnt most fiercely, but this is yet another pitfall which has trapped many, especially police-trained, investigators and resulted in their jumping to false conclusions. For, very frequently, the spark or the small flame that starts the sequence of events causes little damage in its immediate neighbourhood but spreads to more inflammable areas or to fuel; and it is this secondary seat of fire, the seat of development, that leads ultimately to an inferno.

In finding the spot from where a fire originated, investigators carefully consider the time element: when did it all start, how long have certain areas been burning before discovery and alarm, was it a slow or fast build-up with relatively low temperatures or great intensity?

One clue is the *depth of charring* in timber. It is usually reckoned that the charring of hard and soft woods progresses about an inch in forty minutes at the average rate of burning at about 1,500°F. A more slowly burning fire would produce hair-thin, tight-lipped cracks in the wood; faster-than-average burning leaves wider yawning cracks behind. This factor is usually judged just by experience because, it is claimed, 'the investigator has a sharp eye for the depth of charring'.

If in doubt, many investigators use ordinary knives which they press into the charred area, noting how far the blade would go with little or no resistance, because beyond that point, the uncharred wood becomes harder to penetrate. Others may merely scrape off a bit of the charred wood with their fingernails. Forensic laboratories can measure the depth of charring accurately but this assistance is rarely required by the investigators whose reasons are manifold. They like to reserve this weapon for the most serious or spectacular cases where they are reluctant to commit themselves because there may be many questions asked in court or at a public inquiry.

They are usually also not encouraged to incur this extra expense and they have a rather low opinion of the potential value of any scientific assistance. In America, several people mentioned yet another reason: 'The accurate measurement of charring is still no proof to convict an arsonist. So why bother?'

A simple engineering gauge, perfectly suitable to do the job accurately, does exist. A former investigator, now a high-ranking British civil servant to whom anonymity and oxygen come in one breath said: 'Oh yes, I used to have one. Found it very handy. What? No, come to think of it, it was never a standard issue. I guess nobody thought about making it one. I saw it in some engineering shop and then picked one up second-hand in a street-market. One or two other chaps in the service used it, too.'

In principle, the value of accurate measurement is contested because charring is influenced by many factors like moisture content, intensity of flames, and the uneven progress of fire-fighting that lets certain areas burn longer than others. Scientists therefore attach no more than casual attention to it. In practice, however, all studies on investigation deal with it repeatedly and at length, all fire investigators are quick to mention it whenever their work is discussed, and reference is made to it in nearly all final fire reports.

Another important clue investigators use concerns *windows and mirrors*. Very slow and not very intense build-up of a fire, like the smouldering of an upholstered chair, means incomplete burning. It emits a great deal of smoke and so heavily stained windows indicate such a fire. Melted glass with rounded corners shows a slow build-up that reached a high temperature. Faster accumulation of heat in a room would crack the glass in many places but would leave it fairly clean. If a big fire flares up in less than three or four minutes, the windows will hardly be stained at all but the glass will crack in clean lines and large pieces round the frames.

The examination of *walls* also yields useful clues: if the plaster has fallen off but the general damage is not too severe, a sudden big rise in temperature is indicated. In a slower large fire where the flames have not reached the wall, the wallpaper smoulders and leaves a black coating on the plaster where the paper pattern often remains visible. Investigators usually term this as 'charring' but in fact *pyrolysis*, heat decomposition, has taken place without actual combustion.

In scientific terms, practically none of the common fuels for fire does actually burn. 'Wood, coal, plastic, and many other solid organic compounds *do not burn*. When they are heated, they decompose to smaller molecules with greater volatility and flammability, and to carbon. This is the process of pyrolysis, and it is the fundamental explanation of nearly all fires.'*

It is the gaseous material released by pyrolysis that burns, creating and feeding the flames. When volatile liquid fuels are heated, they produce a vapour which burns readily well before pyrolysis could take place. These processes start many chains of chemical reactions which, in turn, create further useful but often confusing clues, like colours of smoke and flames, for the investigator. Photographs, particularly if they are taken in colour during the fire, can thus be very helpful.

To reveal the intensity of the fire in certain areas and to serve as potential arrows marking the direction from where the heat came to a given spot, the difference between heat and actual fire damage is a good ally of the fire detective. Chromium and most types of shiny metals, for instance, would discolour to a fairly regular extent if they were subjected to heat. Light fixtures, toasters, irons have frequently indicated with considerable accuracy the temperatures at different points and even the progress of the fire. The colours range from yellow (due to about 450°F.), through brown, blue, shades of red, salmon, lemon and white to sparkling white (from 2,400°F.). After cooling, the lighter colours of low and high temperatures disappear, but the darker (medium temperature) circles around them are a more permanent discoloration and indicate the previous presence of great heat.

In structural fires several rooms will often remain unburned but will be 'heat damaged' and discoloured by soot, condensed moisture and a dark, greasy film. These are mostly the by-products of pyrolysis and so their laboratory analysis could perhaps reveal what was the original fuel that burned; but practically no research appears to have been carried out in this respect.

* Kirk: *Fire Investigation*, p. 64.

It is a tremendously complex and time-consuming task to interpret all these and other vague clues correctly and find a way out of the seemingly endless maze of possibilities. A relatively simple case may illustrate this point.

Reginald E. F. Whillock, a Divisional Officer of the London Fire Brigade, was once called to a fire at dawn in a three-storey building. He noticed that the fire had caused the most severe damage in an office on the first floor, but it was in the second floor flat where a dead man was found:

'He was lying face down with his left arm hooked over the right-hand corner of a two kilowatt electric fire which had also supported the upper part of his body. His arm was almost totally destroyed, his head and trunk were extensively burnt. He was fully dressed and wore slippers. How would the fire on the first floor reach him up there? Or could it be that his death started the fire and the burning spread to the floor below?

'If the fire spread upwards, it would be a most unlikely coincidence that he would collapse over the heater. I examined the heater. The switch was in the ON position and connected to a 15 amp. adaptor inserted into a three-pin socket in the skirting board next to the fireplace. The socket switch was also in the ON position. It appeared a likely possibility that he had collapsed for some reason, and fallen unconscious over the heater which ignited his clothes and body. I checked the fuse: it had ruptured the electric heater circuit, but I knew from experience that there would be plenty of time before that for the fire to start.

'The first firemen on the scene told me that they had found the door and windows closed when they got there. Walls, windows, everything including doors and furniture were heavily stained which was a pointer to slow, low-intensity burning for a considerable time—at least six or seven hours. In such cases, the smokey windows prevent anybody outside seeing the flames, even if there are any, for a long time, and a particular danger is that when the door or window is finally opened the sudden supply of oxygen creates a ferocious flashover.

'What the staining implied was supported by the fact that the man was fully dressed. I checked his bed: it had not been slept in. The television set was connected to the same circuit as the heater and so it had also been cut off. But I found that the TV set was still switched on. All the evidence was therefore falling into place in the jigsaw. Later, in fact, the pathologist's report confirmed that the man had died from natural causes and the severe burning of the body occurred after death. This was an unusual case as the majority of deaths in fires are due to asphyxiation. Though people say that so-and-so was 'burnt to death', it hardly ever occurs for it's the fumes that kill most victims and the flames damage only the corpse.

'In this particular case, all that remained for me to do was to discover the connection between the fires on the first and second floor. Beneath the body I found that the carpet and floorboards had burned through in a very slow, smouldering manner. There was hardly any lateral spread. This charring continued into the concealed, timber-joisted space between the floor and the ceiling below. In this confined cavity, the heat would build up gradually. The fire would not spread much because of the limited amount of air to support it. Eventually it did burn through the lath and plaster ceiling. The charring round the hole there was consistent with the theory of a downward burn. In the room below, there was hardly any immediate burning around the hole in the ceiling. Through the hole, burning particles would fall and cause a secondary but more extensive fire.

'When in the morning I spoke to people who used that room on the first floor as an office, they described the contents of the room and this, too supported the findings: under the hole there were enough inflammable materials to serve as a seat of development of the fire, but not enough to feed flames that would reach the ceiling like a torch, had the fire started there in the first place.'

Having located the original seat of this fire and estimated the approximate time of the outbreak, Whillock was in a comparatively easy position to determine the actual cause, the material that was first ignited, and the way the fire spread to the seat of development. In many fire reports, however, the supposed cause is given in almost meaningless laconic terms, like 'over-heating of electric motor', that give no guidance to future prevention (what caused the over-heating? whose fault was it? could it have been foreseen and forestalled?).

Naming the first material to catch fire, the initial fuel without which the heat would have remained harmless, is also frequently omitted together with sufficient answers to other vital questions—why and how did the fire spread, how and when was the alarm raised, was there any delay in discovering the fire, was the turn-out and performance of the fire brigade satisfactory, was there any negligence or lack of precaution or lesson to be learned?

CHAPTER SIX

FIRE BY WATER

A FAMILY was away for only a week in October. Arriving home at Withington, Manchester, the wife entered the bedroom and noticed two thin, long burn marks on her dressing table. No friends or relatives were supposed to visit the house in their short absence and there was no sign of a break-in. The mystery of the burns puzzled them enough to ask the local firemen about it. Luckily, they touched nothing in the room until a fire prevention officer called and discovered the cause of a potential fire disaster that would have become a 'cause unknown' case.

On the lower, middle section of the dressing table stood a fairly powerful hand-mirror. Its magnifying side had a focal length of eighteen inches. By an odd coincidence, this was just the distance between the mirror and the opposite wooden side of the well of the table. By yet another coincidence, the mirror faced the window just at the right angle to pick up the sun-rays and reflect them in a piercing spotlight on to the table.* The rest was like the children's game of setting fire to paper with the aid of a magnifying glass. The horizontal burn marks clearly showed the movement of the sun. They were interrupted only at two points where glazing bars would throw a momentary shadow on the mirror. Why two lines? As it was autumn, on every sunny day of the week the sun travelled on a lower course and so the reflection would rise to a higher level. As the meteorological records revealed, there were only two days in that week with more than an hour's sunshine: three hours on one day and five on another. In summer, and if tissue paper or other more readily combustible material than wood had received the reflected sun-rays, a major fire would have obliterated all the evidence.

* See illustrations between pages 152 and 153.

The chronicle of fires is full of such freak causes. In Chicago, the role of the Manchester hand-mirror was played by a spherical glass bowl containing flowers in water, and the result was a smouldering fire in an upholstered armchair.

The radiation of sun-rays has often been suspected as a cause of hay-stack fires but, in most cases, the evidence was missing. An exception was when, after a devastating blaze in a concrete barn, spontaneous combustion could be ruled out completely. Arson remained a possibility and the owner came under suspicion because the barn was usually locked and there was no sign of a break-in. The local fire brigade called for specialist assistance and the scientists who visited the scene noticed a strange 'spotlight' on the floor of the barn—near the area where the heat had been fiercest during the fire. They found that a small triangular window in the top corner of the barn was so situated that it would have focused the sun-rays into this spotlight of about two inches in diameter. Watched by the scientists, it grew brighter and brighter as it travelled on the floor just after noon. About an hour later, following a parabolic course, the light came to rest on a lens-shaped glass, the bottom part of a broken milk bottle, which had ultimately created a powerful enough concentration of hot light to start the fire.

One of the strangest conflagrations is still *sub judice* in Germany: it was caused by water. There was a not very menacing fire in a factory and some workers volunteered to tackle it while waiting for the fire brigade. The workers knew that a store, next door to the seat of the fire, had already been subjected to a great deal of heat, and in order to prevent the flames from spreading to the store, they turned their hoses on a considerable quantity of magnesium in there. The spectacle they soon witnessed was unique and exceptionally beautiful—but they were lucky to live to tell the tale. For what happened was that the water generated hydrogen gas, an excellent fuel, from the hot magnesium. The apparently minor outbreak suddenly turned into a blaze that took hours to control.

Water is known as a fire hazard in chemical laboratories. Heavy rains started several fires at factories where the roofs leaked. Potassium, for instance, becomes spontaneously explosive when it is treated with water. It decomposes water into hydrogen and potassium hydroxide and generates enough heat to ignite the gas. Water mixed with carbide may release acetylene gas that is highly explosive under certain conditions.

Animals figure prominently among the freak causes of fires, even though they are probably the least culpable fire-raisers. Many fires have been attributed to burning cigarette ends or smouldering small pieces of wood and rubbish supposedly carried and dropped on inflammable materials by birds. It was a British bird that came perhaps nearest to conviction: in Canvey Island, Essex, a nest in a timber merchant's garage was found smouldering when the fire brigade was called to attend to a small fire below the nest. The flames were not big enough to have reached the nest, so the conclusion was that the inhabitant of the nest must have picked up perhaps a cigarette end and a burning piece fell from the nest and caused the fire. A fireman commented: 'We hosed the nest, the bird flew out, no one was hurt, not even the bird.'

In November 1969, a report from Périgueux, France, alleged that a fire had been caused by a cat. Witnesses said that the cat's fur caught fire when it lay too close to an open hearth in a farm house, and that the frightened cat then ran out and started a blaze in a hay barn. The cat died in the fire and the damage was estimated at 65,000 francs. This kind of fire is, however, much disputed. Most animal furs do not flare up when ignited: they merely singe and curl up. An exception to the rule is the presence of some insect repellent compound with which the animal's fur could be treated.

Some investigators have even suggested that insects and butterflies may transmit fire to combustible materials, but most authorities completely discount this as a possible cause. Wiring and electrical appliances are, on the other hand, an area where animals may cause considerable damage. No exact information is available for, so far, too little attention has been paid to this hazard and only a few behaviour studies of the various species have been carried out in this respect.

Australians have obtained direct evidence in a case at Yeo, in the Ballarat district of Victoria, in February 1968. A possum climbed an electric power pole and was electrocuted, so causing a short circuit. The pole and grass at its foot caught alight, but a local fireman with a knapsack pump managed to avert what could have become a major bush fire.

Basil Nixon, Provincial Fire Marshal in British Columbia, reported a most unusual case. Firemen were summoned by a housewife. They found that only a three-way plug and a long extension cord, leading to a sewing machine, were burning. There was an important clue: a puddle round the socket. It did not take 'long to figure out there was some doggone dirty work afoot and on questioning the housewife the truth came out. She admitted that . . . on hearing an unhuman cry of anguish' she rushed in to see 'her pet poodle beating a hasty retreat with what she swore were sparks emanating from the posterior section of the animal'. It is quite conceivable that a dog would create sparks or even arcing by urinating on an electric plug and socket but the shorting of the circuit would cause a fire only if the fuse was tampered with for this purpose or if over-heating from the regular use of the machine had over-loaded and worn out the insulation of the circuit.

A significant part of the account is the reference to the woman's *admission* to anything. The investigator, in fact, 'quickly deduced the source of the puddle of water but try as he did, could not get an admission from the lady that the dog had been trained specifically for this type of incendiarism'. Arson in this way is a most unlikely proposition. In 'set pieces', as investigators sometimes refer to arson, criminals sometimes attach burning materials to the tails of cats and push them through an open window or a gap in the wall. The cats, trying to escape, run around and set fire to stores of chemicals or hay barns, but the burnt carcasses are usually found and supply sufficient evidence against fraudulent insurance claims. The same would probably happen if, as is quite conceivable, a dog was trained to urinate on certain chemicals that would react predictably in accordance with the arsonist's expectations.

Rats have a much simpler way of starting fires: they gnaw cable insulations. Recent observations have indicated that cable-chewing is not really a feast for rats for they never actually *eat* the insulating material; in fact they seem to be specially attracted by certain colours—possibly grey is their favourite—and they prefer plastics to rubber. There are already rat-repellent plastics but they are expensive and the repellent tends to become ineffective over the years. It appears that rats attack the cables for three reasons: to sharpen their teeth, to obtain nesting material, and to clear the way if the cable obstructs their run.

Rats and mice which may chew match-heads have also been accused of fire-raising. This again is strongly disputed, but there is some evidence that when rodents carry matches in their mouths, they may strike the match-head against rough surfaces like walls. At least one mouse was almost caught red-handed. There was a fire in the men's changing room of a factory and it was put out by automatic sprinklers. It was proved beyond doubt that for about a couple of hours before the fire nobody could have entered the room. The fire started in the pocket of a foreman's coat hanging from a nail on the door. The flames spread up the coat and that was when the sprinklers came into operation. The foreman remembered that there had been a box of matches in that particular pocket, and some charred match-sticks and pieces of the box were found in the remains of the pocket and below it, on the floor. These pieces of wood bore clear marks of tiny teeth indicating that a mouse, probably attracted by some wax on the coat, must have nibbled at them. The result was the fire and the mouse was lucky to have escaped both the flames and the subsequent torrent.

Cynics may be tempted to treat this example with a certain reservation as the case comes from one of the largest sprinkler manufacturers. It is, however, beyond any doubt that sprinklers can teach us more about the causes of fires than most other experience, research and experiment, simply because they do preserve precisely the vital evidence that usually goes up in smoke if the fire has a chance to develop fully.

Some of the best examples of this have been recorded in Australia, where the Fire Protection Association and, particularly, its chairman Harry Marryatt managed to persuade an unusually high proportion of property owners to instal sprinkler systems in factories, department stores, supermarkets and other buildings even where this protective investment was not required by law.* About ninety-eight per cent of the Australian installations give a direct alarm to the fire brigade whose

* Harry Marryatt compiled a unique record and analysis of automatic sprinkler performance between 1886 and 1968. It was published by the Australian Fire Protection Association in 1971.

personnel, together with the sprinkler manufacturers, can therefore investigate these fires without any delay.

This is what enables Australian fire records to show up new causes of fires as soon as they become a menace. When the use of fluorescent lighting spread, sprinkler-stopped fires revealed these fixtures as new causes of outbreaks. In the cotton industry, where the inevitable presence of highly inflammable fluffy materials in the air has long been known to be a hazard, sprinklers preserved singed fluff in machines where sparks had ignited it. In several cases, the sudden flood of water stopped fires developing in dustbins and provided all the evidence fire detectives could dream of: half-burnt cigarette ends surrounded by ashes and charred paper.

Harry Marryatt, who has spent forty-seven years in the fire protection business and set up the Australian FPA originally as a hobby, has two favourite cases to demonstrate that sprinklers are the best fire investigators.

One happened in a department store at night. The building was empty until half-past one in the morning, when the cleaners arrived. A few minutes after they had begun to work with their vacuum cleaners, there was a big flash, a torrent came down and the alarm went off. A small fire would cause the automatic operation of no more than three sprinklers. In this case, twenty-five sprinkler heads went off all at once. Even though the fire was quickly under control, the worst damage occurred around a small display island, where ordinary wax and butane candles were sold at a circular counter. Most of the other damage covered a fairly large area—at floor level only. Two minutes later, the entire building might have gone up in flames, killing the cleaners and destroying the evidence. Here, however, clear indications of the cause remained to be seen. Not long before closing time, a customer must have examined a butane candle and turned it on without lighting it. The shop closed at seven in the evening, and so the gas, which was in a large special container for demonstration purposes, had more than six hours to escape: the gas, being heavier than air, settled near the floor and firemen found several pools of butane which would have burned up if the fire had developed. The cause of the ignition was also found: an electric spark must have come from a faulty vacuum cleaner.

The other fire started in the small hours of the morning and, according to Marryatt, 'the fire travelled in such devious ways, that it might very easily have remained a "cause unknown" case'. The building was being redecorated, and electricians were preparing the change-over from direct to alternating current. On the first floor, fresh concrete had been laid over wooden boards and, apparently, the cleaners washed this 'green' concrete with plenty of water. Some water seeped through and shorted the lamp fitting on the ground floor ceiling. The fuse failed to clear at the board from where the wiring ran up in a vertical duct to the fifth floor telephone switchboard. There the new A/C switchboard was ready and in place, but the old board, still in use on direct current, caught fire. Luckily, it activated a sprinkler, and the whole strange story was revealed.

This selection of unusual or even exceptional fire hazards is only intended to sample the tremendous variety of possible causes a fire investigator must always look for. After he has found the supposed seat or origin of a fire, he bears the old triangle formula in mind and proceeds to spot the source of heat which, using oxygen, set fire to some inflammables. As soon as he has a suspect, he will cross-examine it by raising the question: could this source produce enough heat to warm the fuel nearby to the ignition or flash point of that particular material? The volume of heat immediately available from the source—say, a burning match—is not his sole consideration. In the right circumstances of restricted ventilation, a comparatively low temperature object, like an electric light bulb, can accumulate dangerous heat in time. So all sources of heat are potential hazards.

America, Australia, Britain, France and many other countries compile long lists of specific causes with their fire statistics because the essential premise is that the more details are available the better chance the hazard-spotter will have. (It is, of course, regrettable that the majority of the fire reports, on which these lists are based, are rather vague and often unreliable; and that not all American states and fire marshals were required to compile statistics so that the available figures bore no uniformity, right up to 1970!) In contrast, the Soviet Union, for instance, seems to prefer to publish simplified statistics with a great deal of generalization, although more detailed lists are available for internal purposes. (Moscow records thus reveal that almost forty per cent of the building fires are caused by 'careless adults', more than twenty per cent by 'careless children', and seventeen per cent by 'heating installations and irons' all lumped together in a somewhat unhelpful fashion.)

For general, lay purposes one could separate *two major groups of heat sources*: the direct burning ones, including anything from cigarette ends to welding equipment; and other sources of heat like friction in rapidly moving machinery, electricity or spontaneous combustion—this is if we leave aside explosions which are sometimes the cause but frequently a result of fires.

The manner in which these sources actually do cause fires can be divided into three main categories: (1) arson, (2) carelessness and negligence, and (3) accidental operational hazards which, however, may reveal a certain degree of negligence because most of them are preventable by due care, foresight and regular checking.

For the investigator, *electricity* as a cause of fire poses very special problems. One of these is that the number of fires attributed to electrical causes has risen so very rapidly and in proportion to the increased use of electrical power, that corresponding improvement of preventive measures and increased awareness have obviously not accompanied this important development. Considering that most fires in buildings are caused by using fuels in one form or another, and that electricity is becoming the major fuel, it has been predicted and statistically proved that 'unless remedial measures are taken quickly, the usage of electricity will become a dominant cause of fire by 1975'.*

Another peculiar problem is that although the guilt of electricity can be deduced from the clues it leaves behind, the evidence is so elusive that a Munich investigator described electrical causes of fire as 'our trickiest customer'. The court of inquiry into the causes of the Australian Templestowe Day Nursery fire led to fairly typical results.

In the afternoon of the last day of January 1964, most of the babies and small children were asleep in cots and beds. After a very hot morning there was, at last, a drop in temperature from

* D. I. Lawson: *Fire Research in the United Kingdom.*

103 to 71 degrees Fahrenheit. Two children woke up, and the owner of the establishment took them from the nursery to the main building to change their nappies and give them a drink. This meant she had to walk for some sixty, possibly seventy-five, seconds with her bad feet although there was a changing table in the nursery bedroom and water was also available there. She noticed 'smoke or dust over the nursery' but did not think that there was anything wrong. She entered the main building and 'then heard my son-in-law screaming'. There was a fire, and soon, seven babies were dead. The authorities were surprised to hear that the building was a nursery.

The Coroner found it incomprehensible that the owner was in the nursery just one minute before the disastrous conflagration and yet failed to notice anything. In his findings, he also mentioned that 'the regulations governing the control of this type of establishment appeared to be adequate'; nursery registration was compulsory, but short of door-to-door searches it would be impossible to detect the existence of all such businesses. That is why this nursery could remain unregistered. The Coroner doubted 'if it was ever intended to be registered' because a witness connected with the business stated in 'an unguarded moment' that the official requirements for registration were considered to be 'rather onerous and unwarranted'.

Although it was not suggested that proper official control would have required the closure of the nursery, it seemed ominous that no parent had ever asked if it had been registered. (This apathy from parents must be blamed for many infants' deaths in several countries. A London nursery operated for three years without a licence. A licence application would have resulted in regular inspections and a ban on the use of two oil heaters which caused a fire in January 1971, and killed four young children. People set up kindergartens to take advantage of the great demand for such places, and mothers entrust them with their children without questioning their qualifications, competence or the suitability of the premises. Many housewives look after working women's children for a small fee. The registration of such activities does not even arise. There are many cases when women, who work on night shifts, supplement their wages by 'looking after' children in the daytime. Naturally,

they want to sleep for a few hours during which the children
are supposed to play on their own. This is how, recently, an
American woman escaped from an inferno that killed her own
children together with those who had been left in her care.)

Following the Templestowe fire, Arthur Pitfield, now Chief
Officer of the Country Fire Authority, State of Victoria, and his
team carried out a painstaking investigation which involved
sifting through the debris. They tried to identify every single
article they had recovered and, with the aid of a large plan of
the nursery, they produced a chart that showed where each
article had been before and probably during the fire, and where
it was found after the fire brigade had finished their work.
This chart helped considerably to eliminate some of the ten
final theories of likely causes. 'However hard we tried,' he
remembered in his office in Malvern, Victoria, 'we could not
come down to a single supposed cause.'

This uncertainty was clearly reflected by the Coroner's
summary: of the ten submitted theories, he found two—spontaneous combustion and electrical fault—the most likely
causes. His 'inclinations were towards' the latter but he had to
register an open verdict with the remark that 'if the cause of the
fire is an electrical fault, the nature of such fault can only be
guessed at . . .'

This kind of guesswork is often the product of far less conscientious investigation than that carried out in this particular
case. It is just as usual to blame electrical causes wrongly as it is
to overlook their fatal involvement completely.

Sometimes, because of the misuse of some appliances,
electricity is the obvious cause. A woman was receiving high-
frequency electrical treatment in a thermal bath sanatorium.
She lay peacefully on a couch which suddenly burst into
flames. She suffered extensive injuries. It was found that the
mattress contained spiral springs of copper-steel in which the
radiation induced electricity. Heating and sparks were produced and these ignited the stuffing all at once. The introduction of foam-rubber mattresses has since proved to afford
adequate prevention.

Tear-gas is not exactly the best welcome to customers in a
Hamburg bar and it is certainly not the way to persuade the
ladies of the nearby Reeperbahn to bring their valuable custom

and wait for clients there when every minute makes their eyes more red and tearful. So the owner of the bar showed understandable concern when he was initiating an inquiry which ultimately not only traced the tear-gas but also saved his premises from an approaching conflagration. It was found that the heat of the electrical supply had gradually led to a breakdown of insulation resins, causing the lamp-holders, which had been exposed to the most direct heat, to emit a vapour with a chemical combination that closely resembled actual tear-gas. The electrical installations might have burst into flames at almost any time.

A breakdown of insulation often occurs because of neglected old wiring or faulty repairs particularly by do-it-yourself enthusiasts. Like veins in the body, wires are everywhere in buildings. Did they start the fire that burnt them?

Investigators rely on a vast number of clues which they try to find in order to substantiate their assumptions. Yet when you discuss these clues with the investigators not only in different countries but also in different parts of a single country or town or even with colleagues in the same fire department, many disturbing discrepancies come to light. Most investigators seem to agree that, for example, metal parts of an electric motor are more likely to melt and fuse if an electric fault in the motor started the fire than if there was an external cause and the heat came from outside. They would also put a similar interpretation on clues like those concerning fuses: an *overload*, including a leakage to neutral or earth, will melt or burn the wire without blackening the fuse bridge, while a *short circuit* will cause the fuse to blow with some violence and badly discolour the bridge face. But when it comes to the evaluation of a short circuit—was it the cause or a result of the fire?—there are wild disagreements. It appears that the most frequent serious mistakes are due to the widespread practice that when an investigator spots a short circuit (even in a secondary circuit) by having found some melted, fused wires, he jumps to the conclusion that what he sees is the *cause* of the fire. In fact, a short circuit is a much less likely and less frequent cause of fires than overloading particularly by faulty earthing and especially if the wiring is the faulty product of an amateur electrician.

Fire detectives always pay particular attention to the state

wires are found in. There are a number of clues to help differentiate between internally and externally heated or even melted
wires. One of these is that if the heat comes from the outside,
insulation will be burnt first and if any of it is left for the investigator, it will usually adhere tightly to the wire and will be sticky,
difficult to 'strip'; on the other hand, if the heat is internal and
so starts burning the insulation from the inside, the remaining
insulation will be loose round the wire and slip off easily like a
sleeve. But beyond a few basic rules of thumb, there seems to be
a great deal of uncertainty and guesswork.

It is therefore most disturbing to find that despite all the
doubts, confusion and inaccurate judgments, despite the frequency and significance of the problems fire detectives encounter
when they try to pin down electrical installations as causes of
fire, *very little scientific assistance is readily available or indeed asked
for.* Although electrical investigation is the most extreme example, the lack of urgency to employ scientific help is equally
deplorable in chemical, engineering, and other spheres of fire
investigation.

Once again, the findings of the special study carried out for
the British Home Office are not untypical of the international
situation.

The greatest advance in fire investigation would come from
better and scientifically aided techniques for the examination of
physical evidence at the scene of fire. The aid required would
have to be greatly varied, ranging from advice by men with
broad scientific background to laboratory tests and long-term
research projects. Fire research scientists can give some general
guidance or answer occasional queries but have no staff to deal
with a flood of questions which may arise from thousands of
investigations every month. The result is that the investigator
must rely greatly on his own experience which is often inadequate to tackle complicated technical or scientific problems—or
he will have to seek advice from firms or specialists even though
these may be interested parties.

Fire research in general is an immense subject. It is concerned
with fire patterns in various structures, the behaviour of all but
especially new types of materials in fire, fire-fighting, causal
experiments, statistics, the efficiency of fire protection and its
economy, and thousands of other problems. Each year, the

mere titles of the new books and other publications on the subject fill several volumes of reference books. No scientist can ever hope to be able to read them all. Although the number of publications on actual fire investigation is far more limited, this author found that very few of even these are read by fire investigators anywhere. Just to take one example: we have seen the vital importance of electrical wiring in building fires, but hardly any investigators even in America know that a very useful research project on this subject has been carried out at Washington State University.*

Forensic scientists provide the most regular contribution to fire investigation. This assistance is essential and most valuable in cases of suspected arson and breaches of regulations. Yet even in these cases, the initial decision—recognition of possible incendiarism and request for assistance—must be made by the investigator in charge who has no scientific training. 'To aggravate the situation even more,' several people admit confidentially, 'forensic laboratories are usually so overloaded with work that they cannot spare more than a few minutes on an average fire investigation request.'

In cases of fatal fire, the pathologists can also help a great deal. As practically all deaths in fire are due to asphyxiation caused by the inhalation of carbon monoxide, a by-product of virtually all fires, the post mortem blood test will show a high or low level of saturation. Considered with some less important circumstantial factors, the high level will indicate a large, perhaps sudden, fire and a great concentration of the gas to which the victim was exposed; while a lower level of saturation may indicate a minor, possibly smouldering fire which made the victim breathe smaller quantities of gas adding up to a fatal dose only gradually. Such findings will help the investigator to correct or prove his theories.

Practically all Western countries have some sort of fire research organisation similar to, although in range nothing to compare with, the American Underwriters Laboratory. Here, scientists thoroughly test every single new product before its marketing is permitted so that any predictable risk to life, limb or property is eliminated, and evaluate what contributions any

* B. V. Ettling: *Electrical Wiring in Building Fires*. The work was partially supported by a grant from Northwest Fire Investigation Association.

materials and constructions may make to the fire risk. But when it comes to helping actual fire investigation, the scientific factor is dismally limited. In 1963, at the annual conference of the British Institution of Fire Engineers, F. Capron, a Warwickshire member, expressed concern that is still valid today and typical internationally:

'It is rather disturbing . . . that the only direct approach to fire investigation on a scientific level is when we or the police have the thought that there may be arson. I feel that there should be a separate group of scientists possibly attached to the forensic laboratories who could be readily available at relatively short notice to fire officers and fire brigades, to help them in their investigation . . .'

To this kind of criticism and suggestion, answers came on three levels from participants at that conference and subsequently from many other sources. *Forensic experts* hasten to point out that they are grossly overtaxed by various police duties and that they are not really fire specialists in the sense that scientists at the fire research organizations are. *Research scientists* emphasize that their funds are earmarked for more general subjects than individual fires, and that, apart from testing structures and materials, their most useful contributions may be if they could introduce new basic concepts such as more efficient use of water in fire-fighting; study of fire as a system; and improved ways of spending the money available for fire protection by revealing wasteful over-protection in certain areas, for example car parks, or by proving that the most expensive item on the life protection bill for buildings, the means of escape, may perhaps be better spent on other life-saving provisions.

Dozens of interviews revealed, however, that the most stubborn opposition to greater scientific participation comes from the *investigators* themselves and, especially, from the officers in charge of fire-fighting to whom this detective work is often no more than an extra, routine chore.

Reginald Whillock of the London Fire Brigade had a case which was typical in this respect:

'I had to call on a firm to discuss some fire protection problems and when I was leaving the building, I saw a fire engine outside. As there were no flames and I had heard no alarm inside, I went to find the officer in charge and asked him where the fire was. He said it was "nothing, really" only some insulation round a steam pipe was smouldering in a room at floor level. "Some fool must have thrown away a fag end," he told me. To him it was an open and shut case.

'It sounded reasonable enough. The officer might have been suspicious of some other cause had the smouldering started, say, at knee level. But at the floor . . . Anyway, it was only my previous experience that made me strip the pipe, remove some of the lagging and send it for examination by the scientific adviser at the council. The result soon gave a completely different cause: it turned out that this insulating material had been in place round the hot pipes for almost thirty years, and the constant heat caused a deterioration which made the material combustible. The existing regulations do take this hazard into consideration, but few firms bother to check it from time to time. In this case, complete re-insulation of the pipes eliminated the danger, but had a "carelessly discarded cigarette" been passed as a supposed cause nothing would have been done and ultimately there would have been probably a major fire.'

Another consideration that might have affected that young officer's thinking is the general reluctance in fire brigades everywhere to 'trouble the experts'. While firemen in several countries are encouraged to 'plead ignorance and ask for advice without shame or hesitation' if they are in the slightest doubt about fire-fighting problems or about the possible need for calling further reinforcements, they understand that busy scientists, available to them in principle, are not to be 'dragged out of their laboratories every five minutes whenever a Tom, Dick or Harry cannot make up his mind about the obvious', as an insurance specialist in Paris claimed.

In London, a senior fire prevention officer explained: 'Apart from some really serious cases or strong clues of being on to something nationally or internationally important, when we can call on any specialist, one shouldn't cry wolf too often. After all, the brigade hasn't got its own scientists and its primary duty is to fight the fire. If it's an unusual fire, if a couple of our chaps are killed in action, if we can see the possibility of a technical discovery or foresee future litigation arising from the case, we can turn to the Greater London Council's Scientific Advisers Department. But we must never forget that those few chaps there have to deal with millions of problems concerning everything from fire to water, from pubs to pollution, and from food to sewage.

'I remember, in Wales, there used to be a scientist attached to the brigade. He was a professor of something or another and he had a lab. in there, so firemen could just pop in and have an informal consultation without any fuss or paperwork. He's dead now and I believe nobody has taken his place.

'Some arrangement like this could be the answer to our problem but then, who's going to pay for it?'

On the whole, it seems that fire detectives use three objections to scientific assistance most regularly. *The first is a matter of money.* Who is going to pay? An increase of man-hours spent on investigation means higher cost in itself. Scientific man-hours are even more expensive. As it is usually the ratepayer who maintains the fire brigade, the ratepayer would have to foot that bill, too. The question is : what would he get for his money in better protection of his own and of the national wealth? Unfortunately, nobody has yet begun to evaluate how much help, and thus extra expense, would be justified by the potential results.

Some officers at the Board of Fire Commissioners in Sydney are convinced that even a minute extra outlay could bring about considerable improvements. A superintendent gets about 7,500 Australian dollars a year. Five extra superintendents specializing in fire investigation, aided by a few fire research scientists seconded exclusively to this duty, would still cost no more than an additional half per cent of the fire brigade budget (three quarters of it paid by the insurance companies and the rest by the local and state governments) and would go a long way towards ensuring a better understanding of fires and their more effective prevention. (At present, so-called investigations are normally done by the district officers who have to report a supposed cause. Special investigations must be ordered by the chief in cases of unusual significance.)

When fire investigators show an excessive concern about the practicalities of financing more scientific assistance, and when most of them refuse to admit publicly the need for such help even in principle, irrespective of the question of where the money will come from, one is driven to suspect that their second usual objection is behind it all : *they do not think that scientists could really help the investigators.* 'Quite frankly, I don't think it's a matter of money,' said a senior bureaucrat in Sydney, 'for apart from paying the men more or buying better equipment and things like that, I wouldn't know what to do with the extra cash.'

Or another comment: 'We have no training college for firemen in Australia, but the brigades train them for investigations well enough. How could scientists help? Bush fires, for instance, are caused by people and sometimes by lightning. We know that much. What could scientists add? Perhaps more forensic laboratories would be useful. Otherwise, your first suspect for the cause of a fire comes from experience. If the fire is in a cotton mill, you look for foreign metal in the teasing machine. If it's a flour mill, friction in a fan or a faulty elevator belt is your likely culprit. A waste plant? Probably a spark lit the processed waste. A paint factory? Find the possible spillage on hot bearings or the spot where vapour could have met an electric spark and you got your story. More scientific assistance? Money would be better spent on prevention. The question isn't how to improve protection but how to do all we already know ought to be done.'

These observations by two well-known experts, both hiding behind anonymity ('please don't quote me by name in this respect, it's no good to get involved with such controversial issues'), also hinted at the investigators' third objection which is perhaps the most common and most short-sighted of them all: *only firemen can understand fires,* only those who have risen through the ranks can investigate and find the cause, scientists are unwilling to stand on the top of a ladder in a gale, so how can they be of use?

Nobody doubts the immense value of the fireman's painfully and heroically obtained experience. Nobody expects that a scientist, with all his knowledge and brilliance at reasoning, could be any good at fire-fighting. But it would be equally specious to argue about his usefulness if his specialist knowledge of, say chemistry or electricity, was properly harnessed by a man of wide practical experience.

It occurs that, once again, the problem is posed by a basic attitude. The faults of this attitude are best shown up by a comparison with aircrash investigators who, like fire detectives, are all practical experts with great experience. They have been to hundreds of air accident scenes and are themselves pilots, engineers, specialists in electronics or similar spheres, but they regard themselves as 'coordinators' of many 'experts and scientists who have probably never seen an accident and who may know little more about aeroplanes than that those are things which take them on holidays'.

Fire investigators resist this comparison. They point out that two aeroplanes are more similar to one another than two buildings, and that any two pilots are trained to act and behave at times of routine and emergency almost identically, whereas no two people care about fire prevention or react to a fire in the same manner; and therefore it is much more difficult to prevent one fire by the experience from another than it is to eliminate an aviation hazard in the same way. This is certainly true to some extent. But it is false on the whole, because it only shows that fire prevention needs an even stronger aircrash investigating spirit and attitude, and it requires even more experience from cases—of which there is a tragic abundance. After all, this is how the non-scientific practical fire investigator comes to say as a rule that 'if it's a flour mill . . .'

An American aircrash detective, specializing in aviation fire problems, carried this comparison a step further. 'Good investigation has contributed as much to safety as anything else,' he said without any pretence to modesty. 'At the final reckoning, it's the insurance man who judges safety for it's he who has to fork out the money when something goes wrong.

'No insurance company would consider lightly or with particular delight a proposal to insure a man against fire while he is locked up in a fair-sized cupboard with a hundred or a hundred and fifty gallons of petrol. Yet an aircraft is just this kind of a proposition.

'Add to it that three or four hundred people may be together in such a confined space aboard a Jumbo carrying almost fifty thousand gallons of fuel, and that the entire package, surrounded by sophisticated electronics with a maze of wires and machinery built to burn that fuel, floats in mid-air thousands of feet up, and it will be obvious what a great compliment it is to aeroplanes and their operators that insurers do not hesitate to underwrite this apparently risky business. This compliment is not a light-hearted one. It is based on practical, mundane facts and figures that reflect a very high level of safety.'

Apart from scientific achievements and advanced technical know-how, safety in the air stems from care. The basic attitude that even the slightest mishap must not go undetected and un-explained rules the entire operation. With the exception of oil refineries and one or two similarly fire-prone industries, it would probably only happen in aviation that a strip of oily rag burning on a metal tray next to a lathe will produce a thorough investigation and an accumulation of half a pound of paper-work. (This was an actual case at an engineering maintenance plant of Swissair, and the subsequent inquiry disclosed not only how the fire had begun, but also what potential hazards it had created and how this risk could be eliminated by planned dis-posal of waste like oily rags.)

Researching the components of air safety, this author has conducted a long series of interviews with hundreds of airline executives and other employees. Aviation has always been almost over-sensitive about fires both in the air and on the ground and, in order to forestall repetitions, the causes of individual outbreaks have been traced by untiring investiga-tions.[*] In a way, therefore, fire protection is a strong tradition and a state of mind of all airline staff.

In this respect, the interviews at the Australian head office of Qantas were particularly revealing. Qantas has an exception-ally good safety record (they have not had a fatal accident in a quarter of a century) which is due to several factors like 'natural' advantages of operating on a near-optimum scale and having longer-than-average flight stages with fewer take-offs and land-ings; sensible policies such as not trying to economize on train-ing and other safety aspects, 'cashing in' on a peculiarly Australian air safety consciousness throughout government and operators, and meticulous attention to detail which is well illustrated by their attitude to the fire hazard anywhere.

Their Safety Department has a separate fire protection sec-tion. Their special training scheme for ground staff who work in engineering and other maintenance shops is far superior to that of the average industrial plant. Whenever there is *any* fire

[*] See: S. Barlay: *Aircrash Detective*, Hamish Hamilton, 1969.

in any of their premises, they require the completion of a Fire Investigation Report form that is more detailed and stringent than the questions even fire brigades have to answer according to their respective countries' regulations. The first instruction in this questionnaire is fairly typical: 'This report is to be completed by the senior company representative within 24 hours of the fire, explosion or similar event *whether property damage is sustained or not*' (author's italics), although it allows for any further investigation.

'I feel we cannot afford to have different attitudes and standards for flying and ground operations,' said Captain Aubrey Rees, Safety Controller. 'If we continue to insist on the full investigation of any incident or even irregularity in the operation of our aircraft, we must also apply the same principle to our workshops. After all, we are not a mammoth airline. The loss of use of just one of our aircraft would mean a drop of about four per cent of our earning capacity. Delays in maintenance and so in utilization of an aircraft would also be a proportionately great blow. Safety at all stages is therefore an economic factor, too.'

Accordingly, the airline investigates every workshop fire in detail and the result is that, while in comparable industrial plants there was a steady increase in the number of outbreaks, Qantas workshops had a twenty-five per cent decrease (all minor cases) in the last two years.

False alarms are a curse suffered by all users of automatic detectors. If it becomes excessively annoying, usually the fault is repaired, but the system is not cured. Perhaps because false signals by the engine fire-warning lights in aircraft are a nuisance even when they are not a hazard, and because airlines had to do a great deal about the investigation and elimination of the faults that caused them, Qantas conducted a similar investigation of false alarms in its workshops. This led to the more frequent and careful maintenance of all installations, with the resulting reduction of such incidents. Where fire alarm buttons, for instance, were found to be liable to early corrosion, a schedule for their more regular replacement was introduced.

Each industry has its own most notorious trouble-maker. It may be a certain piece of machinery, a fan or a power unit. Whenever it catches fire or begins to emit smoke, it is repaired and then used as before. In case of a single minor occurrence, airlines may do no more than that. But their system is based on defect reports, maintenance logs, exchange information from other airlines, and well kept records which are geared to spot recurrences that can ultimately reveal if 'the odd mishap' is, in fact, only the tip of the iceberg. At Qantas, they call the process quality analysis, and their Inspection and Quality Control Department gave several good examples of its effectiveness.

One of these concerned a fault in a high frequency (HF) radio. In May 1964, a Boeing 707 flight crew reported that the No. 1 HF system had become unserviceable. A circuit breaker was found tripped, reset once and again tripped, on the Darwin–Sydney flight sector. At Sydney, during repair, the power supply unit burnt up, causing fire and smoke but no secondary damage on its rack or wiring. The unit was replaced and a number of minor modifications were introduced as additional safeguards for smooth operation. Although the defect was not a hazard to the safety of the aircraft, these measures were regarded only as temporary, and an analysis of records was carried out.

The first finding was that the company had had similar previous occurrences. Then it was discovered that other airlines had also encountered this problem, and that a Boeing service bulletin, the usual note from manufacturer to users about desirable or important modifications, had already suggested the use of a different circuit breaker which aimed at correcting the fault. A check of maintenance records then revealed that this modification had indeed been carried out by Qantas on some of their similar aircraft, but that this 707 was still waiting for its turn. To *cure the symptom* the new circuit breaker was now fitted, and this ensured that if the system failed again it would not burn and cause fire in the unit. Despite these measures, however, the actual cause of the illness had still not been found. The analysis ended with the staccato sentence: 'Investigations proceeding.'

In many industries, a report like this may be left on file, gathering dust—at least until the next failure. In aviation, this is a less likely course. Seven months after that flight from Darwin to Sydney, another sheet of paper was added to the file. It contained only three sentences but was duly distributed to twelve departments, and it informed everybody that, according to specialists, a diode over-heating could have led to transformer over-heating and that locally produced diode replacements were being evaluated. This move aimed at *curing the ultimate cause*. A few months later, with the introduction of these new diodes for all HF radios, the file was closed.

CHAPTER SEVEN

UNSAFE TO LIVE IN?

THOUGHTLESS, CARELESS, NEGLIGENT—these are the words with which most people who have fires, particularly in their homes, are easily branded. Sometimes the saving grace of 'bad luck' or 'unfortunate coincidence' is added. Infrequently, the shadow of 'criminal negligence' looms large behind the words. Usually, it is difficult to draw the line where one description ends and another begins.

Lulworth Castle, an immodestly elegant and haughtily lonesome mansion in a vast green park of Dorset, took decades to build in the early seventeenth century. It took less than an hour to reduce it to a chilly blind shell in 1939. A service lift carried hot ashes down a shaft from the library. The draught made the ashes flare up, and the north-east turret burst into flames. The fire spread fast but the people in the house managed to escape. A thoughtful servant placed an armchair on the lawn from where the owner watched the roof collapse and the house burn down. Most fire brigades in the county sent men to help, but they all had to witness the spectacle helplessly with the owner. The water to fight the fire was there, under their feet, in the newly installed large locked water tank somewhere under the rose garden. The butler, the only man living in the house who knew where it was, had the night off to visit his mother. And he had taken the keys with him. *Thoughtless?*

A London family had four children in 1966. An oil heater was toppled, probably by a child, starting a blaze. Three of the children died. The couple with the remaining child moved to a new home. The wife was pregnant and soon gave birth to a baby. Twelve months later, she had another baby. Not quite two years after the first fire, the oldest child who had already survived a disaster came home from school to find the house in flames. The smoke beat him back from the door and he ran for help. It was too late. The two children inside were already dead. One was eight months, the other twenty months old. The fire was probably started by a toppled electric heater. It was a reasonable assumption that the older child, a toddler, might have pushed it accidentally. The father was at work. The mother returned home shortly after the tragedy. She was out briefly on both occasions. *Careless?*

Near Munich, at a popular inn noted for its traditional Bavarian cuisine, there was a gas-heated, deep-fat frier in the ground floor kitchen. A cook lit the frier and left the kitchen for a short time, but soon a waiter called him in because the fat was smoking. He turned the heater off but suddenly the fat burst into flames. Dense smoke soon filled the restaurant and the fire spread fast, but the thirty-odd guests, helped by the staff, managed to escape. The frier was thermostatically controlled, with a maximum operating temperature of 190°C. (375°F.) It appeared that the fat had been over-heated because of a thermostat failure. Had there been any deaths or injuries, the owner might have been sued for damages because it was not the first failure of its kind. Some efforts had, in fact, been made to rectify this defect but the repairs were not really effective. *Negligent?*

Or a fire in a French provincial department store—was it a case of criminal negligence?

The alarm, operated by automatic detectors, went off at 10.20 in the evening. Firemen found that the main damage was in the linen department on the second floor from where the fire had travelled via an open timber staircase to the third floor, and by convection through windows to another part of the building. Lateral spread was restricted by well-placed fire-doors most of which were properly shut.

The seat of the fire, according to all available clues, appeared to be at a spot behind a counter on the second floor. 'The staff were permitted to smoke in that area,' a French fire officer explained, 'but we found a "carelessly discarded cigarette", an unlikely cause. All the staff had left the building at about six o'clock, more than four hours before the alarm. Had somebody thrown away a cigarette even in the last minute, and had it caused a fire at all, the alarm would have gone off much earlier.

'But behind that counter, there was an odd recess in a main division wall. We found that there had been pairs of spring-loaded steel fire-doors there. Those doors were not required for escape from either side—their purpose was merely compartmentalization of the floor area so that lateral spread of the fire should be checked by them. On the far side, the doors had been welded shut while the nearer pair had been wedged open. In the recess so formed were completely burnt remains of some textiles.

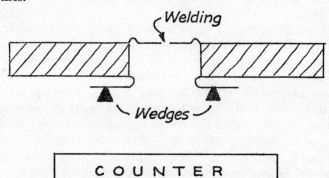

'The manager who arrived at the scene at dawn gave a simple explanation. As the doors had not been in use at all, it was simpler to shut them permanently and use the recess as storage space for stocks of towels, blankets, and bedclothes especially now that the summer sales were approaching. The cheapest way to shut the door was by welding. A brick wall would have been more messy, too. And the welding was carried out that afternoon from the far side!

'This was an important piece of information. The heat from the electric welding equipment could have easily been transmitted through the steel door to the stocks which would begin to smoulder. Heat would build up in there to the point of ignition—undetected! For when the fire detection system was originally planned, nobody expected that the space between the pairs of doors would be used for storage. Detector heads were therefore not required in there.'

This alteration, like so many that cause disastrous fires, amounted to misuse of an area and rendered the fire regulations

4

ineffectual. And yet, because it was not an escape route, the law was not broken.

'Stupidity, negligence, call it what you like,' said a Home Office Inspector of Fire Services, 'but whatever the cause, people who use welding equipment are a traditional and constant menace. All heating appliances represent a certain amount of danger. The man who takes home a blowlamp for the first time ought to anticipate a devastating fire. Yet again and again we hear people say that "I didn't ever think it could do" this and that.

'Oxy-acetylene equipment is the worst of all. Or rather its users are. Especially if it's not part of some routine manufacturing process which a firm is geared to. It's mostly in repair or demolition jobs where it causes trouble.'

The Dudgeon's Wharf fire was a good example. Huge, 150,000-gallon tanks were being cut up with oxy-acetylene burners in July 1969. The tanks contained myrcene residue and not surprisingly, this highly inflammable chemical caught fire. The brigade was called and as they tried to control the fire, there was an explosion killing five firemen and a worker.

'The lunacy of it all,' a fireman commented, 'is that quite regularly, men on repair jobs use oil-soaked tarpaulin to screen their welding equipment. It's like trying to stop the spread of a blaze with gunpowder.'

The textbook case occurred on a cold day in a Leicestershire maintenance plant for large open-cast mining machinery. In the morning, workers found that water had frozen even in the underground pipes. The foreman instructed a three-man gang to dig up the pipe and thaw it out. They dug a foot-deep trench, lifted the pipe, put it on bricks and wrapped it with rags which they had soaked in waste engine oil. All they needed was a match and the scene was set for a most effective thawing operation. What they ignored was the fact that the pipe ran alongside, and only some eighteen inches away from, a wooden store packed with some four thousand huge rubber tyres. Within a few minutes, the fire was totally out of control. The damage? More than half a million pounds. The cause? Complete thoughtlessness.

A German fire insurance specialist commented: 'When we talk about fire protection and the education of the public, we often make the mistake of trying to teach people about every imaginable situation. This is an effort doomed to failure. The best we can achieve is to convince people that whenever any form of heat is produced, they must look for likely fuel that might be ignited by it.' This is, of course, wishful thinking. Statistics do not project a promising picture anywhere. In 1970, New York City claimed that forty-three per cent of its almost four hundred fires a day had been caused by negligent, drugged or drunken citizens.

People in their own *homes* are most frequently and most regularly exposed to the damage and tragedy caused by thoughtless, careless, negligent attitudes. Governments must respect the freedom of the individual—they have no power to control the fire protection of private homes or the use of appliances by householders. Parents or others can only be prosecuted in special circumstances when it is proved that a small child in their care has been killed or seriously injured because of an insufficiently guarded fire. Statutory requirements, even if they are full of loop-holes, offer increasing protection in public places, offices, factories. No such safeguard exists for homes.

Automatic fire detection for the average house would cost about two hundred pounds. In Britain, this would involve some four thousand million pounds to protect twenty million homes. Even if mass production on such a scale would bring down the price very considerably, the potential savings do not justify the investment because, despite the great number of home fires, the material loss due to them is only a few million pounds in any year. To put sprinklers, the ultimate answer, into homes would be several times more expensive than the detectors.

The greatest loss due to fires in homes is counted in the very high number of fatalities: an average two-thirds of the annual fire deaths occur in homes in Western countries. Among the victims, the overwhelming majority are the least protected— the very old and the very young, especially when they are left alone. The single precautionary step of better care for these would produce a tremendous reduction in fire fatalities.

It is left to the householder to protect his family yet comparatively few will positively think about it. Tragedy usually makes good headlines. The fire-caused tragedy is an exception unless

the case is also spectacular. Thirty or forty people dying in one
go, pictures of burning multi-million properties with half a
dozen terror-stricken inhabitants jumping from fifth-floor
windows—these may capture the editors' and readers' attention
. . . momentarily.

A haphazardly conducted test demonstrated this point on a
small scale. Regular newspaper readers were asked about fires
reported in their own towns or countries within 'the last week
or so'.* Apart from one or two big fires which happened to
occur in any particular area within the few days in question, the
response was almost identical, the average answer being 'oh
yes, there was something about a fire somewhere, now let me
see . . .' and then a complete blankness of memory. Altogether,
more than ninety per cent of the people asked gave this sort of
answer. Some excused themselves by saying, 'I'm not interested
in morbid things', while others claimed that 'there are so many
of these little fires and so regularly that one doesn't pay attention to them'. A few people admitted they disliked news about
fires because it made them feel guilty about shrugging off the
thought of prevention.

All those who carried out the questioning of some eight
hundred people read the local papers carefully: each reader's
own regular paper was found to have carried on average
thirteen news items about fires in that one week. The following
examples are but a small selection of the fairly typical news
that failed to make big headlines. They were missed by the
readers altogether or did not make a sufficiently memorable
impact.

A Hamburg family returned home from holiday. A few hours
later, the father went out with friends for a beer. They were
sitting on a terrace nearby when he suddenly saw flames breaking through a window of his flat. He and his wife had been
married for fifteen years. In the first year she had an abortion
carried out by a small back-street surgery because they thought
it too soon to have a child. Two years later, they wanted a baby,
but she had one miscarriage after another. They laid out a small

---

* The test was carried out with the help of local friends and other volunteers in
London, Manchester, Leicester, Munich, Frankfurt, Cologne, Hamburg, Paris,
Nice, Geneva, Zurich, Florence, Amsterdam, Stockholm, Copenhagen, Salzburg,
New York, San Francisco, Chicago, Los Angeles, Toronto, Sydney, Melbourne,
and Hongkong, where, in all, 808 people were asked.

fortune on specialists. After nine years of struggling for a baby, she spent almost eight months in bed—four months in hospital —and they had a son who was now three years old. The mother, who had been watching television only next door to the child's room, was badly burned trying to rescue him. The father ran home with friends and suffered crippling injuries when he attempted to get to the boy. His friends had to carry him out to stop his hopeless efforts. The child was dead.

In New York, seven children died when fire swept through a three-storey building, in Brooklyn. One child was found in his bed, two were in a kitchen huddled together between a refrigerator and a stove, two were near a window on the floor, one sat asphyxiated in a chair facing the TV set, and one was incinerated near the apartment door. The firemen arrived to the rescue after a crucial delay: a hoax alarm call had sent them in full force from their station nearby to an address twelve blocks away from the real fire.

British school teachers were on strike and two girls, aged five and eleven, 'wanted a lie-in that morning', said their mother. A fire broke out and killed both children. The cause of the blaze has remained unknown, according to the West Cheshire Coroner.

An elderly couple died in their Paris home. It was believed that the husband was reading and smoking in bed after his wife had gone to sleep. It was his habit to stay up late. It was thought that probably he had dropped his cigarette on the blanket when he, too, fell asleep.

A Swedish mother watched helplessly as her husband and two children died in a fire that consumed their wooden summer chalet at a holiday resort near Uddevalla on the west coast.

An old couple died in a fire that destroyed their house in a Melbourne suburb on the day they had made the last payment on their mortgage. They had celebrated the occasion with friends all night. It was believed that the fire had started at dawn, just before they went to bed. The husband's sister, who lived with them and was to inherit everything, survived the fire but found that the fire insurance on the house had expired as renewal was long overdue.

Not only the horror of it all, but also the tragic sentimental stories of love, devotion and heroism seem to fail in making an impact on, let alone shocking, readers. The false sense of security in the ostrich attitude of 'it couldn't happen to me' worked against readers' identification with the victim, although many cases were reported bearing a considerable similarity to the following one:

An invalid, bedridden man and his wife were looking after their three grandchildren on the day when a pan-fire got out of hand in the kitchen of their home in Nice: the grandmother braved the flames and dense smoke, and rescued the children but obviously could not move her husband; she broke a ground floor window to push out the children, told the eldest to run for help, and returned to her husband's bedside; the firemen arrived too late to save the couple who were found in each other's arms on the husband's bed both trying in vain to shield the other from the inferno.

The similarities do not end at the nature and descriptions of tragedy. For, what is worse, most fires in the home are due to *a small band of notorious causes* that do not recognize national, racial or class-inflicted boundaries.

'*Children playing with fire*' is internationally claimed to be one of the major causes of fires in the home. It is often rated as highly as the cause of one in four outbreaks. Mostly, it is supposed to come about by children playing with matches. Mostly, there is no, or at least only unsubstantiated, evidence for it. And mostly it can also be described as gross negligence by parents.

Undoubtedly, fire fascinates children and grown-ups alike, and the only difference is that children have less resistance to this attraction because they understand the hazard less. Matches are their easiest means to the positive act of creating 'fire out of nothing'—as an eight-year-old defined it with pride. Children under the age of five show a great demand for knowledge and experience of fire. There have been several suggestions made for satisfying this demand under imaginative supervision.

In the United States, where burns top the list as the leading cause of home accidents, where each year fire kills almost two thousand children, mostly under four years of age, and maims or cripples thousands of others, Dr. Harry Dietrich, a Californian authority on child accident prevention, suggested that children should deliberately be made to play with matches.

His advice was that, having reached the stage of compulsion to light matches on their own, children should be seated in the middle of the driveway or some other safe place and be given a large box of wooden matches. They should be encouraged to take out matches, light and blow them out one by one, the idea being that the novelty would soon pale and the tedious repetition should make them lose the fascination for what is forbidden.

'Children playing with matches' is frequently the most convenient and irresponsible excuse for finding a scapegoat. Investigators do not make any secret of it that when, after a fire, all clues have been examined and all likely causes have been eliminated, children who might have had access to matches tend to get the blame on rather flimsy evidence. If, say, a neighbour saw some children playing nearby with matches, that would count as quite a positive indication of the cause.

It is only occasionally that there is some stronger evidence. French children were acting out the last moments of Joan of Arc. They tied a little girl to a wooden post and lit a rubbish fire round her feet. Luckily, she was rescued by a passer-by almost immediately and got away with superficial injuries. (Oddly enough, this was not an original game. Similarly realistic performances have been reported from various parts of the world. In 1962, a seven-year-old girl was tied to a tree in Wilmington, North Carolina. Playmates made her stand on straw which was set alight and almost became her funeral pyre. She was taken to hospital with serious burns.)

However tragic and truly accidental such cases may be, in most of them there is a strong initial element of parental negligence: either the children are left alone in the house or apartment or they are left without supervision in rooms where they have easy, perhaps invitingly easy, access to matches. Examples of this occur in practically every town and every village. All the reports are painfully simple: mother went to dentist, three children aged two, four and six, died in fire caused presumably by matches; mother went to 'get some sweets for the kids at the shop round the corner' and found house in flames on her return when she made desperate attempts all in vain to save the children; grandmother 'only went to visit neighbour', mother watched television in the caravan next to hers 'just for a quarter of an hour' . . . one, two, five, children died.

A woman in Marseilles who worked at night looked after her own two and another three children during the day. Just before Christmas she went shopping with the children in the morning and bought some sparklers. She left them on a sideboard. In the afternoon, she lay down to sleep in the room. All the children had to stay with her, and she made sure that the door was locked and no child could get out or into mischief. An hour later neighbours broke in and rescued her and the baby in a cot. She was unconscious from the inhalation of smoke. The other four children were dead. Under the bed, there were half a dozen shiny metal sticks left from the sparklers. Although all matches nearby would have been burnt by the fire, the indication was that the children lit the sparklers under the bed where they would be at their most glittering, and threw away the burning matches, which started a smouldering fire.

A New York Fire Department official commented on the fire statistics of the town in 1967: 'People in the slum areas are no more careless than those of Park Avenue. Very wealthy people are burning themselves and their children to death in about the same proportion as those in the Ghettoes.'

Oil heaters, wherever they are, spell a potential threat to life. Even the most carefully tested ones may kill if not handled with care—especially if unsupervised children are around. Thousands of disastrous fires are started when burning oil heaters are accidentally knocked over, carried and dropped, and even when just a draught causes a sudden flare-up and something above it is ignited. In all countries where oil or paraffin heaters are used, various acts of legislation have attempted to safeguard users, but unscrupulous door-to-door salesmen still fob off old models 'as brand new' upon the unsuspecting. (In 1970, a mother and two children died in a London fire caused by an oil heater that had just been sold to them as 'the latest safe type' although it had been manufactured in 1959, before new safety standards came into force.)

A particularly tragic case occurred near Port Radium, on the shore of the Great Bear Lake, in Canada, and ever since a father has felt full responsibility for the accident that wiped out his entire family. They had a wick-type paraffin heater which was left burning all night in the living room downstairs. At dawn the father was awakened by the smell of smoke, went down the stairs to investigate, and found a menacing fire in the living room. The front door of the house opened directly into that room, so he dashed out to get help . . . but left the door open. The incoming air fed the flames and, as the natural course of fire is upwards, the fire spread up the stairs. By the time he returned, a full blast of heat and smoke hit him in the face. It was impossible to get through. A neighbour ran half a mile to telephone the fire brigade but nothing could be done for the man's wife and six children who were all asphyxiated sleeping in their beds.

Open fires of all kinds, not excluding bars of electric heaters, also claim a vast toll of lives, especially among the young and the old. Children light paper or anything else at hand. Once again, a tragic abundance of cases can be found in any country. In Rheims, a four-year-old boy ignited a plastic monster on an electric heater. He was frightened and threw the burning toy on an upholstered chair which burst into flames. He and his baby brother were soon trapped. Their twelve-year-old sister stood outside, paralysed with terror, shivering, unable to cry or scream for help. The mother, who was out shopping, arrived back home just in time to rescue the children. They had all inhaled a great deal of smoke but could be resuscitated. The eldest needed a year's psychiatric treatment for shock and its after-effects.

To the old and infirm the danger is that even without being careless in any way, they may just collapse and burn or electrocute themselves.

Sometimes it takes just a moment's thoughtless behaviour to open the way to trivial coincidences that so often bring tragedies. In a castle at the heart of a large estate, Lady L., daughter of a British aristocrat, slept peacefully. Lady L. was eighteen months old. Her French nursemaid made sure that everything was in order on the nursery floor, then went to do some ironing in a room below. It was the butler who raised the alarm. The nurse found Lady L. unconscious on the floor among the flames in the nursery. The evidence indicated that a slight draught in the room had moved the curtains which then touched an electric heater and caught fire.

The child was rushed to hospital. At first she responded well to treatment for shock and the effects of smoke, but then there was a relapse and she died sixty hours after she had been rescued. Her father ordered that all the gates around the estate should be closed in mourning. But they could not keep out the tragic after-effects of the sorrow. For the death of the child is said to have contributed to the break-up of the parents' marriage . . . and all because of a slight draught.

Clothes that catch fire are the single cause of perhaps the largest number of deaths and crippling injuries in the home. This is one of the oldest fire hazards and, despite massive research and preventive legislation, it is responsible for almost half the fire deaths in buildings in most Western countries.

Lady Dorothy Nevill, daughter of the Earl of Orford, a vivacious member of nineteenth-century society, was one of the lucky few who lived to tell their tale and turn a hair-raising experience into an anecdote to amuse friends. She wrote in her *Reminiscences** :

'That was the day of that monstrosity, the crinoline, which once came near costing me my life; in fact, I only escaped a terrible fate mercifully through retaining my presence of mind. It was in the drawing room one evening after dinner at Dangstein before the gentlemen had joined us, and at the time my dress caught fire I was showing a lady an engraving of Mr. Cobden which he had just given me, and which hung near the fireplace.

'Somehow or other my voluminous skirt caught fire, and in an instant I was in a blaze, but I kept my presence of mind, and, rolling myself in the hearthrug, by some means or other eventually beat out and subdued the flames. I was rather badly burnt about one of my arms, where the marks remain to this day, but otherwise I was unhurt, and, oddly enough, not at all frightened; in fact, having common whitening made into a paste with water, applied to my arm—an excellent receipt for burns of which I had but a day or two before been reading—I came downstairs again in time to meet the gentlemen coming from their coffee. My not having been frightened is rather puzzling, but I have an idea that the thought of trying this new

* Published by E. Arnold, London, 1907. It was quoted by the *F.P.A. Journal*, No. 48, January 1960.

receipt took up my attention. None of the ladies present could of course do much to assist me, for their enormous crinolines rendered them almost completely impotent to deal with fire, and had they come very close to me, all of them would have been in a blaze too.'

The day of that monstrosity passed, but new monstrosities like highly inflammable flowing nightwear caused hundreds of deaths in each country each year. The campaign against dangerous fabrics met staunch opposition from well-meaning champions of individual liberty. Why should governments tell them to use this material not that, or wear pyjamas not a nightdress because of greater safety? The campaign at last gained some impetus when it was shown that the most likely victim of burning clothes would be a woman over the age of sixty-five—or a child under the age of five. Statistics have also revealed that fatal and serious burns were suffered by ten times as many people wearing nightdresses as those in pyjamas.

Further research and investigation into the circumstances of such accidents called attention to particularly hazardous situations. One of these was the old and seemingly unshakeable habit in British homes of putting a mirror over the mantelpiece: wherever there is a mirror, people will stop and look at themselves—even if this means standing close to the open fire or, in the case of children, if it means standing on a chair, close to and *above* the flames.

In most countries, including Germany and Britain, it was shown that the manufacturers' efforts to *sell safety* had been a glaring failure. People refused to pay more for the safer materials and shops found it convenient to mention the difference in prices which could be as much as fifty per cent. In the 1960s, winceyette and flannelette-type fabrics, imported cheaply from the Far East and sold chiefly in street markets, were branded as a particular hazard.

In principle, all fabrics can be burned in some way, but there are huge differences in how they can be ignited and how they burn. Disregarding the special treatment that can render fabrics less inflammable, some basic rules of fire behaviour of the most widely used fabrics can be summarized for guidance.

Wool can be ignited only with great difficulty and, like other fibres of animal origin, it will hardly sustain the fire. Cotton is probably the most dangerous in its untreated form : it ignites easily and burns freely. Linen is rather like cotton, and rayon is only a shade safer. Synthetic fibres, like Nylon, Orlon and many others in common use, are on the whole much safer than natural fibres : they have a very low flammability and usually they melt rather than flame.

Despite all the evidence from tests and actual cases, legislators took a long time to make really positive decisions, thus proving not only that the 'law is an ass' but also that it is as slow as a tortoise. One problem is that a great deal of research and consultation is needed before a national standard of minimum requirements is evolved. This is, however, usually no more than a strong recommendation, and many committees away from a law.

British Standard 3121, for instance, was only a specification for low flammability of fabrics and, many a death later, it formed the basis of more committees, more conferences, more Parliamentary debates and, finally, Home Office regulations that eventually turned fire-performance requirements of all made-up children's nightwear into one of the few legally enforced British standards. (The regulations define the necessary non-flammable properties of such fabrics, which must be able to retain these qualities after regular washing, so that a child's nightdress made from one of them will always burn slowly enough to be extinguished or to be pulled off safely.)

Another way to prevent clothes from catching fire is the use of adequate *fire-guards*. It is typical that in Britain, where there are so many open coal, oil and gas fires and electric heaters with bar-type elements, it is only now that improved, safer standards for firmly fixed fire-guards have been established, soon to be followed by more stringent legal requirements; and that at last, Lambeth Council, a local authority—and still the only one in Britain—has decided to prosecute parents whose carelessness with oil heaters might have led to death or injuries to children.

Laxity, delays and complete lack of uniformity in legislation are much less surprising in the United States than in Europe. In addition to individual liberty, the independence of all American states, towns, minute local authorities, is most jealously guarded. Their National Fire Protection Association formulates many cautiously termed recommendations of hoped-for national standards but even these can be achieved only by the most diplomatic lengthy consultations with everyone concerned if any effectiveness at all can ever be expected from them. Such NFPA standards have, in fact, been published, covering 'wearing apparel' and fire tests of textiles, but the various state legislative acts show little or no reflection of these.

It is indeed a phenomenon when now and then a hopeful ray of sensible and speedy legislation breaks through the clouds of calamity. A survey, reported in a specialist journal, disclosed that, in Switzerland, a new nylon product was made inflammable by its special treatment, dyeing and finishing. Despite the fact that this particular fibre had caused only one fatal accident, Swiss regulations for fire testing of clothes were revised immediately to deal with this latest development and forestall the possibility of a new menace.

Technologically advanced legislation coupled with reliable fire-guards may cut the dangers down considerably, but ultimately, thoughtlessness can negate all the beneficial efforts. In 1968, a Northampton family had a fixed fire-guard specially installed for their open coal fire because there were three children, all under the age of ten, in the house. A few days later, the mother did the family washing and, as it was a wet winter day, she left the clothes spread out to air round the house. The new fire-guard seemed a particularly favourable place for quick drying. She popped out to see a neighbour. On her return, she was met by black smoke and flames. Firemen found the children—all three were dead.

Faulty wiring is responsible for many fires in homes and elsewhere. The dangers are obvious and although builders and contractors conform to local regulations, householders are under no obligation to take care of the wiring or seek expert advice when they decide to renew it themselves without professional help. If you add to faulty wirings the *do it-yourself electrical installations and misuse of appliances*, the second most lethal fire-raiser, you have the cause of about a third of all fires in the home. The majority of such cases are simple : circuits are overloaded, faulty equipment is used, amateur repairs break down, and heaters stand too close to furnishings.

It would be impossible to illustrate all the varieties of mishaps misguided human ingenuity can produce, but a few examples may indicate what weird killer-contraptions do-it-yourself enthusiasts can dream up.

In San Francisco, near Lafayette Square, lived a family of four in a seventh-floor apartment. The daughter was a keen reader and the father rigged up a special lamp for her: it would fit to a four-feet adjustable arm or could be detached to stand anywhere or be clipped to anything so that when she decided to sit up and read at the foot of the bed, she would still have no problem about getting enough light. Soon enough, their younger child, a five-year-old boy, decided to make it a condition of his promised greater efforts at reading to get a similar lamp in his room above his bed. This was done in due course.

One early morning, the boy knocked on the parents' door. The father did not get up but called out curtly to him to go back to bed. About ninety minutes later, the wife woke up and heard some noise. She smelled smoke. The parents rushed out and saw flames coming from the boy's room. Luckily, before they could risk their lives by trying to get in for the boy, the child appeared from the kitchen.

The family escaped unhurt and the boy was able to explain what had happened: he woke up very early, tried to go to his parents' room, was told to return to bed where he played putting the lamp under the blanket, grew tired of the game and went to the kitchen. He remembered some 'funny smell that burned my eyes under the blanket'. It must have been the beginning of the fire caused by the bulb coming into contact with the bedclothes. What made the initial situation particularly dangerous was that, the previous night, the bulb in that lamp had blown out and was replaced temporarily by a very strong one from a spotlight in the living room.

In Wiesbaden, Germany, a trader of furnishing fabrics disconnected the central heating in his small store because he was convinced that the dry air was bad for his bronchitis. He installed electric fires with bars everywhere and connected them all to a single switch near the entrance so that all of them would be turned on at once as soon as the light was switched on in the dark hall. For the summer he unplugged the heaters one by one. He spent the winter of 1967 in hospital and during his absence the store was closed. Early next summer, he was still away convalescing and asked relatives to remove some stocks. They knew nothing of the peculiar wiring of the store and forgot to switch off the light in the hall when they left. Some heaters, which stood too near the shelves packed with textiles, set the building ablaze.

Inundated by too many similar cases, fire protection specialists strongly object to the use of multiple adaptors. There have been many cases when housewives plugged in vacuum cleaners, moved electric heaters on the same circuit near bookshelves or upholstered armchairs while cleaning the room, then switched off the vacuum cleaner—not the plug—while answering the doorbell or making a cup of coffee, only to find the room on fire when they returned.

A simple, but in many ways very typical, device that caused a serious fire was reported by the *Sheffield Star* in 1970. A local couple, who were 'hooked' on early cups of tea in comfort, rigged up a heating element with a kettle between their twin beds. The nearest plug was outside the room, at the top of the stairs, so the lead was hidden under the carpet all the way. One morning they forgot to switch off the element. The husband left for work, the wife was busy spring-cleaning the house, and the fire, that began in the bedroom after an early 'cuppa', had plenty of time to build up to menacing proportions. The flames consumed one bed and ruined the other, burnt a large hole in the floor-boards and caused irreparable damage to all the furniture in the room. A great deal of fallen plaster indicated how fierce the heat had been. The wife was lucky she did not go out shopping: a little more delay in the discovery of the fire would have destroyed the entire house.

Electrical appliances are under constant scrutiny in all Western countries. In Canada, Sweden, Denmark, Norway, West Germany and New Zealand it is prohibited by law to sell any unsafe, sub-standard product. Britain is still way behind these countries: the latest Home Office recommendations, yet to be accepted by manufacturers, still fail to demand flatly that no unsafe electrical goods should be sold. The law, of course, can protect people only from faulty insulation, earthing or design—not from themselves.

Electric blankets account for about 80,000 fires in Western countries every year. Today, about six million blankets in British homes do not comply with the current recommendations and are four times more likely to cause fires than the 'approved' ones. But sub-standard products are not the only danger in electric blankets. Most fires from this source are caused by what is known as 'misuse of these appliances'. Yet one is driven to suspect that 'misuse' is sometimes a misnomer.

Real misuse was demonstrated by a fire in December 1968. The *FPA Journal* reported: a little girl had wet her bed and the parents decided to cover her for extra warmth with an electric blanket. This was contrary to the instructions which specified that this was an under-blanket, to be used under a sheet and definitely not as an over-blanket. As the child moved in her sleep, the blanket crumpled, over-heated and set fire to a flannelette blanket. The ensuing fire killed the girl, aged two, and her ten-month-old brother.

When electric under-blankets are used in their proper place, the hazards should be minimal even if thoughtless people forget to switch them off before falling asleep. Unfortunately, many users leave them on overnight, gambling on the reliability of the device that is supposed to prevent over-heating. The worst problem is however, that with regular folding, the crumpled blanket may break the element and cause a short circuit. The instructions always warn against folding these blankets for summer storage, but dangerous creasing may occur when the blanket is slept on, even though it is merely performing the duty it was produced for. So if eventually there is a break-down in the wiring of the blanket, can the fire it causes be attributed to 'misuse of the appliance'?

Similarly, it is considered a misuse to pile blankets or other such insulating material on top of the electric blanket because this creates an opportunity for heat to build up dangerously. This is particularly so around the middle of the electric blanket because the thermostatic controls are mostly located round the edges and it might be too late by the time the heat from the middle affects them. In Baltimore, Maryland, a case was reported of a family pet, a large Labrador, which slept on top of the middle of an electric blanket with the switch in 'high' position; the dog got away with a fright when the heat and smoke suddenly gave him his marching orders.

A German psychologist, who once advised Cologne police officers on fire investigation, remarked that 'bed is a very dangerous place: people will do any stupid thing to keep warm in bed'. The truth of this observation has certainly been borne out in Japan where the centuries-old bedwarming practice has caused millions of fires, many of which led to deaths or serious injuries.

Throughout the very cold winter, traditional Japanese homes are heated with the *hibachi*, a 'porcelain pot, half-barrel shaped, about 18 in. in diameter and a foot high' in which charcoal burns and which is moved from room to room. S. Freeman, an Australian New South Wales fire officer, reported with obvious horror how entire families plus visitors sit around the *hibachi* 'over which a blanket has been laid to deflect the warm air down around their hands and feet tucked underneath'. The night practice is an even more direct invitation to disaster: 'In cold weather the whole family, father, mother, brothers and sisters and sometimes visitors sleep together in one large bed on the floor with feet towards the middle. A few hours before retiring an earthenware pot with a lid (like an old-fashioned butter cooler) containing charcoal fire is placed in the middle of this bed beneath the bedclothes to warm it up, and left there when the occupants are asleep.

'Imagine the fire risks prevailing with about six or ten pairs of feet tucked around it, whilst their owners are asleep. Little wonder I attended quite a few fires caused by this pot being kicked over . . .' Freeman's general comment was therefore not surprising: fires in Japan are large and very numerous, and fire prevention is much neglected.

Television sets are a constant fire risk in the home. People forget to switch them off for the night, the sets get over-heated and ignite some furnishing, mostly curtains in front of which they usually stand. Carelessness is therefore rightly blamed. But after so many of these fires, would it not be timely to build in some fuse or safety device that would switch off the current automatically when over-heating begins?

The number of TV fires has sharply increased everywhere

(ten thousand a year in the U.S.A. alone) despite the better safety standards of more recent models which incorporate protective devices against the most common faults that can cause electrical fires. For many fires which were started by TV sets—on average five times more than those caused by radios, record players and tape recorders—it would be easy to blame carelessness or, charitably, mere thoughtlessness. But it is equally easy to understand the old woman who forgot to switch off the set after the picture had failed—she paid with her life for her mistake—or to see the Toronto housewife's point of view that induced her to say in a court case brought against her insurers:

'It's no good telling me that it's my duty to ensure that the set is wired to the mains plug properly! I don't know what it means. All I know is that I bought the set, took a sample plug to the shop, they fitted a similar one to the wires and told me all I had to do was to plug in the set, turn the knob and enjoy myself.'

Fire protection specialists warn us that 'merely switching off the set is no guarantee against current reaching the parts that use more power and generate far more heat than a radio. Not even the switch at the socket is a proper safeguard overnight. The only real way to make sure that the TV set won't kill is to disconnect the plug before going to bed or leaving for a long period'. Once again, a haphazardly conducted poll of house-holders in several countries produced a startling fact: eighty-two per cent of those who answered the question had never heard that they ought to unplug their sets overnight. Only one half per cent did actually take this precaution regularly.

Television engineers sometimes dispute the fact that un-plugging helps: they believe that the switches are safe enough, and that if the transformer that builds up voltage to work the tube (up to 25,000 volts for colour) over-heated and ignited faulty insulation, fire would occur long after switching off. They advocate that people should sniff at their set at bedtime and be warned by unpleasant fumes.

Fat pan fires in the kitchen were the subject of a recent investigation by the Joint Fire Research Organisation.* Although it is a common hazard, surprisingly few housewives know what to do about it.

* Fire Research, Note No. 654 by E. D. Chambers.

They studied a hundred fat pan fires which had all been discovered by the occupiers who called the fire brigade. More than half of the fires had been extinguished one way or another before the brigade arrived and only eight of these fires caused injuries. The statistical examination of the cases revealed that there can be vast differences between the 'one way' and 'another'.

The *correct way* of smothering the fat pan fire—with a lid, towel or cloth, preferably glass fibre cloth—was used only in ten cases and it was successful every time without causing a single injury. A third of the people involved still turned to water for help despite constant advice against this. They threw buckets of water, turned on the garden hose, and were probably surprised to see that their efforts were mostly unsuccessful. They were also lucky because only one of them was injured, although using water on burning fat creates a reaction that has caused some of the worst burns. Thirty-four people out of the hundred merely phoned the fire brigade—some of these did not even turn off the cooker. The worst possible course of action was followed by fifteen people: they picked up the burning pan and tried to take it outside. Some succeeded, some did not, but that was irrelevant. What mattered was that six of them were injured whereas of the other eighty-five amateur fire-fighters only two suffered burns.

The list of hazards in the home is, of course, very long, for even such seemingly innocuous household equipment as an *aluminium kettle* can become a killer of the old and lonely. A forensic scientist recalled that within a twenty-mile radius he once had two such cases in a single week.

An old woman put an aluminium kettle to brew a cup of tea on a gas ring which was connected with a composition pipe to the main. Waiting for the water to boil, she went down to the cellar for some coal, stumbled, broke her thigh, and lay helplessly, unable to call the neighbours. When the kettle boiled dry, the aluminium began to melt and drip on the piping. In turn, the pipe melted and ignited the gas that burnt fiercely like a blowlamp. There was little left of the house. Investigators reconstructed the tragic events only from the molten aluminium, the old woman's position on the stairs with the coal bucket, and the post mortem that revealed the fracture.

In the other case, an old man put on the kettle, went to the

lavatory, had a seizure, but died of asphyxiation when the
kettle boiled dry, melted, burnt a hole in the rubber tube that
connected, improperly, the gas ring to the pipe, and ignited the
gas that burnt out the flat.

As there are safe kettles available which will not melt even when
they are boiled dry, blame if any ought to be put on thoughtless
relatives or welfare officials who failed to warn the old people.

In the entire 'thoughtless, careless, negligent' group of
attitudes to fire hazards the worst and most widespread is the
complete disregard for the frightening fact that several fires
start every minute somewhere. Yet it just does not seem to
occur to people to go out of their way and seek advice on how
to prevent it happening to them. There was nothing more
pathetic than the elderly woman, living alone in Munich, who
confessed to a local fire officer that 'I am so worried about having a fire and being unable to do anything about it, that every
night I take a rather large dose of sleeping pills and even so, I
am sometimes too worried to fall asleep'. When he visited her
home, he listed fifty-seven fire hazards ranging from frayed
electric extension cords snaking all over the flat to mountains of
old newspapers and magazines stacked everywhere even on top
of an electric cooker. He volunteered to help her clear out the
flat and repair the faulty appliances. This she accepted grate-
fully, but she refused to understand that barbiturates are
dangerous to the lonely, and that had there been a fire she
would have been doomed to lie there in a stupor unable to
recognize the danger, wake up and escape.

All countries make some provision for giving advice on fire
problems to anybody any time—in principle. In practice, lack
of requests from the public and also a chronic fire brigade
staff shortage prevent the service being of much use. Fire
Prevention Weeks and other special safety promotion campaigns have some effect but most people simply ignore the
warnings. Free pamphlets pushed through the letter box seem
to get a similar reception.

Much more effective is, for instance, the American Home
Inspection programme, particularly in rural areas. Its secret
is that unlike a poster, a spoken word of warning, accompanied
by a pointing finger, is related directly to somebody's home.
The hazardous level of conditions is then made obvious to each

householder—there is no more excuse that 'it couldn't happen to me' because the creation of a risk, the first step to a fire, is already shown to be happening to him. The figures speak for themselves. In a single year, Los Angeles firemen visited 199,482 'residential and light business occupancies'. These inspections disclosed 10,418 hazardous conditions 'each of which posed a threat to life and property'.

Short of actually visiting a home, the simple striking leaflet and checklist, distributed by the Country Fire Authority of Victoria, Australia, appears to be one of the most effective forms of warning because it is provocative, and evokes curiosity and subconscious identification. (Although several of the questions cannot be applied to urban conditions, when it was shown to fifty-two town dwellers in the United States and Europe, it persuaded twenty to copy out the checklist for subsequent inspection in their homes. A remarkable result when one thinks about the direct route for leaflets between letter-box and dustbin.)

The availability of personal advice varies a great deal not only from country to country, but also from town to town, and there are sometimes considerable differences between suburbs of the same town. The situation in London offers an interesting example.

Under the Fire Services Act 1947, every British fire authority must provide facilities for giving advice on request from anybody including private householders. They have no right to inspect private homes except by invitation and they have no right to enforce the acceptance of their advice. Fire prevention officers are convinced that there ought to be some basic fire-fighting equipment in each home. They can tell people what sort of extinguisher to buy or to have a garden hose or at least a bucket handy, but this they can do only when asked to.

When occasionally firemen offer door-to-door advisory service, the reception is not very favourable. A North London brigade tried it with very limited success. A fire prevention officer said : 'At first people thought we were policemen and this embarrassed them. Then they got worried that we wanted them to spend money on something. Finally they were offended that their homes might be considered unsafe to live in. The trouble is that all too often their houses actually are unsafe.'

Borough councils have too few, and not always really well-trained, home safety officers. In Lambeth where some exemplary initiatives have been taken and where the chief safety officer, Earl Sinclair-St. Clair, Ph.D., also happens to be the head of the British and international organization of municipal safety officers, the safety office has eleven employees including administrative staff looking after a population of 336,000. (650 hours of unpaid overtime for Sinclair-St. Clair in a single year is not exceptional.) When Lambeth organized a free house-to-house advice campaign, 'reception was rather sceptical, sometimes hostile, and one was made to feel a bit of a nuisance'. Earl Sinclair-St. Clair said: 'The education of people is not much more than a cliché because whatever the subject is—fire, road safety, accidents in the home—there is too little centralized planning, little or no back-up support including financial facilities, and a lack of knowhow and trained personnel.'

Most Londoners—or others in Britain, for that matter—have no idea of their rights to call the fire brigade and ask for advice or even an inspection of their homes with no obligation on their part. 'Perhaps it's lucky that they don't know,' commented a fire prevention officer, 'for we certainly couldn't cope with a flood or even a mild increase in such requests.' They do indeed have a tremendous backlog of inspection they are required by law to make, and a reluctance to take on such private visits was fairly evident when several test requests were made in various parts of town. This author's own attempts showed clearly that the local brigade, as one officer put it, was 'not quite geared to giving this service'. Here are the notes taken on December 8, 1970.

15.10: called nearest Command headquarters, girl answered and made some inquiries; was cut off, called again; was told that yes, visits can be arranged but only through London HQ; was given number.

15.17: called London HQ; was advised that brigade had no right to inspect and that owner's permission was needed; gave assurance that owner of premises was making inquiry; 'oh well, yes, then that's out of the way'; was advised to phone local Division HQ.

15.22: called Division HQ; operator had to make inquiries; was put through to somebody whose name appeared to be 'what's it about, sir?'; was told that 'due to pressure of work' visits were hard to arrange but inquiries could be made in writing or by going to the office in person; insisted that London HQ had said a visit would be possible; 'well then, hang on for a minute'— nothing happened till 15.33.

15.33: hung up and called again; number engaged.

15.37: another call—number engaged.

15.39: could not say who caller had talked to; operator put through call to prevention branch; found wrong man who made inquiries in office and then promised to transfer call to right man; silence, except voices 'oh no' and 'sorry, wrong number'; waited in vain until 15.45;

15.45: another call; phone ringing but no answer; tried again, let it ring until 15.52, then again for three minutes.

15.55: called telephone exchange and operator managed to get through at 15.58; fire brigade phone operator explained that switchboard was old, calls were usually cut off if transferred; now he would stay on the line until the right man was found, but must wait; prevention branch lines engaged.

16.03: was put through to branch—yet another man to be given the full story; like all others, he was polite, friendly and a little patronizing, promised to pass on request and to arrange that an officer should return call in a week or so and make an appointment. The time:16.13.

This was achieved in sixty-three minutes. A less persistent caller, driven by a more casual idea of 'let's see if everything is all right in the house', would probably have been put off half-way through.

Thirteen days later, on December 21, a prevention officer rang the door-bell without appointment. He was friendly and most sympathetic, walked through the house in less than five minutes, omitted a couple of rooms, failed to spot long electric extension wires and few multiple adaptors (against both of which he later advised), and asked if the purpose of the original inquiry was the purchase of a fire extinguisher. When he was told that this approach was, in fact, just a test, he seemed to be relieved and explained his puzzled looks: 'We have so few such requests that I kept wondering, what is he worried about? It's a well-kept house, no hazardous conditions—we can spot them as soon as we enter—so what is he up to?'

This officer's manners and impeccable appearance would have allayed the fears of a friend who, when he was asked to make a similar test in South London, said: 'My god, no! What if they really come and tell me I must spend a lot of money on fire escapes or whatnot' and, when he was reassured that he would not have to comply with any regulations, added: 'Sorry, I really don't want a brass-helmeted fellow clomping all over my house in his dirty waterproof galoshes.'

Then, as just an after-thought, he remarked: 'What could they tell me anyway? That I shouldn't drink petrol and light a pipe at the same time or that I shouldn't throw my burning cigarettes into the bin where I keep my powder dry?'

Perhaps even such banal pieces of advice would not be completely wasted. A fire-eater with Winship's Wild West Circus did, in fact, suffer burns to his throat, chest and face when petrol was used by mistake instead of paraffin for his trick. When he blew the petrol from his mouth on to a burning torch it exploded, unlike the paraffin, which would burst into a supposedly harmless ball of fire. Luckily, he had the presence of mind to shut his mouth at once to exclude air, a basic component of the deadly fire triangle.

As for discarding cigarette ends at work and in bed, it seems the warning cannot be repeated often enough. Statistical examinations of rising tobacco consumption and paper production revealed a direct relationship with the increase in the number of fires. It appears that currently there is one fire for every six million cigarettes sold. This evidence is inconclusive but it will be interesting to watch this trend now that the anti-smoking campaign is gaining momentum: will a reduction of tobacco consumption lead to a reduction in the number of fires, and will the menace of lung cancer at least help to check the frequency with which people are burning themselves to death?

CHAPTER EIGHT

FAG-END

THE WORK-DAY ended with the usual tidying up and New Yorkers who were employed in 7 East 22nd Street left for home. Next morning when they returned they found themselves without a job. The building was to become a parking lot. During that night in October 1966, there was a fire. Had one of them smoked a last cigarette while washing his hands? Nobody knew. Who would remember? It was only a cigarette. . . .

First it was a 'one alarm' fire and the usual contingent, three engines and two ladder companies, responded. The blaze in the cellar looked 'pretty bad'. It was a commercial building, deserted at night, and the Chief on the spot tried to control the outbreak for some time before putting through a second alarm.

The cellar and the ground floor were occupied by an art dealer who imported cheap, mass-produced but original oil paintings from Europe and sold them to retailers. The paintings and frames stored there were highly inflammable. What made it worse was that at the back of the cellar, some damaged frames were retouched while others were repainted completely in gold if the customer wanted a 'real antique' look; and so paint, too, was stored in there. The prospect was not promising.

Fire-fighting began with a frontal attack, but the heat down there was tremendous. As the block ran right through to 23rd Street, some firemen had to go round to see if they could attack the flames from the far side or if that building behind needed protection from a possible spread of the fire. The two buildings that formed the block were separated by a wall. On 23rd Street, the cellar and ground floor were occupied by a drug-store.

A chief with some men went down into the cellar. At the far end was the wall behind which they knew the fire was raging. 'The men moved round to see what they could from there,'

said Chief Vincent Canty who investigated the case. 'All they
can do in situations like this is to use all their senses: smell the
air for smoke, feel the walls and the ceiling if any spot is getting
warmer, listen and look for clues. There was some heat coming
through and a bit of smoke issuing. They considered ripping a
hole in the wall and putting through a hose.'

On the ground floor above, two Fire Chiefs and a dozen men
started the same investigation. A little smoke seeped through the
floor there but a fireman later described the conditions in the
drug-store as 'not worse than what you'd see at a quiet poker
game'. So he and another man were sent to have a look round
on the first floor. They spent about three minutes up there
looking, sniffing around. They found nothing suspicious. The
reconstruction of timing of a routine job like this is impossible.
Perhaps it was just a last touch of a wall to feel if it was getting
hot. Whatever it was, it saved their lives by the very fact of
delaying their return to the ground floor by perhaps no more
than thirty seconds.

The Chief who led the men in the cellar of the drug-store,
suddenly had a hunch. The ceiling was getting too hot to touch.
More smoke came through the wall. Although there was no
fire there, the heat had become more obvious. He knew something was about to happen. Perhaps the fire would break through
the wall from the art dealer's cellar. It could trap them all down
there. He ordered his men to get out at once.

They rushed up the stairs and reached the shop on the ground
floor when a blast of red-hot air with a tremendous whoosh and
bang swept them off their feet. They dived for the door only a
couple of feet away. The radiated heat that hit them was fierce
enough to burn the left side of each man through his clothes in
the few seconds they needed to get to safety.

The same few seconds were enough for some of them to see
what was happening at the back of the shop. The floor opened
up under the feet of the firemen in there and a furnace seemed
to reach out to them. In a fraction of a second they were all
swallowed by the inferno below.

Two Chiefs and ten men perished. Within minutes, more and
more engines and specialist assistance like field communication,
mask service and searchlight units converged round the building,
but even so it was only in the morning that the last remains of

the twelve incinerated bodies were brought out of the cellar. A post mortem showed they had all met instant death.

There were immediate accusations of carelessness on the part of the fire department. Newspapers asked why good men should be sacrificed for an empty building? Nobody was waiting to be rescued in there, so why were these men sent into the unknown?

'That question was easy to answer,' said Chief Canty. 'You can't wait for the fire to come to you. If you don't attack it, you soon lose a block or even a street. You must go in, make a stand and fight—within reason. And that's what puzzled us most: how is it possible that there had been no warning on that ground floor of the impending disaster? Why was it that two very distinguished Chiefs and ten thoroughly experienced men had seen no reason to get out? or did they make a mistake after all?

'We had to find out what happened. What caused the fire? What caused the disaster? We had to do justice to the memory of those men.'

At the site there was no sign of a break-in or illegal entry. Away from the site, marshals of the Bureau of Fire Investigations looked into the affairs of the art business. All suspicions of arson and motives for incendiarism were soon eliminated. The lucrative import was booming and the owner 'was on to as good a thing as he could find', said an investigator.

The first dramatic discovery was made when firemen had a chance to examine the layout of the building. Normally, each of the two buildings that make the block would occupy half the site. Here, at one time, the two buildings had been joined into one, then separated once again by walls on each floor. The result was that although the ground floor of each went only halfway through, the cellar of the art dealer was some thirty feet longer, and so its far end, with the frame-restoring section, was right under the rear section of the drug store! This meant that the two Chiefs and the ten men had been standing all the time right on top of the seat of the fire. How was it possible that they had no indication of what was to come?

'The fire had gutted the building and quite frankly, there was very little hope to find out what had caused it all,' said Chief Canty. 'The normal course of action would have been a quick demolition job because of the dangerously leaning unsupported walls, but with the loss of lives it was simply a must to examine every bit that came out of the ruins. We had our own photographers and demolition squad there. As the cranes lifted out the remains of the floor, our investigators marked on the floor-plan where each piece came from, tagged it with careful markings and sent it to the firehouse where all the debris was laid out and examined. We even reconstructed certain parts, particularly those where the fire began, and, right above it, where the first collapse occurred killing the men.

'We also assembled the full history of the building, contacted former occupiers, checked the records of construction and all subsequent alterations. We found nothing illegal or irregular, but the records, together with the material evidence, yielded an important explanation: we understood, at last, why those good men enjoyed a false sense of security right up to the moment of inevitable disaster.

'The floor had been constructed of good pine beams in the days when things were expected to last forever. These beams were embedded in the walls so well that an earthquake couldn't have moved them. Then one occupier grew tired of the wooden floor, laid concrete on it and covered it with tiles. A few years later, the new occupier disliked those tiles. So down went another layer of concrete and new tiles on top of that. The result was a several inches thick floor resting safely on the pine beams.

'These layers acted as a perfect insulation against the heat below. The floor let through very little smoke and remained cool under our men's feet right to the moment when the last inch of the wooden beams burned through and the whole construction suddenly collapsed. Our men had been cheated by these conditions. All we could do was to exonerate them. The cause of the fire? A mystery. A last cigarette?'

Thus even after a meticulous investigation like this, the answer to the cause of an outbreak may remain very unsatisfactory. It is not untypical that we have by now encountered smoking as a possible, probable, supposed cause of fire several times. We have seen how an intelligent guess at the end of a fruitless investigation may serve as a solution—a German policeman admitted that 'I often read "smoking" as "I don't know" '—and how many firemen maintain that such 'guesses' should be credited with accuracy because of the experience of the investigator. It appears, however, that in this case, the word *experience*, supposedly an accumulation of knowledge by observation, is merely the symbol of the status to which a traditionally acceptable presumption has been elevated by regular usage. On the other hand, scientific experience, supported by experiments, shows that while a vast number of fires may indeed be caused by careless smoking habits, it is very difficult to start a blaze with a burning cigarette—except in 'favourable' circumstances.

The glowing coal at the end of a cigarette has an average surface temperature of 287.7°C (550°F). A standard cigarette burns for about fifteen minutes—and not more than about twenty-five minutes even if it happens to burn all the way. A carelessly discarded cigarette-*end* will, of course, have only a few minutes' burning time left. The low temperature of the tip can just about char a little a smooth-surfaced board or even much more inflammable material like cotton. If the burning cigarette is covered with some light, loose material, like cheese-cloth, the heat dissipates long before the material under or over the cigarette could reach ignition temperature.

Newspapers are among the most inflammable type of paper, yet in still air, a burning cigarette dropped in a stack of newspapers will probably char no more than the top two sheets just under the tip. On most upholstery, a burning cigarette will usually produce only a linear scorch. Highly inflammable plastics and even the particularly dangerous foam rubber padding will probably be charred in a similar way, merely melting *away* from the heat.

All this is not to say that thrown-away cigarettes can never cause fires in the above circumstances, but a blaze as a result of such conditions is so unlikely that scientists and specialists view many investigators' findings with great scepticism.

The likelihood of fire increases dramatically when there is a draught or any air movement. The glowing tobacco temperature will then rise to about 426.6°C (800°F) and will cause a faster build-up towards the ignition temperature of the material on which the cigarette is resting. But the final real hazard evolves in most cases only through the accidental presence of some kind of insulation that can prevent the dissipation of heat while being imperfect enough to ensure a sufficient flow of air supply to maintain burning. Then the cigarette will soon burn at the temperature 510°C (950°F). This can easily produce a smouldering condition in the surrounding material. As the zone of smouldering expands, air currents are induced and these, in turn, increase the rate of burning. When the heat production builds up to the ignition temperature of the material that surrounds the cigarette, the gentle glow bursts into much faster-spreading flames.

This is how fire starts after a half-stubbed out cigarette-end, together with other contents of an ashtray, is thrown into a waste-paper basket or some plastic container. Many pub, hotel, restaurant and home fires start in this way.

The carelessly discarded burning cigarette-end may also find its way into an insulated spot—a gap among loosely packed inflammable materials in a store or factory, and among dry grass or leaves where the invisible origin of many disastrous forest and bush fires is known to be. In these cases, however, the initial appliance of smoking, the flaming match, is the most likely and most frequent culprit.

Two of the ideal black spots for such accidents exist in the home: one is the bed, the other is upholstered furniture with cushions. The much advertised ideal cigarette with its 'round, firm and fully-packed' construction has not only excellent smouldering but also exceptional rolling qualities. When it is dropped, it quickly finds its way into gaps under cushions, the folds of bed-clothes, and between the seat and arms or back-rest of furniture.

There are only a few situations in which investigators can conclude with any degree of certainty that the cause of a fire was a cigarette. The most definite proof is when a reliable witness is available, and circumstances confirm the account. It was a case like this in September 1968, when Divisional Officer Samuel Johnston of London Fire Brigade had a call at 10.46:

'It was a six-pump fire in Fulham Road and because it was a "Persons Reported" call—which means that there were people in the burning premises—the attendance by an investigator was automatically required. It was a terraced building with flats on the four upper floors and a small stationery shop on the ground floor. The fire was raging on the ground floor, beginning to affect the upper floors. Two people were trapped upstairs: a man was rescued by escape ladder from a second-floor window, and his teenage son was carried by firemen down the smoke-logged staircase. Both had to be taken to hospital suffering from shock and smoke exposure.

'I talked to people who were in the shop when the fire had begun, and I can only wish that everybody would stick to simple facts and observation like these did. It would make our work much easier. The account of events they gave supplemented each other and fitted to the material evidence. A customer, an Egyptian girl visiting Britain, selected some postcards and sweets in the shop, then stood in front of the cash register to pay for them. She had been smoking and holding the cigarette between the fingers of her right hand. She remembered quite clearly that the cigarette was still there when she accepted some change from a pound note in her outstretched hand. Not being familiar with English money—this was in the days of half-crowns, twelve-penny shillings and other sources of endless puzzlement for foreigners—she held her palm open counting the change mentally.

'At this time, her hand was over a sloping, open sweets display rack which stood on a glass-fronted display cabinet. Suddenly, she remembered, the cigarette slipped from between her fingers. It disappeared immediately from view. So she stepped back to see where it had fallen and noticed it behind the glass inside the cabinet.

'Unfortunately, she never had a chance to pick it up. She saw that the cigarette set fire to something that began to emit a lot of smoke and burn with frightening bangs. What she did not know was that the cabinet had been full of fireworks.

'The smoke was spreading so menacingly that she and the shop assistants fled to the street. That's how they escaped, for soon the whole shop, with its timber wall linings and more fireworks stored on shelves at the rear, was aflame with the fire spreading fast up the stairs to the first floor landing.

'The cabinet where it all began was damaged beyond recognition, but it was a fairly safe assumption that the top of the cabinet had not been as tight-fitting as it should have been.'

In many cases, however, witness accounts can be seriously misleading. In Hamburg, a middle-aged woman died in the fire that burnt out most of her home. Her husband and grown-up son told the police investigator that they had left her sitting on a sofa and smoking a cigarette only some *twenty minutes* before the

fire was noticed. The two men then made several dangerous
attempts to rescue her—this was seen by neighbours—but only
the firemen managed to get her out in her dying moments. On
the basis of the witness account it was subsequently accepted
that 'the fire had been caused by a lighted cigarette which she
must have dropped when she fell asleep momentarily and which
must have set fire to the sofa'.

This explanation is just about possible—but extremely
unlikely. Among cushions or in a corner of a sofa, where the
cigarette has the necessary air supply and insulation, the first
forty minutes or so usually result in a smouldering area of some
six or eight inches in diameter.* Flaming combustion will not
start for at least sixty but usually ninety minutes. Therefore, if
the woman in Hamburg was seen awake and still smoking only
some twenty minutes before the fire, the chances are that either
something else caused the fire or the witnesses got completely
confused with their timing in the excitement.

Timing can be of paramount importance. If a fire is discovered in its early, developing stage in a cinema in the morning, it is unlikely to have been caused by a carelessly discarded
cigarette because nobody is supposed to have been in there for
eight or ten hours—but this may indicate other causes or illegal
entry by unauthorized persons.

In certain conditions, the material evidence can be substantial enough to prove that a cigarette must have been the culprit.
One clue is that during the early, smouldering period, combustion is incomplete and, as we have seen, investigators will find
fairly heavy staining by smoke deposits on windows, etc.

If such a fire is discovered and put out before near-total
destruction is brought about, the chair- or bed-centred pattern
and heavy charring under the suspicious furniture will give
guidance to investigators. The notorious 'last smoke in bed' has
been blamed for many fatal fires. People in bed are tired,
mentally prepared to rest, and are liable to fall asleep involun-
tarily. In many such cases a considerable alcohol content in the
body was revealed by the pathologist even though most people
know that drinking greatly increases the likelihood of a last
cigarette causing tragedy. The burning cigarette finds perhaps
the most favourable conditions in bed: there are hundreds of

* *The Fire and Arson Investigator*, October 1960.

folds to kindle the fire surrounded by highly inflammable materials like cotton which can sustain smouldering for a long time and produce the killer amount of carbon monoxide.

Jumping to 'obvious' conclusions, however, can be just as misleading in these as in more mysterious cases. In a small, derelict forest lodge of northern Sweden a fatal fire gave all the indications of an accident caused by the owner's habit—well-known to friends who gave evidence—of having a last cigarette in bed every night. The body was burnt beyond recognition. Identification by the teeth proved to be impossible because of the lack of dental records. Unexpectedly, an insurance claim was entered by the supposedly dead owner of the lodge. It was then that the mistake was discovered.

The owner was a homosexual who had broken off a long-standing relationship with his friend and went abroad for a few weeks. The friend, a known drug addict, had a key to the lodge, went there, and probably started a slowly smouldering fire after he went to bed in a presumably drugged condition. As the owner could not be found at the time, the investigators accepted the most likely assumptions of the given circumstances.

They had at least one genuine excuse: they had examined the springs of the mattress and found one of the most important clues that would identify a fire that started in beds or upholstered furniture. This is that even when a chair is only between thirty and seventy per cent destroyed by internal fire, the springs usually soften or collapse—a very unlikely event if the piece of furniture is burned and destroyed to the same extent only from the outside. Tests in an electric furnace indicated that furniture springs will normally collapse under their own weight if the temperature reaches at least 621°C (1150°F). In experiments, cushions have produced this temperature after about three hours of smouldering. Increased hardness of collapsed springs usually indicates that fire reached the upholstered furniture from the outside and the collapse was brought about by the sudden cooling action of the firemen's water jets.

A pipe or cigar may cause fires in ways which are similar to the effects of dropped cigarettes. Because of the increased amount of glowing embers involved, they are more likely to burn holes and start the spread of smouldering faster, but they are no less over-estimated than cigarettes as causes of fires.

Cigarettes have also been regarded by inexperienced police-men and investigators as one of the arsonist's favourite tools. Although the possibility cannot be ruled out completely in some odd cases, this idea is probably yet another fallacy. Apparently, the developing ash caused by reducing temperature acts as an insulation round the tip and if the cigarette is not given enough time to build up heat, it cannot ignite even petrol vapour. (In laboratory tests, cigarettes were put out in dishes of petrol because, just like water, the inflammable liquid cut off air supply. Cigarettes which were puffed by a special air-pump failed to ignite or blow up explosive vapour-air mixtures even if the ash was frequently knocked off.)

Car fires have often created a highly controversial issue: could a single cigarette result in the complete gutting of a car? American criminologists proved in experiments that the answer was positive.* The question that remained was: could such a car fire destroy completely the occupants' bodies?

In 1966, it became imperative to find the answer because of a suspected murder case. In a deserted mountain area near Kamiah, Idaho, the burned-out shell of a car was found with the remains of two bodies which were destroyed so completely that all attempts at identification failed. The car and its owner had been missing for several weeks. Detectives were puzzled. What nobody knew was whether additional accelerants were needed during the blaze or if such a thorough devastation could happen purely accidentally.

At that time, a research project was under way at Washington State University.† It involved the deliberate burning of the carcasses of two ewes in two cars, a Nash and a Plymouth, recovered from a junk yard. Both cars contained the usual floor mats, seat cushions and fabic lining. A carcass in each car was set on fire with the aid of accelerants (gasoline). In one car, after thirty minutes of smouldering, the heat cracked the windows and the fire was allowed to continue for another thirty minutes before the flames were extinguished and samples were removed for laboratory examination.

In the second car, a heavier ewe, weighing 170 pounds, was

---

* *Journal of Criminal Law, Criminology and Police Science*, 54, 1963.
† Bruce V. Ettling: 'Consumption of an Animal Carcass in a Fire', the *Fire and Arson Investigator*, April 1968.

laid on its back on the front seat and eleven quarts of gasoline
were ignited. A door and a window were left open for free air
supply. In thirty minutes, the flames totally consumed everything—except the carcass. This was a crucial point in the
experiment: the car had already begun to cool down, but a
very small fire continued to burn under the carcass. Could that
bring about as complete a destruction as that in the Idaho case?

The scientists then made a vital observation. The carcass
was still suspended on metal parts. Fat kept dripping on the
char and ashes underneath which maintained the small flames
like a candle-wick. The flames rendered more fat—this, in
turn, continued to feed the 'candle'. The cycle continued for
more than three hours, by which time the carcass, with the
exception of the skull and pelvic regions, was completely
burned.

The conclusion was that the ewe, and presumably a human
body, too, could be thoroughly burned irrespective of the
presence of accelerants if the body was suspended in a way that
the fat fed the flames below. The evidence was further supported
by a report about the difficulties over destroying corpses in Nazi
extermination camps. Apparently, many attempts were made,
always in vain, to burn piles of corpses on the ground with the
aid of gasoline. The solution reached by an extermination
specialist was to place the corpses on a rack and light a fire
beneath them. (That specialist obviously knew his gory trade
for he ordered the corpses to be so arranged that the ones with
the most remaining fat content should be at the bottom of the
pile.)

As for the Idaho case, the scientific findings did not rule out
the possibility of murder, but they did prove that the two deaths
could have been entirely accidental. If the couple fell asleep and
a burning cigarette was dropped on the sloping seat, rolling
naturally into the corner, the fumes could have asphyxiated
the two people and the ensuing fire could have reduced the
remains to the state in which detectives eventually found them.

In many fires which are supposedly caused by carelessly
discarded cigarettes, the negligent or absent-minded smoker is
not solely responsible for all tragedies that may follow. In a
European case, which is still *sub judice*, it seems likely that the
eventual findings will blame a burning cigarette as the probable

cause of the fire that ultimately killed several people in a factory. Smoking was permitted everywhere in the premises despite the fact that the materials stored all over the place and the products were highly inflammable. This possible laxity of the company regulations would not have resulted necessarily in fatalities, had the fire escapes been properly maintained, had the escape routes been kept free of obstruction, had the staff been instructed in fire-fighting and evacuation drill, had quick notification of the fire brigade been arranged in advance, had fire-doors to check the spread of flames and fumes been kept closed according to regulations, and overall, had the management *and* the local supervising authority ever paid but passing attention to the likelihood of fire.

The single flicked-away cigarette cannot be blamed for everything.

CHAPTER NINE

UNSAFE TO SHOP IN?

FORGET FOR a moment what you ever heard or thought, knew instinctively or learned reluctantly about fire precautions. Give yourself a legislator's seat and read a three-point proposal for the safety of *department stores*. You will be forgiven for thinking that this is a joke or a mistake and that the proposals must have been devised for the first department store in history.

People in charge of stores with sales floors and storage area exceeding 2,000 square metres (2,392 square yards) and of certain buildings which house highly inflammable materials, must take the following steps: (1) Avoid fires; (2) Fight every fire right from the beginning quickly and efficiently; (3) In case of fire, (a) give the alarm in the building, (b) make sure the speedy evacuation or safety of all occupants, and (c) call immediately the fire brigade.

The interpretation of these proposals is, of course, subject to detailed regulations for fire prevention. Yet it seems almost unbelievable that these were the *new* moves made by Belgian authorities in 1968, *after* the *Innovation* fire—the biggest department store disaster in history.

As a momentary legislator you would be ill-advised to jump to hasty conclusions condemning the Belgians. They are not alone in putting up traffic lights at obviously dangerous cross-roads only after a series of fatal accidents.

In Brussels, many ancient hazards were rediscovered after 250 deaths, 166 serious, and 50 minor, injuries. It is a harrowing tale not only because it amounted to a national tragedy, but also because of the state of affairs it revealed.

It began between approximately 13.20 and 13.30 on Monday, May 22, 1967. A salesgirl returned from lunch to her counter in the children's wear department, on the first floor, near the main staircase. She noticed a small flame reaching towards her through an opening in a partition wall. The department store, *A l'Innovation*, in the densely built shopping centre of the town, had its own firemen who went into action right away, but apparently they used only dry powder extinguishers and ignored the wall hydrants and hoses nearby. The store was having a special 'American Week' and a great deal of highly inflammable display and decoration materials filled the huge unenclosed expanse of the sales areas under the glass cupola of the central light-well. Yet it must have seemed such an innocent little fire . . .

How innocent it was can be seen from a brief timetable. At 13.34 the nearest fire station received an alarm call on the direct line reporting that some smoke had been noticed; at 13.36, the first engine's crew, on their way less than a mile from the store, noticed a large pall of black smoke and asked for immediate further assistance; at 13.38, when the first appliances reached the store, about a hundred people were hanging in bunches on the façade of four floors or balancing on the narrow cornice near the top, at least another hundred heads kept appearing and disappearing at windows screaming for help, and the street below was already littered with the bodies of those who had lost their balance or had been forced by the flames to jump. This was only four minutes after the fire brigade had been alerted—and perhaps ten minutes after the first insignificant flame had been seen.

At 13.45 the glass dome shattered—air supply was now unlimited. At 13.50, the whole building was an open furnace—nobody still inside had a chance to live. About another ten minutes later, the oldest of the store's three sections, the one next to *Priba*, another store, collapsed. The most modern section at the far end held out for another two hours. Then its unprotected steel pillars gave way on the ground floor and it felt like an earthquake as the steel buckled and massive concrete and metal structures collapsed into a flaming heap of ruins.

This was the moment that threatened most of Brussels with destruction. The inferno raged freely on all the two and a half acres of the *Innovation*. The in-rushing wind blew the flames through the gaps so that the roofs of adjoining buildings caught fire. Flames also jumped across Rue du Damier, the crammed street at the back, and started a secondary fire in the building opposite.

Fire engines had to fight their way to the scene: all the streets around are very narrow, usually packed with parked cars and jammed traffic. Firemen, Red Cross, Civil Defence and other volunteers poured into the area. Trying to stop the spreading blaze, the city fought for its life. The struggle went on all night. Some 30,000 gallons of water were used. On Tuesday, more than twenty-four hours after it had all begun, the hot ruins were still smouldering. Yet it was in the first ten minutes or so that the massacre and the threat of an even bigger disaster were already an accomplished fact.

The investigation found the exact spot where the fire had started. Suspected incendiarism as an anti-American demonstration was ruled out. The cause of the fire is still unknown, but it is clear now that apart from the initial delays, confusion and unpreparedness, the incredibly swift progress of the flames was the main factor in the holocaust.

It appeared as if the decorative displays, false ceilings, and inflammable partitions of the many storage cubicles had all been designed to spread the fire. The grand staircase proved to be the ideal route for it to reach the upper floors. In addition to the tons of combustible goods, large tanks of butane gas, which were stored for heating appliance demonstrations, fed the flames. Synthetic materials were everywhere. These produced immediate vast quantities of dense, black, toxic smoke and inflammable gases. Survivors thought that the electric power supply had failed from the start, but it was proved that the lights had remained on for a long time—they had only been made invisible by the density of the smoke.

The biggest slaughter took place in the self-service restaurant on the third floor of the most modern section even though this was the last part to collapse. About two hundred people were in there. A waitress yelled when she saw black clouds rolling in from the carpet department. Fire alarm? Survivors did not remember hearing it, but it is known that the alarm was sounded late, and the system was insufficient anyway because it had often been mistaken for routine shop service signals. The restaurant was hit by sudden darkness as the poisonous gas filled every crevice within seconds. Many customers never had a chance to leave their tables. They were overcome by smoke. Others did not know their way out. Staff became disorientated. Groups were groping around in the dark until they lost consciousness and their piled bodies waited for the flames.

Iron escape stairs led outside the wall all the way down to the interior courtyard. A member of the kitchen staff, who had her schoolgirl daughter with her, knew that the stairs could be reached through a window. She smashed the glass and led some people out. But through the windows of lower floors smoke swallowed the stairs. As more and more people tried to follow her, the pressure on her mounted with every second in the darkness until she was thrown the last few feet to the ground. She escaped with injuries. Others fell from higher up under the pressure. Many of these died. The few in the restaurant who were still fighting to retain consciousness smashed windows. The fire flared up. To escape the flames many jumped to their deaths.

Some escapes amounted to miracles. On a narrow fourth-storey ledge, a group of men and women were trapped. Firemen, who saved in all some two hundred people, could not yet get to them. But the heat and the smoke did. Their situation was desperate. People in the street below got ready with a jumping sheet. Then a window opened on the far side of the street and a member of the store's maintenance staff threw a reel of thin rope to the group trapped on the ledge. They fastened the rope, then slid down one by one, although the rope burnt some people's palms to the bones. But one woman chose to jump. Like many others in the store—and in similar panic situations elsewhere—she refused to let go of her handbag. She was caught in the jump sheet and survived with back injuries.

In spite of all this horror, in retrospect, the most spine-chilling story appears in the findings of the fire investigation: practically every hazard that had existed in the store and was now recognized as a serious fire risk could have been spotted before the tragedy. It was a very conscientious inquiry. Nobody tried to hide anything, everybody concerned was most anxious to learn everything the disaster could teach them. Major Edmund Rombaut, Chief Inspector of the Belgian Fire Services, gave a full acount of the fire to the forty-fifth annual conference of the Institution of Fire Engineers. He gave a long, detailed list of the lessons taught by the *Innovation* holocaust. These range from a revision of dangerous constructions and materials to essential escape facilities and alarm signals, from the need for sprinklers to the threat in delays and unpreparedness. What is amazing is that *none of the lessons is new in any way*. Experts in various countries received this report with understandable consternation: of course the staircases and lift-shaft must be walled-in, of course the unprotected steel structures have too little fire resistance, of course this and of course that, and yet, what is frightening is that despite the similarity of essential facts, people who are concerned with the safety of buildings in many countries have still a lot to learn from this disaster.

The Belgians themselves demonstrated this point three years after the *Innovation* fire. The fourteen-storey headquarters of the Common Market Executive Commission was completed in 1969 at a cost of thirty million pounds. A year later, after complaints about working conditions and strikes by the staff, outside experts found that the underground conference area must not be used because of fire risks and inadequate ventilation. Materials used for wall panels and interpreters' cabins did not meet the fireproofing requirements.

Every country has had its share of department store disasters. In Marseilles, seventy-five people died in 1938. In New Zealand, the toll was forty-one lives in 1947. The United States had several fatal store fires in the 1950's with from twelve to twenty-two victims each. In Bogota, Colombia, eighty-three people were burned to death in 1958. In the 1960's there was a marked improvement—until the Brussels case. And Brussels had not had such a disaster before. So now in each country everybody asked: *could the same happen here?* Officially, the answer is invariably 'no'. Anybody in charge of such matters could otherwise be accused of criminal negligence. But if it is to be 'strictly off the record' fire prevention experts' answer is 'yes, to a lesser extent, something like that could also happen here'.

The façade of the *Innovation* was, for instance, mostly covered by aluminium sheets which formed blind gables to give a modern appearance. These hindered fire-fighting and rescue operations—until, finally, they began to melt away. Luckily, they then revealed the old windows behind them. Major Rombaut believes blind gables ought to be forbidden. 'I know that they are much employed in the United States and Germany,' he said, 'but I am convinced that considerations of doubtful value such as those of beauty, fashion and commercial exploitation must not be allowed to outweigh public safety.'

Or take the good many British specialists who were quick to be outraged that there were unprotected steel structures in the *Innovation*, that there were serious shortcomings in the detection and reporting system, that there were big undivided floors, and open staircases. Yet a fortnight before the Belgian disaster, fire destroyed a British department store.

It happened in Blackpool. The fire brigade was called shortly after midnight. The second storey was already burning fiercely and, according to the Fire Protection Association report No. 5736, 'fire was spreading rapidly to the first storey, assisted by undivided floor areas and open staircases, escalators and lift shafts'. Does the phrase have a familiar ring? And that is not all. Most of the Blackpool store was destroyed, with an estimated damage of almost two million pounds, and 'some collapse occurred, unprotected steel columns being doubtless a contributory factor'. There was an automatic heat detector system in the building but it so happened that this did not cover the area in the lighting display section on the second floor where—investigation revealed—the fire had probably started due to a fault in an electrical installation.

It is impossible to say whether there would have been a Blackpool disaster if the fire had begun during the day when the store was full of shoppers. Perhaps the fire would have been discovered in time, as it was not during the night, when nobody noticed the developing blaze. (The nightwatchman's clock tape registered a last visit in that section some six hours before the discovery of the fire.) Perhaps evacuation would have proceeded smoothly without loss of lives. But it is a fact that a sprinkler installation was due for completion only a month later, and that before this outbreak a fire authority inspection had resulted in 'recommendations . . . regarding additional means of escape and staircase enclosure . . .'

So in the wake of the Brussels slaughter, while the public was fed with smiles and reassurance, a big international gathering of fire officers, builders, store managers, insurance and fire protection specialists took place in Zurich in 1968. It was no news to these distinguished representatives of fourteen countries (including the United States, most of Western Europe, Yugoslavia and Czechoslovakia) that the fire hazard, in whatever form, had no national boundaries. But they all seemed to be utterly amazed that each country had its own prevailing thoughts about the best way of protecting department stores, and that all these best ways not only differed widely but also often revealed wildly contradictory views.

Their amazement is incomprehensible for at least two reasons. One is that improving communications, frequent international conferences and goodwill visits, and exchange of masses of relevant literature should have long disclosed all these differences at least to the extent of removing the surprise element. The other reason is that practically all aspects of fire prevention views and legislation show the same vast amazing differences from country to country.

This Zurich conference perhaps promoted a little more international understanding—if not cooperation. It certainly provoked (and gave ground to) some 'strictly private views' with which the participants still make scathing criticisms about one another. The great French reliance on the private brigades of the big stores receives some vitriolic comments. The Americans are maligned for lack of centralized uniformity in legislation, and for leaving 'too much to the insurers who value the protection of property more than that of lives'. Whatever the validity of this latter view, it is a fact that pressure from the insurers has led to sprinkler protection in almost all American department stores, and also that American insurers and store managers were understandably dumbfounded when they discovered in Zurich that most European department stores regard sprinklers as a superfluous luxury. (Pressure by insurers works in a simple way: the insurance of an unsprinklered American store costs a dollar for each hundred dollars to be protected—or a hundred thousand dollars a year for a store that is worth ten million including the building and all the goods; if it is fully protected by sprinklers, the cost can be as low as seven cents per hundred dollars—or seven thousand dollars for the same store; as a comparison, an unsprinklered Austrian store is insured just about as cheaply as an American fully sprinklered one.) Some Europeans criticize the Germans for 'over-policing' and the Germans, in turn, criticize the British for not giving enough powers to the controlling authorities.

The participants at the conference, however, found at least some common ground: they were all highly critical of what they saw in Zurich. First they were shown round a then new department store. Several people now hold the view that in their respective countries the safety of that Swiss store would be judged insufficient even though it seemed superior to what they were afterwards shown in a number of other stores in the town. (Open escalators, lack of compartmentation of sales areas, manually operated sprinklers, and too few public stairways are some of the specific features they mention.)

It is interesting to note that although all these ardent and sharp-eyed critics raised valid points of argument, it is easy enough to pick holes in their own attitudes. As in many European countries, in Britain, for instance, there is heavy reliance on legislation that only follows, almost invariably, the trail of destruction. Laws are later subject to amendments, and then to amendments of the amendments to patch up the cracks caused by further fires.

In 1960, the Henderson department store fire in Liverpool was one of the major turning points. Eleven lives were lost (ten people were trapped on the fourth floor), the direct damage was more than a million pounds, and it called attention to most hazards in the book from open staircases and escalators to the causes of a tremendously fast spread of the flames, from manually operated fire alarms (automatic detectors were just being installed) to delays in evacuation.

The Henderson fire had a direct bearing on the birth of the 'Offices, Shops and Railway Premises Act, 1963' which was to control department stores. This, in turn, was followed by the 'Building Regulations, 1965' for existing buildings in England and Wales, in addition to the Building Standards for Scotland (1963) and the old London Building Acts (1930–1939). In 1968, the new British Standard Code of Practice recommendations for fire precautions devoted an important section to shops and department stores, and interested parties could also refer to the guide 'Fire Prevention and Fire Precaution in Department Stores' prepared by the FPA and the Retail Distributors'

Association. If you add to these the various amendments, local regulations, advice from fire brigades and professional organizations, and the frequent warnings that the law contains only minimum requirements and managers can do a great deal more to safeguard their stores and customers, then it will be fairly obvious that even specialists find it a strenuous exercise to keep up with it all.

Most British store managements take the rules of the game seriously. It was not quite exceptional that a manager of Harrods had the nerve to switch off all the demonstration television sets just before the blast off of the American moon shot in 1969 because the crowd watching it had grown so big that it represented a serious menace to evacuation in case of fire. On the other hand, in the absence of such good sense, the enforcement of the law appears to be rather lenient and ineffectual as a deterrent.

Recently, the Greater London Council brought a prosecution against the owners of a department store who had failed to comply with certain safety requirements. There were four charges: lack of an alarm system that would be audible everywhere in the building; lack of outlets for smoke and hot gases from the basement; the Fire Brigade was not provided with basement plans; hose reels that had been installed as required were not connected to the water supply. The owners pleaded 'guilty', and they were fined a total of £190 with £25 costs.

Fines like this amount only to little more than gentle prodding, but then it must be admitted that even the best and most strictly enforced laws cannot fully alter basic human attitudes—to which, unfortunately, many store managers are subject as much as anybody else. After the Ibrox Park disaster in 1971, the London *Evening Standard* raised the question 'how safe are you in a crowd?' and investigated where else a mass movement of people could trample dozens to death as at the Scottish football ground. Turning to crowd behaviour in big stores just before Christmas or on the first day of a sale, reporters asked managers about the hazard. The answers were reassuring: people in a store are supposed to move in all directions, in and out of several entrances, and 'there is no set time when all of them are trying to go in the same direction or do the same thing' as at the end of a football match. The effect of fire, alarm

signals and evacuation order—and the possible panic—would
however, set up just the situation managers did not seem to
visualize at all.

If the fire hazard was not uppermost in these store managers'
minds, a British supermarket manager got his priorities wrong
to the extent of putting security of wares before safety of people
and so contravening specific laws and regulations in February
1969. The two attitudes, however, stem from the same falsely
reassuring 'it-couldn't-happen-to-me' syndrome. After the fire
had broken out, five employees of this Buckinghamshire supermarket were trapped in a store-room. Soon they were so panic-
stricken that they threw tins of food to smash the glass instead of
simply opening the window. But the window-pane was not the
only obstacle to their escape: there were iron bars which had to
be cut by firemen to rescue those inside. The escape door was
padlocked with no key available. The firm was fined £660 after
pleading guilty to three breaches of regulations.

Supermarkets are a comparatively new hazard in most European countries and regulations that apply to them are often
full of loopholes. In Australia, where fire prevention specialists
realize that the state-to-state differences are indefensible and
national legal standards are badly needed, practically all department stores have installed sprinklers which are compulsory
in supermarkets only if their floor area is beyond a certain limit
—thus providing a ready-made loophole for clever planners.

In the United States, the Life Safety Code makes special
provisions for supermarkets and self-service stores. It recognizes
that where customers use wheeled carts or buggies, there is
an increased risk of obstruction to exits. The Code therefore
recommends that adequate space should be given for the
transit and parking of these carts, and that railings or other
barriers at the cash-desks should not hinder customers or staff
if they have to escape.

This Life Safety Code is an excellent guide for the entire
United States. It was assembled by painstaking nationwide
consultations under the auspices of the National Fire Protection Association and it utilized the knowledge and experience
of all the leading specialists. It has been revised and updated
regularly since 1913. The current text is worded appropriately
for direct legal use so that any local authority, which wishes to

make it mandatory in part or in full, can simply adopt and pass it as law. Yet it is up to them what to do—the Code is no more than a guide or reference document.

The Code acknowledges, for instance, that in a department store the fire hazard is increased if highly inflammable goods are stored, displayed or handled without protective wrappings or containers, and therefore it *suggests* extra-stringent escape facilities for the staff and public. The Code also makes special provisions for *exhibition halls* but again, it is up to local authorities to make use of them. And even if they are made law, it is often doubtful how well the law is enforced. It is a sobering thought just to look through the invitations to disaster that were listed after a Chicago fire.

The McCormick Place exhibition centre was a modern building on the shore of Lake Michigan. It had been completed only in 1960. The forty-sixth exhibition of the National Housewares Manufacturers Association was to open there on Monday, January 16, 1967. At two o'clock in the morning, when only cleaners and security guards were there, a fire began on the third (top) floor. Only a few hours later, the centre would have been packed with visitors. The theatre alone had seats for five thousand conference delegates.

People on the spot made a haphazard attempt to fight the fire. One man tried to beat the flames out with a broom, another used a piece of carpet. A couple of buckets of water were thrown but, apparently, nobody tried to use a hose from a nearby hydrant. The fibreboard cubicles were excellent food, decoration materials and polyethylene-wrapped kitchen gadgets were a delicacy for the flames. Crates of advertising leaflets, readily combustible plastic, wood and rubber products were everywhere and, after an initial 'hesitation', the fire spread fast up and sideways.

The fire brigade was called after about six minutes' delay. Firemen tried to fight the fire inside the building, but in about four minutes, flames surrounded them and, then, the water pressure dropped until only a trickle came from their hoses. The men had to be withdrawn. They tried to use the outside hydrants in vain. They tried the internal hydrants and found no better pressure. Once again they had to be pulled out when the roof began to collapse.

Investigation eventually revealed that the water supply came from the Chicago mains via an unattended pumping station about a quarter of a mile away. The pumps were owned and looked after by the authority that operated the exhibition centre. Several pumps were faulty. Automatic equipment that should have operated further pumps in case of increased demand was also faulty. Some of the hydrants on a ring-main round the centre were defective while others had been turned off. Even the most determined attempts of the fire-fighters failed except in preventing the blaze from achieving a complete devastation of all parts.

The roof collapsed only forty minutes after the first report of the fire. The firemen were not in control of the situation until almost ten in the morning. The damage to the building was estimated at twenty-two million dollars and the value of the exhibits that had gone up in smoke was far in excess of that. In all, the loss must have been about seventy million dollars.

In addition to the inadequate water supply, partly a result of insufficient inspection and maintenance—the 'invitations to disaster' included many factors the Code tries to eliminate. There were totally unprotected steel structures. There was no sub-division in the main exhibition area. The staff were not trained properly: they delayed giving the alarm and were apparently not familiar with all the exits. (The one casualty, a security guard, died after he had failed to find his way out of the building.)

The probable cause of the fire was an electrical fault. Although the permanent wiring in the centre had been installed in accordance with good practice, the temporary installations had many shortcomings like poor circuit protection and incorrect earth connections.

Only about eight per cent of the building space was protected by automatic sprinklers. An executive of the Centre argued that sprinklers would have been ineffective because of the height of the ceiling. The NFPA, however, maintained that sprinklers had been used successfully in similar large industrial and storage buildings for many years, and tests after the Chicago fire supported this view. An independent consultant concluded before the fire that any outbreak in the main exhibition areas would be a flash-fire which would not generate enough heat to weaken steel structures and make them collapse. The actual fire clearly proved this assumption incorrect—but have we not seen all that before?

There is always an explanation. People in charge of department stores are not criminals. Are their costly mistakes due to carelessness? Ignorance? A touch of negligence? The public seems to trust them. No shopper ever looks for escape routes and fire exits in a store. There is so much else to look at. Many customers in that Belgian *Innovation* were not even sure on what floor they were when it all began.

CHAPTER TEN

ACTS OF FOLLY

LEGISLATION FOLLOWS the trail of destruction. This is the well-trodden path that leads towards law-making in practically every country, but perhaps four British examples will best show this tragic routine at its worst. Like most legislative steps everywhere, these four served to increase the safety of people in various types of occupancy and to remove obstacles from their escape routes in case of fire.

One was the Amendment of the then twenty-one-year-old Cinematograph Act. This Amendment came only a few months after the Glen Cinema disaster at Paisley in Scotland on December 29, 1929, and the direct cost was the loss of seventy children's lives. All were between the ages of three and fifteen, all were suffocated or crushed to death in a panicky stampede when eight hundred children tried to escape from smoke and a fire that was not really dangerous and was quickly put out by the firemen who were on the scene within two minutes. There was a general lack of preparedness, escape routes were unmarked, and corridors led to locked and barred emergency doors.

The other was the Eastwood Mills fire at Keighley on February 23, 1956, when the loss of eight lives called attention to many alarmingly widespread mistakes and shortcomings (lack of alarm system and fire drill, insufficient escape routes, etc.), and opened the way to a revision of the Factories Act in 1961.

The third was the Henderson's department store blaze in Liverpool where, on June 22, 1960, eleven fatalities provided the jolt that was needed to bring about the new Offices, Shops and Railway Premises Act of 1963. (Many of the disastrous features here could have been eliminated by learning from cases like

the Keighley Mill fire and from the already proposed Factories
Act, but one must appreciate the idiosyncrasy of law: fire may
make its own equations but human nature, and so the legal
attitude will always differentiate between a store and a factory
or, for that matter, a cinema, dance hall and other places where
people gather for a different purpose!)

The fourth was the tragic case of the Top Storey Club at
Bolton, Lancashire, on May 1, 1961. The first result: the
Licensing Act in 1964. The cost: nineteen lives. But at least
it started off a slow train of thought that is still huffing and
puffing ten years later though not quite getting anywhere.*

The 'cost' of these pieces of legislation is, however, only the
direct cost which does not take into account all the lives lost in
similar situations elsewhere throughout earlier months, years
or even decades. Take that Paisley cinema disaster with its
locked doors, lack of regular inspections and law enforcement.
It was *not the first* of its kind. The following are but a few of the
more horrifying examples that preceded Paisley and contained
many warnings for precautions in public places of entertainment:

1876: Consay's Theatre, Brooklyn, New York	283 deaths	
1881: Municipal Theatre, Nice	150	,,
1881: Ring Theatre, Vienna	450	,,
1887: Opéra Comique, Paris	110	,,
1887: Theatre Royal, Exeter	186	,,
1888: Theatre, Oporto, Portugal	240	,,
1897: Charity Bazaar, Paris	124	,,
1903: Iroquois Theatre, Chicago	580	,,
1926: Temporary Playhouse, Drumcollagher, Co. Limerick, Ireland	50	,,
1928: Theatre, Madrid	68	,,

After Paisley, with the development of the safety curtain,
better venting of the stage, emergency lighting, clearly marked
obstacle-free exits, the huge theatre disasters began to disappear,
but typically, Paisley was *not the last* of its kind. Boston's Cocoanut Grove night club holocaust was just one, and the French
dance hall disaster was another of the carbon copies of the old
slaughters in the theatre. The hazard is still very much with us

* See Chapter XI.

and perhaps the greatest miracle is that there has not been a repetition in Japan, where the traditional theatre has no aisles, only narrow catwalks which are most unsuitable to cope with any rush among the audience. Japanese actors warm up around open fires on a sheet of galvanized iron on the floor in their dressing rooms where sparks fly freely among the masses of silk kimonos and other inflammable materials even during the show when these rooms and fires are left unattended.

The inability to learn from other countries' disasters is not a Japanese speciality even in these 'enlightened' days of international fire prevention efforts. The United States, for instance, had scores of extremely tragic school fires like the one in Chicago in 1958. At that time the toll had reached such appalling proportions that the authorities had to step in. The worst-risk schools had to be closed down, prevention was improved in others, but it was far from achieving a complete overhaul: several American experts claim that possible school disasters are still on the cards.

One would expect Europe to be alarmed by the American example. The headmaster of a German school with about eight hundred children in his care declared that 'we can but try to do our utmost even if at the final reckoning we're in the hands of God'. The question is, what is our 'utmost'? And the same question could be repeated many times in France. A high-powered French government official, in fact, asked this author: 'Don't you find it rather ominous that an unduly high proportion of the worst fire disasters in history took place in France as a whole, and in Chicago?'

His concern was particularly understandable at the time, in 1967, when France was still in a state of shock after the bewildered survivors of a Savoyan orphanage fire had been counted: eighteen children were dead and thirty were injured out of the hundred and eighteen there. The orphanage was in a converted thirteenth-century building in the village of Taninges, near Annecy. The fire began at night, and when the smoke awoke the staff and children in the second-floor dormitories, the building was already engulfed in flames. Many ingredients of the old disaster recipe could be found in the orphanage: lack of automatic fire detectors and alarms; unprotected old timber beams which supported the roof but were ready to burn and collapse; and an unenclosed staircase that became smoke-logged and flame-blocked so fast that children who could not jump from the windows were trapped under the burning roof before it came crashing down on them.

British schools have mercifully escaped the spectacular fire disasters that force the hands of legislators, but will their luck last forever? On an average, there is one large school fire each week in Britain. A survey by the Fire Protection Association shows that British schools are inadequately protected, many buildings have fire-prone structures, escape routes and emergency training are frequently insufficient and, in general, many British schools are no better as fire risks today than were those American ones which suffered the high death rolls particularly in the 1950's. A. W. J. Lewis, a Labour M.P., asked the Secretary of State for Education and Science in 1971 whether she would ensure that all schools within the jurisdiction of her Ministry had at least four fire drills each year. He also urged that all schools should teach fire prevention and give instruction on the action to be taken to contain fires until the firemen's arrival. These, he recommended, should be part of the ordinary education syllabus. The answer he received was, of course, totally non-committal. He was told that these were matters for head masters and responsible authorities, and also that 'the Standards for School Premises Regulations 1959 include requirements about safety from fire', and a Ministry pamphlet, 'Safety at School', *recommends* periodic fire drills in all schools . . . Governmental hands can be washed, the ball of fire is in the local educational authorities' court.

In some respects, and not merely because of its inherent cumbersomeness, it is only natural that preventive legislation is behind the accumulation of new hazards. Fire prevention is costly and negative. It is hard to prove that fire could, or in fact would, have occurred had a certain preventive measure not been taken. Prevention work is not sheer joy for firemen. As Chief Fire Marshal Martin Scott of New York's Fire Department once put it: 'Correcting dangerous conditions has no popular glamour; cautioning people about potential fire hazards often brings personal rebuke. Inspecting and regulating hazardous occupancies is a task that is never finished.'

Another natural cause of delay is that the concentration of

wealth and people progresses at a much faster rate than defensive techniques and awareness. More people and more wealth are crammed into our rigidly allotted space for living. Single aeroplanes now carry hundreds. Single multi-storey buildings house thousands. Vast numbers of fatalities in single disasters are entirely feasible.

Warnings against having unprotected wealth packed into limited space came early. The Great Fire of London in 1666, with flames spreading from warehouse to warehouse, was perhaps in a class of its own. The Great Block Fire in Melbourne, in 1897, was another. Then came many conflagrations in the world's big cities which were no longer regarded as oddities. In oil refinery fires, a whole series of explosions can only be expected. Feyzin, France, 1966 . . . Rotterdam, Holland, a year later . . . In 1965, at an American petrochemical plant on the Ohio River, one explosion was followed by another nine in thirty minutes, then another eight in an hour, and one more six hours later. Not only the plant and all residential areas in its vicinity had to be evacuated, but river traffic had to be stopped, highways on the far side of the river had to be closed, and air traffic had to be diverted from the nearby airfield. The cost: a dozen lives, scores of injuries, and about ten million dollars.

The tremendous concentration of wealth, with the resulting multi-million loss potential, is not restricted to the richest countries with the, comparatively, most sophisticated fire defence. Only ten or fifteen years ago, nobody would have expected the port of Karachi, Pakistan, to suffer fires with damage of half a million pounds (January 1969) and then almost three million pounds (50,000 bales of cotton plus buildings) only a month later.

Modern technology is also progressing so fast that fire prevention is frequently left behind by new products and new materials. Although, ideally, everything new ought to be tested for fire hazards, many products slip through the net. There are painful gaps in international cooperation and these also result in frequent duplication of scientific effort and expenditure. When disposable paper panties were found to be a potential fire risk, some big stores in France, Italy and Britain stopped selling them, but many other shops carried on regardless. In Britain, several tragic accidents revealed the menace in some cheap spectacle-frames which burned fiercely like torches. The frames were eventually banned, but the inherent danger really ought to have been spotted before they caused accidents.

It is perhaps the building trade that is most exposed to a constant flow of threats through the introduction of many new —often cheaper, more efficient, longer-lasting, less corrosive, structurally stronger and even safer—materials, which, however, may seriously intensify the propagation of flames or, in burning, release large volumes of toxic products. Plastics are particularly dangerous in this respect and their use is increased by up to twenty per cent a year in most Western countries. While this figure shows their popularity stemming from their various advantages, it also emphasizes the tremendous burden on fire research establishments which must evaluate them and propose safety measures.

Take, for instance, P.V.C. (polyvinyl chloride) which is today perhaps the most widely used plastic material. About a third of the world's plastics production is P.V.C. and about a quarter of all P.V.C. products are used in the building industry. (Its application is universal, ranging from cable and wire insulations to upholstery, handbags, floor tiles, luminous ceilings, panels, packaging, book bindings, records, and, in its foam version, padding, cushions, and all sorts of gadgets like fishing floats.)

P.V.C. was thought to be a relatively safe product, particularly if it contained a fire retardant, because normally it tended to melt rather than burn. On the other hand, it was found that in fire it generated a great deal of carbon monoxide, the main killer in most disasters. Then there occurred a not very significant fire in an electronic components store in Denmark. The fire damage was not serious. There was, however, a consequential loss of about a hundred thousand pounds due to corrosion of electronic stock. Even though there was only a small quantity, no more than twenty pounds, of P.V.C. involved in the fire, this material was proved to be responsible for all that corrosion because of its hydrogen chloride content. A great deal of research is still being done in most countries* so that more

* Dr. G. Purt of Switzerland read an important paper at a symposium on this corrosion problem in Sweden, at the Swedish Fire Protection Association meeting in April 1969.

stringent ways of controlling the use of P.V.C. can be worked out.

This kind of delay is understandable: it is always difficult to justify the allocation of still larger funds for preventive scientific research. It is, however, quite unforgivable that once a hazard becomes known legislation should still trail behind devastating fires.

In the early 1950's, Britain suffered several heavy fire losses which showed up a type of fibre board lining as a serious risk. Although authorities had been warned, the delay in action was clearly reflected by one fire report in which the investigating officer emphasized that 'this fire also illustrated the necessity of the steps taken to prohibit the use of [these] combustible building boards in industrial and other premises'. These boards were eventually banned in Britain, but even then, they were used merrily in France, Italy, Germany and several other countries.

No less condemnatory is the example Australian fire officials mentioned in interviews. A new cheap synthetic insulation material had been introduced and was soon widely used in the building industry. Like all other products, it was tested by the building research station and was found to be highly inflammable and capable of producing large volumes of toxic fumes. In several outbreaks it helped the fast spread of the flames. It was possible to give it more fire resistance but then it would have been less economical. Then there was a fire near Canberra where two people in the building were killed by fumes. The insulation material was strongly implicated in the deaths and the Coroner recommended at the inquiry that its use should be stopped. Yet most states of Australia paid no attention to this. In Sydney, a fire officer said: 'We could, of course, recommend its ban to the committee that advises local government on building regulations, but we know that builders and manufacturers would put up a great fight against restrictions particularly while a big civil action concerning damages is still pending. Unfortunately, we must use our warnings sparingly to avoid the protests from businessmen who would readily accuse us of trying to stifle their trade.

'Some building regulations are still in a rather rough state in Australia. National legislation is only in the preparatory stage. In factories, for instance, our Board can force owners to provide adequate, approved escape facilities *above* and *below* ground. Most owners are very conscientious about it and do not try to create hazards for their employees. But if somebody decided to build a factory which has only a ground floor, nothing above or below, he could cram ten thousand people in there and cut costs by providing only one entrance-exit for all —and legally, we could do nothing about it.

'Or take *high-rise buildings*. Many of them are designed to be just slightly under eighty feet in height simply because it saves quite a bit of money to them that we have only advisory and not enforcing powers regarding such buildings. Another important expense-barrier is the hundred-and-fifty feet mark. More than eighty feet high buildings must have automatic fire alarms, and if a building is, say, a hundred and forty-nine feet high, it will need no more than that. From a hundred and fifty upwards, the building must be protected by sprinklers although then the alarm system becomes optional.

'Once again, many owners can see the advantages of better protection. But those who want to make a quick profit, can play with a couple of feet in height and take a chance on the occupants' lives.'

While such complaints can be heard from keen prevention specialists in Sydney, where the above regulations are in force, their frustrated colleagues in the rest of Australia and, in fact, almost everywhere else on earth, envy New South Wales for these particularly advanced regulations, whatever loopholes they contain. Not to mention the older high-rise buildings (with top floors beyond the reach of fire brigade ladders) which are often 'calling for disaster' with their lack of sufficient escape and fire-fighting facilities, new skyscrapers mushroom everywhere in space-hungry cities with no more than minimal protection.

Pusan, in Korea, used to pride itself on its new seven-storey Telecommunications Building. It was a reinforced concrete construction throughout and seemed to offer full safety to the hundreds of employees, mostly girls, working in there. At ten past eight in the morning of March 18, 1968, the fire alarm was sounded. Nobody knew exactly how long a fire in a fourth floor office had been going. But that was the least of their worries. Once the flames had broken out of that room, extensively used wooden acoustic panelling helped the fire spread fast. Lifts stopped, the main staircase filled with dense black smoke, and on the fifth and sixth floors smoke reduced the visibility to nil. At least two hundred people groped about in the darkness unable to find the fire exits. They fled to the seventh floor and most of them were rescued by firemen. Some girls were forced by approaching flames to jump from windows of the fifth and sixth floors. Six people died. Forty-three people were injured, many of them seriously.

Under extreme pressure, like that of the vast population explosion in Hongkong, building developments leave fire precautions and control way behind. Just after the war, Hongkong had a population of half a million. This was trebled in one year. The fire brigade force was totally inadequate to start with and then it fell behind even more severely as the city grew to a population of four million by 1965. Huge fires were inevitable. In 1954, on Christmas Day, one inferno made 58,000 people homeless. Fire destroyed almost as many people's homes every year. Hongkong, even more than New York, had only one way to expand—upwards. In the 1950's, some fifty high-rise blocks were completed each month. By the 1960's, the number increased to a monthly two hundred. It was only at that time that the fire brigade received funds and better support to grow steadily from a personnel of a hundred and fifty after the war to six thousand. Yet even then, despite good planning and modern equipment, the task of protecting Hongkong remained enormous. When it was not fire, it was the typhoon (seven in 1963) or the rainstorm (three inches of rain in forty minutes and fifteen inches in a day in 1964) that drained the reserves of the brigade. 1962 brought a special disaster in the form of an unprecedented drought when, in four days, water from the mains was available only for four hours to fight the more-than-average number of fires.

In the high-rise buildings of Hongkong, water can be a serious problem even when there is no drought. 'To plan for fire-fighting was not a particular priority as the colony grew,' said a Chinese administrator. Anywhere else his words would have sounded cynical—in Hongkong, they merely reflected painful reality: 'As all this is comparatively new, here, you may say that we've missed the boat. Yes, perhaps it would have been better and cheaper to build with fire safety in mind. But the choice was between housing people fast or letting them live in the street longer so as to avoid gambling with their lives.'

He also implied that while housing people was a must, Hongkong had lives to spare. In the peculiar circumstances there, this attitude may even be understandable. No such excuse exists in Western countries where tall buildings have simply outgrown protective measures.

New York, of all cities, must have the money and experience for building skyscrapers. Yet after a fire in a fairly new fifty-storey glass and aluminium building in Manhattan, in 1970, when two security guards were killed and thirty-one people, including twenty-four firemen, were injured, a desperate fire chief was driven to condemn the building as 'cheap and highly inflammable'. He recognized that the building was 'artistically beautiful' but added that 'it's a helluva problem when there is a fire'. A German fire officer commented: 'If it can happen in the States, don't be surprised that it happens everywhere else.'

In Britain, civil servants and various authorities on fire protection bitterly complain that the 'excess cube and excess height' regulations for high-rise buildings are not applied nationally. In fact, only London, Manchester and another five cities control tall buildings and even these concentrate mainly on new ones. The usual argument is, of course, in force: local authorities must enjoy some independence even if the foremost specialists of the country recognize the risk this freedom creates.

The fire brigades of the seven towns that apply such building regulations suffer an acute manpower shortage so that re-inspection of premises is a tremendous problem. For big blocks of flats, the London Fire Brigade recommended the installation of dry rising mains (galvanized iron pipes running up through the building, say, near the staircase, with an inlet on the ground floor where firemen could connect a hose and pump the water up, and valves on each floor where hoses for fire-fighting can be connected); but the maintenance of all this is the owner's responsibility. Firemen know perfectly well that many of those valves are stolen and that the inlet box on the ground floor is often obstructed, damaged and neglected, yet they find it impossible to increase the frequency of inspections to more than a maximum of once a year. Between these tests, the owners are responsible, though prosecution would be of meagre consolation to sufferers of an eventual disaster.

Until about the 1960's, apartment and office blocks were supposedly protected from holocaust by applying the theory of compartmentation—flame-resisting structures blocking the spread of flames from any compartment on fire—and the safety of people in any compartment was served by well-planned alternative escape routes. Actual fire experience, however, revealed that most of these modern blocks contained a built-in hazard to lives: *air-conditioning*.

The ducts of this system cut through the walls of compartments both laterally and vertically, and readily transmit the killer smoke and fumes from the scene of the fire to occupants of far-away compartments who are safe from the heat and so perhaps unaware of the danger of asphyxiation.

The improvement of means of escape from tall buildings is under constant review. One school of thought favours the slight pressurization of escape routes to keep corridors free of smoke. Another recognizes that the construction of escape routes is very expensive (it could amount to half of all fire protection costs in a building) and studies the better fire protection of the structures themselves so that occupants could 'stay put' safely and without undue distress during a fire.

Undoubtedly, *automatic sprinkler* protection, planned from the stage when the building is still on the drawing board, is the ultimate answer. The need for this solution arose, said Richard E. Ritz, a partner in a large American firm of architects, 'because of the considerable number of such [high-rise office block] fires in recent years, with major property losses and some loss of life. A large percentage of these losses brought out the inability of fire departments to easily combat fire and carry out rescue work above the reach of truck-mounted ladders'.*

The installation of sprinklers is, no doubt, expensive. The cost is often used as a major argument against this method of fire protection. The legislation in New South Wales, Australia, not only established a worldwide lead in this field but also produced a great deal of experience in its fourteen years, and showed that

---

* Paper presented at the American N.F.P.A. annual meeting in New York, in May 1969.

the initial investment that loomed so large as a sum for a single item was usually no more than about one and a half per cent of the total cost of the building. It was also seen that apart from the security it rendered, it could help to reduce other cost factors if it was designed-in from the early stages. As a result, the United States and other countries have now begun to think in similar terms.

Talking about the Georgia-Pacific Corporation's new twenty-seven-storey office building in Portland, Oregon, Richard E. Ritz calculated that the automatic sprinklers were likely to *save* money for the owners: he foresaw the saving of two and a half million dollars in a fifty-year period, due to reduced insurance premiums and increased rental space through minor concessions in the layout of escape stairs and access areas.

Such 'savings' are, in a way, imaginary. Unlike an industrial productivity increase or cost reduction, they represent no extra profits. The savings are achieved in a negative way by avoiding the need to pay inflated insurance rates which are imposed in the form of specially loaded premiums on the basis of fire loss experience.

The basic loading would apply to an entire line of business. A recent example is the plastics industry which has suffered some tremendous losses in the last few years. It was found that a high proportion of all 'mammoth' fires occurred in premises where plastics or foam rubber were manufactured, stored or even widely applied. Insurance companies had to react every-where: they put plastics in the top bracket of the bad risk category and increased the fire premium sometimes by as much as seven hundred and fifty per cent (Britain) for the industry in general. For a particular plant the actual quotation can vary enormously and increase or reduce the basic loading according to numerous considerations like the often too inflexible fire risk grading of an area, the quality and distance of the local fire brigade or special fire precautions demanded by the insurers.

These precautions require an initial investment which can be fairly large, but the ensuing reductions can make it pay. A manufacturer of coats and dresses replaced combustible roof linings by non-combustible material, fitted pilot lights to irons, introduced the use of non-inflammable solvents, and committed his firm to sweeping up cuttings daily and to better general housekeeping. These measures reduced his fire insurance cost to one-fifth of the original premium, from an annual £250 to £50. The installation of automatic sprinklers would have made the premium dwindle to £15 a year.

What insurers call concessions, the insured often regard as blackmail. Although the justifiable extent of the special loaded terms imposed is frequently disputed, the pressure is at least understandable. Fire protection associations and others concerned with the 'education of the public' know only too well that nobody likes to be told how to run his business. It is also known that very few people recognize a fire risk when they see one, and even fewer are ready to think the hazard over in full: how big is the risk, how much can the firm afford to lose, should the potential direct loss be fully covered or is partial protection reasonable, will the consequences—ranging from delayed deliveries and temporary shut-down to complete loss of plant—only damage or destroy the business? Answers to these and similar questions, and the decisions based on them, may effect the entire economy of a country. A disturbingly high proportion of firms go out of business after a major fire and this reduces the gross national product. If on the other hand a firm chooses to pay high insurance rates, the cost is invariably passed on to the customer by price increases. It is due to these considerations that insurance pressure is about the most benevolent of all blackmail.

The pressure is most blatant when it comes to automatic sprinklers. The premium reductions after the installation of sprinklers are so substantial that these alone are likely to repay the investment in up to eight or ten years, after which period the company continues to enjoy the benefit of the 'most favoured customer' treatment. A hosiery factory, for instance, was insured against fire for £112,000. Until 1965, it paid an annual premium of £378 despite the usual discount for hand appliances. In 1965, the premium was more than doubled to £850. A sprinkler system was then installed and that reduced the premium to £302—less than it had been before 1965.*

The insurance reduction is not the only encouragement given to those who wish to install sprinklers. Governments chip

* This case was referred to by Winston Osborne: 'The Economics of Fire', the *Institution of Fire Engineers Quarterly*, December 1967.

in with various cash investment grants and tax relief which, when all allowances are added up, help numerous firms to recoup their initial cash investment in five or six years. In 1969, a fire-prone British factory invested £20,000 in sprinklers. This reduced its annual insurance premium of £4,000 to just over £1,600 and, with all the benefits, the fire defence would pay for itself in four years. The only setback this company suffered was when a false alarm set off a couple of sprinkler heads and the downpour of water ruined some goods and decoration—but against this damage the firm had been specially insured for a nominal charge.

The only drawback to government assistance is, as usual, that the various pieces of relevant legislation create sometimes ridiculous anomalies. When certain buildings are forced to install extra escape facilities, tax officials sometimes refuse to accept an outside iron staircase as capital investment—and if it is regarded as a building extension, capital allowance is not applicable. While grants and tax allowances assist and encourage the installation of sprinklers and automatic alarms, these new improvements increase 'the letting value of the building' and so call for an immediate penalty in the form of increased rates. The water rates, too, go up as soon as sprinklers are installed in many areas: the argument is that the quantity of water that *may* one day be required is potentially increased.

These factors, together with the cost of the all-important regular maintenance and testing of the sprinklers, amount to a reduction of the artificially created savings, but the difference is ultimately so insignificant that it is difficult to understand why manufacturers and fire protection specialists who 'sell' sprinklers to the public often choose to be so reluctant to mention this snag.

Sprinklers do not need the boost of sales-talk. Their efficiency record, despite false alarms and hence water damage, speaks for itself. In the United States, for instance, the National Fire Protection Association produced statistical evidence for the forty years from 1925 to 1964, concerning 75,290 fires in sprinkler-protected premises. 96.2 per cent of all these had already been extinguished or were under control by the time the firemen arrived there. Even if it was a very large outbreak from any cause including arson, there was no total destruction.

The less than four per cent inefficiency was due to mechanical failures, defects in manufacture or poor maintenance. A recent assessment of sprinkler performance in Australia and New Zealand showed a 99.7 per cent effectiveness. In the few cases where the system failed despite its faultless operation, and the building was destroyed, the reason was always fairly obvious, like tremendous bush fires raging all round a building and exceptionally heavy demand on the water pressure everywhere in the area. (Apart from water sprinklers, which are most widely used, there are other automatic fire extinction systems to fight specific types of outbreaks—like flammable liquids, dusts, vapours—with gases, high expansion foam and various chemicals.)

A serious menace to sprinkler efficiency is the human element. There have been numerous cases of shutting off the sprinklers too soon, before the fire was completely out, in order to reduce the water damage and save, say, a few jumpers by gambling with and often losing an entire department store; in many other cases, on the basis of the why-should-fire-start-right-now? theory, the system was completely disconnected during some repairs to or the demolition of a building. (This is how a tremendous fire got out of hand in the course of the Sydney Buckingham store demolition, in 1968. Only a few months later, the early removal of sprinklers was repeated in the Brisbane Fruit Marketing building with disastrous results and danger to lives in the entire surrounding area. And, to complete this Australian cautionary tale, if Brisbane did not learn from Sydney, a Sydney furniture factory did not learn from either: only eight days after the Brisbane blaze, on April 19, 1969, fire gutted its building in Marrickville, a Sydney suburb. Paints and lacquer caused several explosions. (The probable cause was a minor welding operation during which the automatic sprinkler system was shut off temporarily.)

Despite the potential human failings in the maintenance and ultimate control of this basically simple system—a heat detector which releases water from the affected sprinkler head on the ceiling—automatic sprinkler protection is, in fact, an anti-stupidity device. It does not ask questions about the cause of undue heat, just deals with it. Stupidity and other shortcomings of human behaviour have always been important factors which

Trapped—but not the worst off, in the Brussels l'Innovation
department store disaster. (*See pages* 125–130)

Photo : Paris Match

The store was having an 'American Week'. Dummies and decorative displays burned fiercely.

Photo : Paris Match

It started with a small flame. Forty minutes later, even the heaviest steel girders had to give way. The cause of the fire remains buried in here.

Photo : Belga

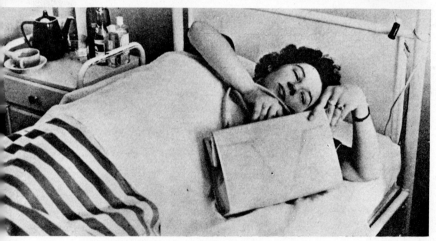

The shopper who would not part with her handbag . . . a sign of 'negative panic'. The jump—fall—and miraculous survival—still clutching the handbag.

Photos: Paris Match

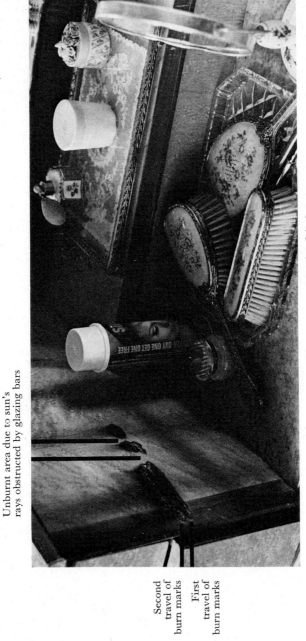

Focal length of concave mirror 18 inches

Unburnt area due to sun's rays obstructed by glazing bars

Distance approximately 18 inches

Second travel of burn marks

First travel of burn marks

Accidental set-up for a freak fire which was prevented only by the calendar—it was October, with short hours of sunshine. The cause would have remained 'unknown.' (*See page* 65)

The alarm call was delayed, but the flames swept swiftly through the Chicago school where the toll was 93 lives. It was the end of the school-day. Parents were waiting under the windows. (*See pages* 1–3)

Photos : National Fire Protection Association, Boston, Mass.

'Nobody could have foreseen such an event.' The bar after the Cocoanut Grove night-club tragedy. Boston, Massachusetts, 1942—holocaust and panic killed more than 500 people in 20 minutes.

Photo : National Fire Protection Association, Boston

Nobody could foresee such an event? The bar after the Top Storey Club tragedy, Bolton, Lancashire, 1961—holocaust and panic killed 19 people in a few minutes.

Photo : P.A

'Who would ever have imagined such a fire? 'A corner and the grotto of the lively Cinq-Sept dance hall at Saint Laurent-du-Pont, France—and what remained of it in 1970, after holocaust and panic had killed 146 people in 15 minutes.

Photos : Paris Match and U.P.I.

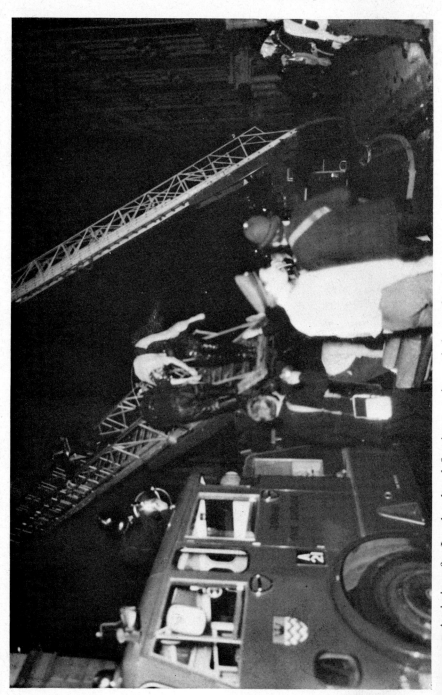

A victim of Leeds's hotel fire in 1971 is carried to safety down a 100-foot turntable ladder.

A London fireman using a turntable ladder as a 'water tower'. Some of his colleagues scaled the wall of the blazing hotel like acrobats with the aid of window-to-window hook ladders (seen just below the flames).

Photo : London Fire Brigade

An 'obstacle course' and readily inflammable materials block the access not only to the fire exit but also to firefighting equipment. And if a worker of this factory managed to fight his way to the door . . .

. . . an unexpected drop and more obstacles would hinder his escape. In any case, the flames would probably beat him to the rubbish strewn along the passage—an invitation to fire in itself.

Photos : London Fire Brigade

A witness said: 'I myself bolted that door every night.' But the photographic evidence shows that the bolt is evenly discoloured by smoke only in the 'off' position. When the door is really bolted, the clean middle section appears. This section must have been protected during the fire by the metal staple holding the bolt in place. So the door was *not* bolted that night. Did the witness make a mistake or did he lie? It may be a red herring—or it may be a clue to arson.

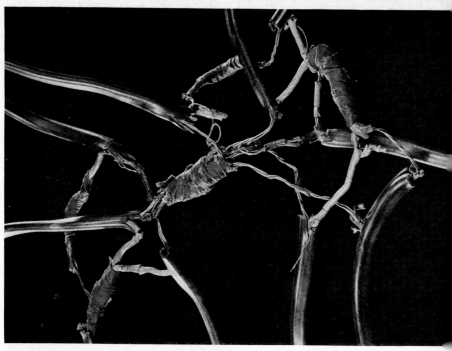

Ingenious do-it-yourself wiring a suburban house by 'unknow artist'.

Photo :

Which electrical appliance is *on* right now? The vacuum cleaner and the heater or the blanket and the toaster or the toaster and the heater . . .? The overloading of power sockets and multiple adaptors—like this—are frequent causes of fires.

Photo : London Fire Brigade

Rat-chewed cable—found before shorting and fire could occur.

Photo : Fire Protection Association

All the icy waters of
Lake Michigan could
not save the
McCormick Place
exhibition centre in
Chicago. There were
just too many built-in
invitations to disaster.
(*See pages* 135–136)

Photo : Oscar, Chicago

'I have got a small fire that has got a little bit out of hand,' reported a workman to the Sydney fire department. That 'little bit' was soon enough to make the firemen run for their lives.

(See page 20)

Photo : Fairfax, Sydney

Nerve centre and operations room for the Australian fire strategists of the Country Fire Authority. Victoria. With the experience of Black Friday (*see pages 242–248*) and other devastating outbreaks they have learned to respect the enemy that may strike simultaneously at more than 200 spots anywhere in 64,000 square miles.

Photo : Country Fire Authority, Victoria, Australia

The Snowdonian National Park alight. The magnificence of such sights may disguise the horror and slaughter that go with them.
(*See chapter* 14)

Photo : Sutcliffe, Anglesey

There was just nowhere to run.

the best of laws have had to ignore. The operation of sprinklers depends on a few specialists. Other fire preventive measures in, say, a factory, may depend on every single person involved in the planning, building, operation and maintenance of the plant, not to mention visitors, passers-by, guards, enemies, practical jokers and vagrants.

The most pertinent example to show that the 'public' are totally unable to learn and that legislation is equally unable (reluctant?) to deal with ordinary human failings, concerns a most elementary fire precaution, the correct use of *doors*.

It was proved almost two centuries ago, and many times again ever since, that *closed* doors in general, and purpose-built fire-resistant doors in particular, are an important line of defence. At least for a while they will contain the fire, and will always slow down considerably the spread of both flames and smoke, the main killer. Universal legislation has therefore required fire-doors to be self-closing—the near-ideal solution, because these remain open for only as long as is essential for someone to pass through.

The problem is that these doors, especially in industry, are in constant use and people carrying anything, pulling goods or pushing tea-trolleys find them an utter nuisance. In principle, self-closing kick-doors are easy to operate, but any young waiter who was punched by one on the nose or had his tomato soup knocked out of his hands would have poignant tales to tell about them. So whatever the laws of a country are and whatever punishment those responsible are threatened with, the practice is that *most fire-doors tend to be kept open by a wedge, a brick, a hook, even a nail or some other simple method*. A quick look at four haphazardly chosen large fires will amply emphasize this point.

On June 22, 1861, the tremendous Tooley Street blaze that started by, it was believed, spontaneous combustion in the hemp storage of Scovells' warehouse, almost resulted in a second Great Fire of London. Once all floors of the warehouse were alight, it was hardly possible to contain the flames which jumped from warehouse to warehouse full of jute, oils, paints, flour, cheese, saltpetre, sulphur, etc., spread to Hay's Wharf and Chamberlain's Wharf, made walls collapse killing Braidwood, the first Superintendent of the London Fire Engine Establishment, and ignited ten thousand casks of tallow that melted and

6

flowed on to the surface of the Thames setting the river ablaze. By exceptional bravery and ingenuity the brigade eventually brought the fire under control—but why was it that the fire had spread at such tremendous speed throughout Scovells'? The answer survived in some parts of the gutted building. The fire-resisting iron doors in the walls that separated the storages had not been closed.

Fifty years later, in 1911, New York's Triangle Shirt Company had a fire which, according to Bernard J. Reilly, now Deputy Chief Fire Marshal of the New York Bureau of Fire Investigation, 'was the perfect demonstration of all the ways how not to use doors in a building. Six and seven floors up long rows of girls were working at their sewing machines. The fire started well below them, but all the fire-doors were open and so the fire spread fast without interruption. Quick alarm might have reached them in time to escape, but there was no way out. The factory doors were locked to keep the girls in during working hours. The locks might have been forced by them in an emergency but their last obstacle was insurmountable: the doors opened inwards and as the panicky crowd surged forward against the doors, bodies were just piled up ceiling-high. 145 girls died—some in the workroom, others in the street after jumping from the windows. If only those fire-doors were kept shut . . .'

Ninety-nine years to the day after the Tooley Street fire, on June 22, 1960, Liverpool's William Henderson & Sons store had a fire which claimed eleven lives. When the full story of the tragedy was pieced together, investigators discovered that in the older section of the store, the doors giving access to the plywood-enclosed temporary timber staircase were all self-closing but had been fixed open with hooks to assist the ventilation of the building. In the newer section, there was a brick-enclosed concrete staircase, but the self-closing hardwood doors that served it had all been wedged open on each floor. The fire began on the third storey. The flames did not spread immediately to the timber staircase, but because the doors were open, it became a chimney within seconds. Some people tried to escape down there, but intense heat and thick black smoke sweeping up those stairs drove them back. It is now known that although the plywood, the timber and the flimsy doors would not have resisted the fire for long, they would have delayed the heat and smoke probably long enough to save the lives of the nine people whose bodies were finally found at the head of that staircase.

Finally, a recent fire in a London factory. It happened at night and so although the flames spread fast nobody was killed. Firemen discovered not only that the fire-doors had been open but also that they had hardly ever been closed: the proof was that the doors were on runners in metal channels in which probably years of rubbish had been accumulated. A brief conversation with a fire officer about the case showed the tip of the iceberg that exists in the murky waters of fire legislation:

Was that factory supposed to have fire-doors at all?

'Oh yes, under the relevant building acts, many premises must have them to reduce the size of compartments.'

Then why was it not discovered before that rubbish had been accumulating in those channels of the unused doors?

'Who should have discovered it? Factory inspectors who visit and control industry might have spotted it but it certainly wasn't their duty to check. They go to ensure the protection of lives. This policy of compartmentalization belongs to the hazy area of who is protecting what. So it's the owner's responsibility to maintain fire-doors in proper condition and see to it that they are kept closed.'

So was the owner penalized?

'He couldn't be. For although those fire-doors were compulsory, keeping them open was not an infringement of the life-protective escape requirements.'

But are fire-doors not also means of escape?

'In certain circumstances, when adjoining to or essential for reaching escape stairs, they are. This was not the case in this factory.'

So was it right that those doors could hardly be forced shut?

'No, it was a misuse of an appliance for the fire protection of the building, but it did not endanger lives. Also, the dirt in the channels revealed bad housekeeping, a constant fire hazard— but the same dirt did not constitute a permanent fastening device of the door which authorities object to. The Greater London Council, for instance, would usually refuse to permit *any* means of fastening on fire-doors.'

In most countries, it is up to the local authority to treat all such irregularities as a crime, a punishable offence or the subject of some reproving remarks. Could anybody in this case raise the question of negligence?

'Only the insurers. It would depend on their leniency in the particular circumstances.'

What did the insurers do or say?

'I wouldn't know. It's a private matter. The owner was the only loser.'

What if the fire had spread through his negligence to other buildings?

'He would have to sort it out with all insurers involved.'

This negligent practice of open fire-doors is so widespread in the United States that an experienced prevention officer advised colleagues to make inspections a vital prerequisite for their preparations against arson and 'civil disobedience' in riot-prone areas: 'Scrutinize and be critical of blocked exitways and blocked or open fire-doors . . . Fire-doors are required in many buildings by law. They are expensive and management should always insist that they are in proper operating condition, not obstructed, blocked, open or held open for any reason. *This violation of fire laws is the most prolific spreader of fire even during ordinary times* [author's italics] but it takes added significance during times of social unrest.'*

There have been many inventive people who have sought some practical compromise with these conflicting interests. They devised various ways to keep doors open but have them shut automatically in times of danger. One such fastener is controlled thermostatically. Another, a magnetic catch, is connected to the fire alarm: when it goes, the doors are released. An American device has a fusible link between a weight and the self-closing fire-door kept open by it: when the temperature rises, the lead fuse melts, the weight drops and the door closes.

Authorities argued that the devices were not reliable. Industry argued that the gadgets were too expensive. (A catch automatically released by the fire alarm would cost about £80 and even a smaller factory may need dozens of them.) Similar

---

* 'Arson Investigation Before, During and After Civil Disobedience', by Donald P. Yuellig, Asst. Superintendent, Fire Prevention Bureau, Cincinnati, Ohio, April–June 1968 issue of the International Association of Arson Investigators' journal.

is the argument against the existing delayed-action door-closing devices which are widely used in places like shops mainly to keep the heat in and the draught out. They tend to jam and their closing speed may become too fast or too slow. 'I'm sure it's a matter of research effort,' exclaimed a frustrated Chicago fire chief who judged it totally unacceptable that 'we can send men to the moon and back, and time their activities including their final splash-down to the fraction of a second but we can't make sure that a damned old door will keep open for only a given number of seconds and then close tight without a hitch'.

There is, however, a simple solution. Some people attribute it to the brainwave a technician had at Boreham Wood, the British Fire Research Station—others believe it was the brain-child of a German or an American—but the idea is known to many people in most countries. Ordinary cabin hooks to fasten doors open are unacceptable and dangerous because they are difficult to reach and disconnect especially in an outbreak of fire when there is a rush for the doors. Nobody could be expected, even if he thought about it, to hold back the crowd and try to undo the hook behind the door. But if the hook was *turned upside down*, only the pull of the spring-loaded door would keep it up in the ring. Then the door would need only the slightest touch to release the hook from the ring and make it drop by its own weight.

A touch of genius? Authorities do not think so. They recognize that in almost any escape situation the door would inevitably be pushed and the hook would drop. They accept that the ease of using this device would help to ensure that elderly night-watchmen, who dislike bending down and pulling the wedges from under open fire-doors, would more readily close all doors on their inspection tours. They do not dispute the various other advantages. They only claim that if the fire approached through an open fire-door and everybody escaped away from that door, nobody would bother—or have the time—to apply that slight pressure that is necessary to let the hook drop. The likelihood of this happening is infinitely smaller than that of permanently wedged open fire-doors, yet few local authorities will allow the use of inverted hooks, only in exceptional cases by special application. Most of them stubbornly insist that people *must* learn, people *must* keep fire-doors shut—whatever tales of negligence and stupidity practical experience keeps telling them.

It is impossible to estimate how much this resistance on both sides costs. A recent statistical examination of large fires has, however, produced some startling results. Admittedly, the sample was small, but it gave a clear indication that in a quarter of these large fires the fire-doors had been wedged open, and the average loss was some £30,000 greater in these buildings than in those where the properly shut fire-doors had prevented costly fires from becoming even costlier.*

Apart from legislative impotence in responding to human nature and its inherent hazards; apart from catastrophic inability on the part of the law-making process to keep up with changing conditions and the rapid accumulation of new hazards; and apart from the inevitable loopholes which are often no more than a failure in anticipating stupidity (for instance, Britain and other countries have laws that specify what fire-fighting equipment, say, a hospital *must* have but do *not* require staff training for its use); fire laws such as exist seem to suffer from a world-wide disease that paralyses statutes into statues. The disease is lack of control and enforcement.

The legislative jungle, the differences in laws and attitudes from country to country and town to town, and their bearing on the actual fire hazard, would deserve detailed studies and volumes of comparisons. But on the whole, there is likely to be a direct relationship between low fire losses and strictly enforced good legislation. It seems irrelevant whether the 'good legislation' is nationally applied or 'voluntarily' adopted by each locality, whether the 'strict enforcement' is carried out by some nation-wide agency or a local watchdog whose existence may be democratically more acceptable, and whether it is the government or some private association, even insurance organization, that lays down the rules and standards as well as controls adherence to them. What is really important is the nation-wide application of the highest possible yet feasible standards a nation's leading specialists recommend.

In Holland, general improvements in controlling the increase in fire damage occurred at the same time as more national legislation was introduced and a newly formed fire protection

* G. Ramachandran: 'Fire Doors and Losses in Large Fires'; Fire Research Note 690.

association began to coordinate the varied local safety standards. France, whose fire legislation and control is somewhat lackadaisical, frequently achieves a number one position among the *big wasters* by losing the highest proportion of her gross national product through fire. Other regular leading members of this ignominious club are Norway, Canada, the United States, Britain, Australia, Denmark, Finland and Sweden.

No country suffers nearly as much gross fire loss as the United States. (Britain, the second big loser, has a tenth of the American fire damage.) But then, no other country is as rich as the United States, and the tremendous concentration of wealth helps to explain away the size of the total figure, because it is not unusual there for a single fire to cause fifty million dollars' worth of damage. No such good excuse can be found, however, when one looks at the per capita loss statistics. For each man, woman and child, the United States lost eleven dollars and twenty-four cents because of fires in 1968. In the same year, Switzerland—by no means the poorest member of the Western world—lost less than a fifth, only two dollars and four cents, per head. It does not appear to be a coincidence that the outstandingly good Swiss results go hand in hand with rather strict fire protection control in many respects.

Although each Swiss canton has its own laws, there is a national uniformity based, undoubtedly, on the best standards and experience known to the whole country. In some cantons no private insurance is allowed, but in most (eighteen of the twenty-five) the market is divided between public and private insurance companies with the former insuring the buildings and the latter accepting the contents liability. Apart from all the usual professional advice being available, the public and private insurance establishments run an inspection service with periodical revisions and major three-yearly re-inspections.

West Germany also managed to maintain one of the best records with per capita losses running at about a third of those in the United States. Fire regulations are somewhat varied in each *land*, but the standard is very similar everywhere, and fire legislation is enforced by a two-tier system: one part of it is that, as we have seen, having a fire is, in a way, a crime and police are supposed to investigate every outbreak; the other is that the fire brigade's protection requirements carry the force of law when the brigade inspectors visit and check shops and places of public assembly every year, and other business premises every three to five years. Some Cologne fire officers believe that this system together with public 'acclimatization to discipline under Hitler' produced the good results and helped to maintain them over the years.*

It seems no coincidence either that in countries where the annual fire damage is very substantial, like the United States, Britain and Australia, firemen complain bitterly about the lack of powers given to them.

The American system is often criticized by more legislation-minded countries. Yet there is nothing inherently wrong with the system—provided that the nationally best available advice is turned into law by local authorities and that effective law-enforcement is exercised in each community. This, however, is not quite the case. Even a simple measure, like the nation-wide uniformity of fire reporting and statistics, has taken several years of hard-fought coordination to achieve. Although the N.F.P.A. recommendations for fire safety are widely discussed, enthusiastically debated and carefully formulated to make them nationally acceptable, and although more and more states and cities adopt them as laws, these local authorities show lack of devotion or experience or a mixture of the two and fail to provide funds or powers or both to enforce their own legislations.

The Cocoanut Grove fire was one good example of this. Another, which infuriates Ralph Nader and other protectors of the American consumer, was reported by Ian McDonald in *The Times*:† 'According to the National Commission on Product Safety 30,000 Americans are killed and 110,000 permanently disabled every year as a result of incidents connected with consumer products.' Many of these deaths and injuries are due to fire hazards. There are already scores of laws in all states to ensure safer products and restrict the use of hazardous ones like inflammable fabrics. 'These would quickly cut the toll of accidental death and injury—if they were enforced.'

A third example is remembered vividly by many people even outside the United States. It emerged on Hallowe'en,

* Quoted by the *F.P.A. Journal*, No. 84, p. 371.
† February 6, 1971.

in 1963, when some four thousand people enjoyed the opening night of the *Holiday on Ice* show at the State Fairground Coliseum in Indianapolis. Many of the audience were children on a family outing. Albert Losche, the Mayor of this Mid-Western city, was angry because he had been late buying tickets for his party of ten. The best seat in the section, where he would normally sit, had already been sold.

As it was the first night of the show, there were some delays, and the curtain went up fifteen minutes late. Nobody could suspect that the delay would be fatal. The programme was a great success throughout. It had now come to the grand finale, the last three minutes' work for the soloists, special acts and the forty-six skaters in the chorus who were just getting ready. Had the show begun on time, the auditorium would have been empty by now.

The band began to play, but a sudden explosion, followed by screams and cries of pain, moans and wailing, drowned the music. Entire rows of seats and people, many of them children, were thrown high up in the air, hitting others at the end of a short flight like cannonballs, flailing hands sought protection for horror-stricken faces, thousands of people tried to escape, dragging hundreds of the injured, but the band played on and so helped to avert complete panic.

It was soon found that the explosion had occurred in the basement, right under the section where the Mayor would have sat. Its force tore up the concrete floor and shattered the seats while gusts of flame shot ninety feet high through the gap. Sixty-eight people were dead or dying. Almost four hundred people were injured. Firemen thought it was lucky that the explosion was directed straight upward. Otherwise the toll would have been even larger.

What happened? Fire officials found four cylinders containing gas which had been used in the basement for heating food and drinks at the refreshment stands. They said that, apparently, gas leaking from a tank had accidentally ignited and caused the explosion. Fire Chief Ira Anderson announced three days later that the gas had been used there illegally. So there was no gap in the preventive legislation of Indianapolis to blame. But why was the use of gas there not spotted before? And why did nobody pay particular attention to the stand at the Coliseum where, as a report in the fire department showed, a dangerous gas leakage from a tank had already occurred four years earlier? Voluntary, locally most suitable legislation can work—and can be excellent—only if each authority is capable and willing to take full responsibility.

Britain, perhaps not surprisingly, seems to be in two minds and so enjoys some advantages and many disadvantages of both national and local legislation. While numerous fire prevention specialists cry out for more and better legislation, for plugging of the loopholes and more effective control, there are plenty of understandable complaints about too much policing and too many inspections and too many authorities who have the right to poke and pry. It is easy to sympathize with both sides. There are thousands of buildings in Britain today which are controlled by four major separate Acts and can be inspected by various departments of national and local government, and also by the fire brigade. At the same time, the legal anomalies that exist in London are not a unique phenomenon in the country.

In January 1971, a Greater London Council committee of inquiry on safety and health at work heard evidence that many metropolitan buildings like Covent Garden, Smithfield Market —which has a vast underground storage—and the Admiralty are beyond the control of the law that compels the smallest shopkeeper to safeguard his employees. There are many restaurants in basements of otherwise very loosely controlled buildings. If the restaurant is licensed to sell alcoholic drinks, customers are protected by strictly implemented legislation which requires and checks the proper maintenance of means of fire escape. But next door, diners at an unlicensed basement restaurant are forgotten by the law and enjoy no such protection.

Over the past twenty years, many fire specialists have frequently sounded the opinion that 'people trust their luck—and when the luck runs out, they trust the insurance companies. If they had to pay for at least a part of their losses, they'd have to think twice about precautions. Offenders against regulations are made to pay in controlled premises, but everybody knows that the penalties are far from stiff enough to compel everybody to take care'. Those whose duty it is to inspect factories mostly rely on the owners' goodwill rather than on the £10 or £20 fine that will not really hurt any industrialist. In principle, an inspector can complain to a magistrate's court which, in turn, can order the temporary shut-down of the factory while the legally required alterations are carried out. But luckily, in most cases, the threat of such action is enough. The word 'lucky' applies to both sides: the owner does not want to lose business, the inspector cannot afford to lose too much time with numerous court proceedings because he is hard pressed even without them. Staff shortage prevents the frequent inspection of factories and four- or five-year gaps between visits are inevitable. Sometimes, after repeated warnings, the fines imposed are a little stiffer, but do they really enforce the law and do they really stamp out negligence? A Birmingham fire prevention officer was quoted as saying in 1968* that 'if a firm transgresses the fire regulations they might be found guilty and fined £300. If twenty people die in a disaster, that's £15 a life'.

Fire regulations put the responsibility of enforcement on scores of different people ranging from various authorities to the owners themselves. Their text is full of expressions, like *effective steps* to be taken or *adequate control* to be exercised, which are open to argument and interpretation—what is effective? what is adequate?—and so help to render half-hearted policing ineffectual and inadequate.

Britain's Factories Act was introduced in 1937. Twenty years later, after the Keighley Mill fire (which eventually led to the revision of the Act in 1961), it was found that between fifty and seventy per cent of the factories still did not comply with the means of escape and fire alarm requirements, and that only fifty-five per cent of the factories had been granted fire escape certificates called for by the Act. One could quite see the validity of the argument: why have legislation at all if there is no enforcement anyway? 'Employ more inspectors' is the obvious answer—but it is far less obvious to say who should pay for this. Insurance companies can increase their supervisory staff because they simply add the wage bill to their premiums. But government officials are paid from the taxes and firemen are paid from the rates, and the people who would have to foot the bill through cuts in public expenditure or increased taxation and rates are councillors and Members of Parliament who would hate to fight their elections with such

* *Daily Sketch*, November 20, 1968.

programmes. On the other hand, disasters and activated death-traps give them marvellous opportunities for righteous indignation.

Fifteen-year-old Anthony Doyle was to move to a better job from the London warehouse where October 19, 1968, was his last workday. It was already late afternoon when a fire broke out. The fire brigade, called by a passer-by, found the rear of the building ablaze with the fire spreading fast up a partially enclosed timber staircase. The only entrance to the building led into a lobby where packing materials, wood, wool and shredded paper were stored. Firemen had to fight their way in through that lobby. On the ground floor, at the rear of the warehouse, they found the bodies of a visitor, the managing director and three employees of the firm. One of the dead was Anthony Doyle. If not through the lobby, why could they not escape through windows? At the front of the building, all the windows had been covered from the inside with sheets of plywood—at the rear, all the windows and even an office roof light had been fastened shut and covered with closely spaced fixed metal bars. The dead director's mother-in-law explained: 'There has been a constant string of break-ins at the warehouse. My son-in-law was forced to barricade the windows.'

The cause of the fire has remained 'unknown'. Unfortunately, it was also unknown why nobody had called attention to the potential death-trap formed by the barred windows, even if windows were not recognized as proper means of escape. Fire prevention experts may insist only on the legal requirements of escape facilities. A Midland fire chief declared: 'We do not think people should have to be acrobats when escaping from a fire.' But were those legally acceptable proper means of escape in order everywhere now, seven years after the *revision* of the old Factory Act? A survey found a tremendous backlog not only in follow-up re-inspections but also in basic first visits. And within a few weeks, barred windows were to stop fleeing people in several fires including a supermarket blaze and a disaster in Glasgow.

The Glasgow Fire Brigade received an emergency call at 10.31 on the morning of November 18, 1968.* Only four

---

* Good summaries of the case and subsequent inquiry were published by the *Fire Protection Review*, January, March and April 1969 issues.

minutes later, the first firemen on the scene asked for urgent reinforcements by sending a 'Make Pumps Ten' message. In the meantime, people in the street witnessed horrible deaths: screaming girls appeared behind windows, smashed the glass with chairs, then tried to pull firmly embedded metal bars from their sockets in vain, tried to get through the gaps but failed, and only a few seconds later, flames engulfed them and the screaming stopped as they disappeared. A lorry driver saw two men going up in a lift. Suddenly the lift stopped and flames swallowed it.

Ninety-three firemen fought the fire. Seventeen jets were used and 3,300 gallons of water were pumped through four miles of hose every minute. All sorts of modern equipment were brought in to assist the battle for those inside but nothing could be done. Only four people had escaped at the outset of the fire. When shortly after three o'clock in the afternoon the blaze was brought under control, twenty bodies were found inside. Another two bodies were not recovered until the following day. The building was in an old part of Glasgow where several big fires had occurred, including one a mere four hundred yards away that had killed nineteen firemen and salvage workers in 1960.

A public outcry was followed by a thorough inquiry. A weird story of minor and not so minor negligence came to light. The building used to be a whisky bond—hence the barred windows. Failure to remove the bars was not illegal. The upholstery firm that had the fire had moved there in June 1967, and had filed an application for inspection, as required by law. The local authority had a substantial backlog of inspections, and priority was given to buildings which, unlike this warehouse, had previously not been visited. Their inspector did not therefore go to the premises before the fire. A factory inspector of the national authority did, however, visit the firm twice. Once he found that the door at the foot of the statutory fire escape stairway was locked and he warned a director, who was to die in the fire, about it. On a follow-up visit, the door was open. But when the disastrous fire broke out, the door was firmly padlocked and no key could be found. It had been locked to prevent pilfering. There were various allegations that the door had been unlocked only once in an 'emergency'—when the inspector came for the second time.

There was a pitiful story about the fire alarm system, too. The local fire brigade, to whose station the system used to have a direct connection, had a record of false alarms from the building. The record also showed that the system had not been tested at all from July to November 1967, but there had been fifteen tests between December 1967 and March 1968. And then the automatic direct alarm was disconnected. What happened? A supervisor from a fire alarms manufacturer visited the director of the upholsterers and there was a discussion about the system. The supervisor testified at the inquiry that the alarm had been installed long before the upholsterers moved in. The new firm in the building was asked if it wanted to keep the alarm. There was no direct answer. Tests and inspection visits continued but the firm finally refused to pay for them. The director told the alarm supervisor that he had 'a terrific roof repair bill to meet. The fire alarm system I cannot have.' That was why, in March, the alarm to the fire brigade was disconnected. A co-director was never told about this. The factory inspector heard about it only on his second visit when he suggested re-connection or some alternative installation, and had the fire not intervened, he would have checked the new arrangements in the course of his next visit that was to be in about January 1969.

The widow of one of the victims told the inquiry that 'they could all have walked out if the door had been open'. Experienced firemen confirmed that at least the majority of the victims would have escaped without difficulty. The widow also revealed that many of the victims had known about the danger. Her husband had once told her that the building was a 'death trap' and 'if ever there was a fire, we would have no chance'. Her husband and other employees thought about starting a strike over the missing key to the padlocked escape door. If only they had done it—if only the union had encouraged them! According to the widow her husband had approached the employers on behalf of the staff, but 'could not get any satisfaction'.

At the Glasgow Sheriff's Court, the company pleaded 'guilty' to failing to ensure the safe operation of the doors that were the legal means of escape. The dead director's brother, co-owner of the factory, admitted the same and also that, contrary to the law, he failed to have the alarm system checked regularly. The judge accepted that he had a lesser share in the internal management of the factory than his now dead brother. He was fined £200 on the first and another £100 on the second charge. The company was fined the maximum of £300 on the one charge.

Law enforcement? Remember the Birmingham fire prevention officer's comment? In the Glasgow case, the maximum penalty was *less* than £15 a life.

If the Glasgow disaster taught us a lesson, there was certainly nothing in it that had not been seen before. 'The tragedy is that much too frequently, it is only a disaster we can hope will be in the interest of the country as a whole—and pray that one will be enough,' said a fire prevention officer. 'You may believe I'm a cynic. I think I speak out of sheer desperation. But you'll see my meaning if you consider the frustration that's our lot in the wake of one of the best pieces of British fire legislation.'

He was talking about the Offices, Shops and Railway Premises Act, 1963, which at long last, brought these buildings under control to protect all employees and visitors in them. The Act makes it the employers' duty to provide 'proper means of escape' and keep them free from obstruction, to mark distinctively all escape routes and put up exit notices of 'adequate size', to install and test regularly 'effective means of warning' (fire alarms), to provide and maintain 'appropriate means for fighting fire' and ensure that all employees know what to do in case of fire. The Act certainly plugged hazardous loopholes in fire prevention and therefore it is even more unfortunate that it missed the opportunity to promote, for instance, the widely recommended international and British standard colour, green, for exit notices, and to make sure that the fire drill for employees will be at a nationally acceptable standard instead of leaving policy decisions in this respect to local fire authorities whose views of what is a suitable method of fire drill may vary considerably. Yet these problems are dwarfed by major anomalies and the size of legislative muddle which were created by the implementation of the Act.

The Act made a great step in the right direction by giving substantial new powers to the fire brigade and nominating it, for the first time, as the enforcing agent of an important fire legislation. What it immediately failed to do was to alleviate the brigade's chronic staff shortage which now, with the burden of these additional duties, paved the way to many potential disasters.

According to the Act, all employers whose premises came under its jurisdiction had to register their firms with the fire authorities within two years—which was 1965. New firms had to do so immediately upon starting business and old firms had to re-register when moving to new premises. The exact number of the firms which ought to be registered is still not known, but so far, more than 700,000 firms have been registered. *Many* of these must receive fire certificates—'many' because their number has only been *estimated* to be about 70,000. The rest of them will not need certificates, but must be advised in writing of what precautions are required of them.

Normally, the fire brigade serves two masters: the Home Office and the appropriate local authority. In this case, however, it is another ministry, the Department of Employment, which is charged with the administration of the Act. So the brigade also serves a third master in this respect. To make things worse, despite the original aim and for various administrative reasons, the fire brigade has not been made the enforcing agent everywhere in the country. In thirteen major areas, like Birmingham, the job is done by the architect's department of the local council.

The control of premises under the Act requires a very substantial effort. Buildings that need fire certificates have to be inspected, and occupiers must be advised about the necessary alterations which then have to be checked. After the certificate has been issued, the premises must be re-inspected regularly. The fire brigade has the right to do that at any time at will. If there is to be any extension of buildings or staff, the brigade must start with another primary inspection all over again.

The Act came into force in 1963. In seven years, still no more than about eighty-five per cent of the premises thought to need *certificates* were dealt with. This was the estimated national figure. London, due to its usually acute staff shortage, was far worse off with no more than about two-thirds of the work done. 'A' Division, the fire district around Chelsea, for instance, got through only some 3,500 of the 5,300 offices, etc. registered with them. Nobody can blame them: apart from all the inspection and advisory work, the fire prevention officers must do all the fire investigations—and there are just not enough trained, experienced men to do the work. When will they catch up? Nobody knows. New registrations are pouring in every day.

And that is not all. Premises which need no certificate must still be inspected and controlled. The number of these is simply not known. It is also unknown how many have still to be visited. An inspection and then a warning letter is far from enough to complete a job. With the means of escape there is usually no trouble and the law can be clearly enforced if an employer is reluctant to comply with the brigade requirements. But fire-fighting equipment is an entirely different matter. Its adequacy is often disputable. It shows a sad state of affairs when insurance companies give a discount of up to twelve and a half per cent to firms which fulfil merely the minimum legal requirements through buying a few hose reels and buckets. Maintenance of the equipment is often totally neglected and many firms regard the annual servicing of extinguishers at fifty pence a time an unjustifiable luxury. Fire officials must write two or three letters —with inspections and verbal prodding in between—before they get results in most cases. The law is not clear-cut and so it is difficult to start legal proceedings against probable offenders.

Fire officials try to patch up and defend the system out of sheer goodwill. They conscientiously weigh the pros against the cons and try to live with it all. The need of a total overhaul appears to be a must if the demon of fire is to be put in chains. But perhaps such plain logic is not convincing enough. Perhaps the current vast damage and death toll are still considered to be on an acceptable level. What Sir Keith Joseph, Britain's Secretary for Social Services, said at the National Association for Mental Health conference in February 1971 is not untypical for most countries: 'Heaven preserve any government from revelations, but when they come they often serve a high purpose.' He explained that a sudden revelation of conditions of which the public was unaware gave Ministers a chance to re-galvanize their colleagues and obtain resources. In the case of fire, disasters are the shape of the sudden revelations that serve the high purpose.

In 1966, a committee was set up under the chairmanship of Sir Ronald Holroyd, to conduct the first major inquiry in thirty

years into the problems and principles of the fire services. The
work was expected to take two years. It lasted for four years. The
final report made several important points which are expected
to have beneficial effects in this field. But on the whole, it came
to the conclusion that no new major laws were needed to restrict
the mounting material and property losses, and that private
enterprise rather than government could tackle the entire
hazard. If the committee had sensed the approaching disaster
situation at all, it was only expressed in the praise and recommendation of the American system in general and the work
of the American N.F.P.A. in particular:

'. . . we are convinced that if a strong national voluntary
association on similar lines were set up here, it would arouse
more enthusiasm among business firms than a purely official
body, however well-intentioned and well-informed, could ever
hope to do . . .'

Similar, although not so far-reaching and all-embracing,
voluntary associations and advisory services in fact exist in
Britain. But the firms' enthusiasm is either missing or falls short
of the target. If the law needs a new determined watchdog, if
the law enforcement agents need a crutch, the role ought to be
played by union safety officers who ought to be experts on the
subject and as ready to strike over fire safety disputes as over
minor who-is-doing-what affairs. In Britain, a really strike-
riddled country, for every day lost in industrial disputes an
average of six days has been lost through industrial accidents,
many involving fire. For wherever there are loopholes in the
law, many firms are only too pleased to sneak through them.
One such loophole is big enough, in most countries, for hotels to
slip out of the fire authorities' net.

CHAPTER ELEVEN

UNSAFE TO STAY IN?

IN THIS age of holiday mass-migration, when public watch-dogs noisily demand—and receive—some effective guarantees for members of our increasingly discriminating consumer society that we get what we have bargained for, that the hotel will not be a foot further from the sea than advertised, that the cuisine will be as 'individual' as promised, and that the view from the hotel window will be worth the small-print of the extras; in these travelling days nobody demands—or receives—any guarantees that the holiday-maker will have a good chance of survival if the dream hotel of his choice burns to the ground.

In a western country, people are eleven times more likely to get involved in a hotel fire than in a blaze in the home.

The following list contains only a few examples of the hazards which have become more and more menacing with the growth of mass-travel. The difficulty in compiling this list was merely to choose what to leave out of the tragic abundance of hotel fires.

AMSTERDAM: Fire broke out when there was a brawl in a bar in Amstelstraat, the heart of the town's entertainment centre. Flames and killer smoke rose fast to the small hotel above the bar. Guests were taken by surprise. Nine people died. For many, there was only one way out—through the windows. Even the firemen's safety net was too hard for a jump from the second and third floors. Of the thirty guests who survived the spectacular leap, many were seriously injured.

TUCSON, ARIZONA: Jumping from the windows presented an even slimmer chance of survival here: the hotel on fire was twelve storeys high. Yet again, guests were trapped and the alternative to jumping was death in a furnace. Twenty-eight people died, thirty were seriously injured.

INTERLAKEN: Switzerland has a good reputation for fire safety. Yet the Schweizerhof Hotel, which was only fifteen years old, was razed by fire overnight. It happened only a month after the Roi Soleil (six hundred beds, St. Moritz) had burned to the ground.

TEWKESBURY, GLOUCESTERSHIRE: This small English town has only some six thousand inhabitants—but it suffered three hotel fires in a single fortnight in January 1970.

AHVENANMAA ISLAND, FINLAND: The conflagration that destroyed a hotel caused death to four and serious injuries to thirteen people.

ATLANTIC CITY, NEW JERSEY: Flames swept freely through a block of seafront hotels and boarding houses—there was hardly anything to control their path. Twenty-five people were killed. A family survived a fifteen-foot jump: they, like others, could not reach the escape stairs because unbearable heat and smoke had blocked the corridors.

NEW YORK: Three people died, nine were injured when a seventeen-storey hotel burned in the Central Park area. The doors had no self-closing device although the fire department had already served the management with a summons for failing to comply with this requirement. Proper fire-doors would have checked the progress of the blaze and smoke.

KOHRIYAMA CITY, JAPAN: A holocaust devastated a three-storey hotel amusement centre. Thirty people died and twenty-four were injured. Delayed evacuation caused panic. Chased by flames along the corridors, three hundred screaming guests fought and clawed at each other in a stampede to safety.

VALLOIRE, SAVOY ALPS, FRANCE: Four guests died and six were badly injured when guests, many of them keen sportsmen, had to jump for their lives from the windows of a blazing hotel at this ski resort.

JACKSONVILLE, FLORIDA: There were almost five hundred guests at the hotel when twenty-one people were killed in a fire. Some women and children managed to escape to the roof and helicopters from a naval base picked them up. Many guests were asphyxiated before they had a chance to escape. Others tried their luck through the windows: some were reached by firemen's ladders; those who relied on a long line of knotted sheets and blankets, fell to their deaths when their make-shift rope tore apart on a window-sill.

LONGREACH, QUEENSLAND, AUSTRALIA: The presence of mind of a young man saved thirteen people in a hotel of wooden construction which was ablaze from end to end within a few minutes after the outbreak of fire. He played the part of a human alarm system by running from door to door, banging and shouting to wake up everybody at two o'clock in the morning.

BANGKOK: In April 1971, the four-storey Imperial Hotel burned out. Only the walls and the swimming pool were left intact. Twenty-four people were killed. Thirty guests were injured. Three Japanese men survived a leap from a window on the fourth floor by landing in a coconut palm.

Wiesbaden, Hongkong, Paris, Spanish and Italian holiday resorts—the story is all too frequently the same. And all too frequently, we hear about the lack of sprinklers, proper fire alarms, fire-doors and escape routes. Many of the restaurants, dance halls and nightclubs also come into a legislative no-man's land where they share with the hotels the splendid opportunities for spectacular disasters. Fire at a rooftop restaurant in Montgomery, Alabama, for instance, killed twenty-five people within a few minutes.

The United States is one of the inexhaustible sources for tragic examples. In 1946 alone, there were three major hotel fires in Chicago, Dubuque and Atlanta, with a combined death toll of 199, which emphasized the importance of the recommendations in the Building Exits Code and paved the way to the development of the more advanced and practicable Life Safety Code to create national standards for public buildings, including hotels. 'This Code is widely used by various Federal, state and local agencies in the United States,' commented Percy Bugbee, former general manager of the N.F.P.A., but he had to admit: 'We still have schools, hospitals and hotels that are substandard; but the responsibility falls on state and local authorities, and many of them are doing quite a lot about it.' The full qualification of the words 'many' and 'quite a lot' is the still endless string of hotel fires.

The competence of similar local authorities came under close scrutiny in Australia, after the Shore Motel fire in 1967. On September 2, at 7.23 in the morning, firemen at No. 61 Station of Sydney noticed flames and the rising finger of smoke before emergency calls started coming in. There was an immediate initial response of engines, ladder and salvage companies from three fire stations, and reinforcements from another two stations were on their way seven minutes later.

The fire report describes the position on the men's arrival in Howarth Street, Lane Cove. The entire office and manager's suite together with the main stair enclosure of the motel were burning fiercely. Occupants of two suites off the staircase were exposed directly to flames, heat and smoke, and were cut off from all means of escape. Occupants of three suites in the annexe and all suites on the first and second floors north of another staircase were also cut off and calling for rescue. There was a great deal of understandable panic. Guests tied bed-clothes together so that children could be lowered from the second to the first floor and then dropped from there to people on the ground. Construction workers, organized by an off-duty fireman, helped with the rescue operations.

A very strong southerly wind blew through the open door and windows of the office where the fire had probably begun, and drove the fast-spreading fire up the 'open flue' of the stair-case. Despite the determined efforts made to rescue those trapped inside, numerous guests chose desperately to jump out of windows—several thus escaped certain death, but others suffered horrible injuries because in their panic they could not wait for the help to come.

Firemen and ambulancemen applied an oxygen resuscitator to six people who then had to be rushed to hospital. Doors in suites were beginning to burn through. A thirty-seven-year-old woman was brought out unconscious. A passing doctor and firemen gave her closed chest cardiac massage and oxygen, but she did not revive. She was dead on arrival at the hospital. A woman ten years younger climbed out of a window on to a roof, fell and was burned, rolled off the roof and was caught by the construction workers. She had suffered forty per cent burns to her legs and face. Four days later she died. An American woman jumped from a rear window. She tried to dive into the swimming pool, but fell on concrete. She had a ruptured liver and a broken wrist.

The ultimate horror of the tragedy is contained in this sentence of the fire report: 'The fatality [the second death came later] and injuries at this motel were caused by inadequate provision for means of escape in case of fire.'

The report also mentioned two other recent fatal boarding house fires. Insufficient means of escape were blamed in each case. Firemen recognized that the design and construction of the motel were greatly responsible for the rapid spread of the fire—and *the hazard was entirely predictable*. They recommended the revision of the relevant laws and better application of fire-resistant materials for hotels, motels and boarding houses.

These suggestions were all the more serious because the Shore Motel was a modern building—only five years old. The Coroner's Court inquiry in May 1968 conducted a careful examination of all the details in order to establish what party if any should bear the responsibility for this tragedy. The Stipendiary Magistrate listened to several witnesses. Finally, he accepted a fire brigade District Officer's view 'that it doesn't take a fire to occur to enable other experts and himself to determine a fire risk (such as was illustrated by the course this fire took)'.

So were the owners or management to be blamed? No. They complied with all the relevant regulations and, in fact, took all the necessary steps for future fire precautions immediately after the fire, according to the advice given by the fire authorities.

If the Board of Fire Commissioners had the expert knowledge to predict the disastrous events, why did they not do so? They were not asked. They were not supposed to be asked. They were not supposed to look at the plans or the building. They were not supposed to advise anybody or inspect anything involved in this case.

But surely, somebody had to approve the plans! Yes, the local council, which indeed passed the inherently dangerous plans without examining 'likely fire hazards and provisions for detecting and fighting fires' in this motel. So was the council to bear responsibility? Not really, because the true culprit was a complete legislative muddle.

Without trying to describe all the details, the basic situation was that an old law which controlled buildings of a certain height did not formerly permit the construction of motels of this size. An amendment later changed the position so that the construction of the motel became legal. (It was built between 1960 and 1962.) The fire regulations in the same law were also amended 'over the years . . . in the light of greater learning and experience' and this legislation, which was relevant to *new* motels, hotels, etc., was dated June 1964! To complete the muddle, there was plenty of room for doubt as to the meaning and interpretation of legal terminology.

The result was that 'no public body looked at the plans for this building' from the fire prevention aspect, and the magistrate found 'that this seems incredible'. He went, however, an important step beyond this conclusion: with reference to the possible existence of other Sydney fire traps that might have slipped through the same loophole, he put it on record that 'it seems to me it is of little use amending the law to provide greater safety, in this case to the public patronizing motels, if no action is taken to ensure that motels already erected are not required, as far as practicable, to meet the new safety requirements'.

Fire specialists in any country would not have been as surprised by this legal anomaly as the Sydney magistrate was. They would not have found it so incredible either what widespread laxity or outright absence of fire control and law enforcement is tolerated even in countries which greatly rely on their tourist trade.

Britain, with her average of seventeen hotel fires a week, offers far from the worst European odds if you want to gamble on your life. Building regulations in general and fire prevention in particular appear to have a much poorer standard, for example in Spain and France. Most Spanish catering staff who start work in Britain—or Italians who take employment in Swiss and German hotels—are amazed when they are required to take part in any, often deplorably elementary, fire drill. Yet the saga of how a British law came to control future fire safety in hotels and other hitherto neglected premises makes a spine-chilling bedtime story for the traveller. Oddly enough, it was not a hotel disaster that set off the sequence in slow motion—the story stretched over a full decade!—but the fire in a club that, like many other premises, had slipped through the legislative net.

Over the rapid waters of the narrow River Croal, next to a stone bridge, in a rather decrepit conglomerate of three early nineteenth-century buildings, the Top Storey Club of Bolton, Lancashire, occupied—true to its name—the top (second) floor, with offices on the ground, and foyer, cloakroom, bottle store on the first floor. It had a not particularly glamorous entrance leading through a passageway from where a door opened to a joinery shop which occupied most of the ground floor. There was an open timber staircase, and most of the ceilings and partitions were of combustible materials. A second timber staircase was shut off, out of use, because it only led into the joinery shop which was locked carefully against thieves.

In the club-room, there was a stage and bandstand adjoining the dance floor at one end, with a bar behind a bamboo screen at the other. Tables and chairs occupied the middle. Four windows were bricked up, while the rest of them overlooked the river—*five* floors, sixty feet, below. The difference in the height of the building was due to a basement and sub-basement which were visible only from the river side. A disused loading door—with only a twenty-foot drop to street level—was almost completely impossible to open. There was no fire alarm.

Those who have read this book so far must already have spotted the potential disaster. So did, of course, the fire officer who inspected the club *at the owner's request* and, in a letter dated February 4, 1961, emphasized that the means of escape were 'totally inadequate' for a club 'and that if a fire did occur on the ground or first floors when the top room was in full occupancy, there would be every possibility of these people being trapped without any alternative means of escape . . .'

In April, the fire brigade paid another friendly visit—they had no authority to inspect the club or demand anything because a club licence, once granted, could not be withdrawn. The fire officer was in for a shock: nothing had been done about fire prevention, the club had changed hands, and the new owner knew nothing about the strongly recommended second escape. A second letter on April 5 re-emphasized the fire brigade's concern. Later it was claimed that arrangements had been made to provide an external escape from the old loading door to the street—but these stairs were not yet installed on May 1, the day when people across the river noticed an orange glow and flames in the ground-storey windows soon after eleven o'clock in the evening.

At about the same time, the manager smelled smoke drifting up the stairs. He went down to investigate. Tracing the smoke he came to the joinery shop and broke in the door. He was never able to shut it again. Drums of cellulose paint and thinner, and half-assembled kitchen units were feeding the flames. He ran to the office, called the brigade (11.07) and tried to return upstairs. Intense heat and fumes forced him back. He ran out into the street leaving the passageway doors open. A second man, who tried to follow the manager only seconds later, had to vault over the landing handrail to the ground because the stairs were already alight.

In the club-room, somebody cried 'fire!' Hardly anybody paid attention to it. The smoke began to force customers away from the stairs towards the bar. The lights went out. A window was kicked out and people ran towards it. They were confronted with the sheer drop of sixty feet to the river. Eight of them fell or jumped out. Five were killed—three survived with shock and injuries. There were another fourteen people in the club-room. Carbon monoxide poisoning killed them all. Apparently, some had tried to seek refuge behind the bar—the rest of the bodies were found round the loading door they could not open.

Downstairs, there was a great deal of fire damage. The club-room was untouched by flames! Only the heat and smoke had left their marks on the fittings, fixtures and the dead.

Whichever way one looked at it, this was a textbook case of senseless slaughter. The inevitable conclusion was that the law —or rather lawlessness—was to blame. The Club was governed by the Public Health Act of 1936 which gave no one the right to prevent the disaster. In a familiarly hasty patching-up operation, an extra paragraph was inserted into the new Licensing Act (just going through Parliament but revised in 1964) to empower the fire brigade to inspect registered clubs and object to the granting or renewals of licences on the ground of fire risks.

The old Health Act was not found to be the only one ruling, so ineffectually, places of public assembly and various other buildings which had long avoided legislative attention. Acts of Parliament, amendments of these acts, the amendments of amendments, bits and pieces of laws like the Cinematograph Acts, various music and dancing licensing acts, even the Pet-Animals Acts and the Disorderly Houses Act of 1751 were in force and could be regarded as relevant to clubs, hotels, etc., depending on the interpretation of the odd paragraph. Ministries, fire brigades, district, rural, suburban, county, county borough councils were in charge of fragmented fire prevention duties, and licensing justices covered some aspects of protection under different regulations without anybody having a complete picture of the situation—and, even less, bearing full responsibility for it.

Hotels were in a special mess: to some people, a hotel is a place of work, so was protection to be administered by the factory inspectorate? There were offices and sometimes shops in hotels, so were these employees to be cared for by some other watchdog? To the public a hotel could be a place of assembly, to staff it was a place of residence, to guests it was temporary residence—was everybody who entered to be protected by a separate authority under a different law?

The matter deserved and got top priority. An inter-departmental committee of leading specialists was set up to consider a uniform fire prevention law, plug loopholes and clean out the stables of Augeas. By assembling titbits from various old laws and drawing up modern legislation, the committee was ready with its proposals by 1963. Then came the first hurdle. It is always hard to get parliamentary draftsmen, a rare and much-sought-after species of the legal jungle, but the committee fought for them and trapped them. At the beginning of 1964, the draft of a new comprehensive Fire Precautions Bill was ready. The Home Secretary promised to introduce the Bill in Parliament soon. The Bill was printed by June 1964. It seemed that places of residence, resort and assembly, flats, pubs, theatres, halls, hotels, hostels, clubs, would all be dealt with at last. But pressure of work never allocated precious parliamentary time for this Bill to be read. Its priority was insufficient. The memory of the Bolton club disaster, now three years old, began to fade.

The committee had its hopes raised by the coming election:

civil servants know from experience that when a new government takes office, there is always a shortage of its very own, ready-made legislative packages on the shelf, so a Bill, properly drafted, has a good chance to go through even if it enjoys a low priority. In October 1964, the Labour Party took over from the Conservatives. But somehow, there was still no time for fire prevention. In March 1966, there was another election. The government was re-elected, many already drafted Bills preceded fire laws in the queue, and although Home Secretaries kept promising early reading in Parliament, there was just no time.

The situation in fire prevention kept changing. There were new problems to deal with, new legislation to consider. The Bill had to be altered, more draftsmen had to be enticed, a continuous review of the position had to be kept. Bolton? What happened in Bolton?

Firemen, appalled by the conditions in many buildings, were left to their own devices. So they introduced their own 'law' which they called the Bluff & Persuasion Act. This is how it worked in a particular case.

The Offices, Shops and Railway Premises Act came into force in 1963 and gave firemen the duty to inspect premises of this kind. Working on the tremendous backlog, a prevention officer visited a hostel for the destitute in 1969 to inspect, according to his rights, nothing but the offices in the building. He noticed various fire risks in the hostel and gave some friendly advice, but this was declined. Persuasion failed. Probably no funds were available for preventive measures.

Soon after this visit, there was a fire in the hostel where some four hundred people spent the night. The fire report recorded the supposed cause as 'Careless disposal of lighted cigarette end or match set fire to foam rubber mattress'. The investigation spotted numerous hazards. There had been no fire drill, nobody knew what to do in fire. An electrical alarm system could be sounded only from one point, but it was out of order. The manager did not know that the alarm needed regular testing. Some residents had been recruited to act as 'night security patrol' for bed and board but, needless to say, these failed to discover the fire in time. Foam mattresses were stored on the landings. For maximum utilization of space and for the provision of some privacy, cubicles were erected everywhere—and the result was a most 'intricate maze' from which the casual resident would never find his way out.

Making use of the collected information on similar cases and of the fire that gave everybody a fright, the brigade now applied the delicate mixture of bluff (what if there were fatalities next time? the law might seek the culprits . . .) and persuasion, which is best reflected in a letter. The prevention officer who wrote it certainly knew how to walk bare-foot on hot eggs. He set out his suggestions for prevention gently. He explained that the lack of legal obligations was a mistake and must not be relied on. He emphasized in complimentary terms the great work of the hostel caring for people who could not fend for themselves, let alone help to ensure the safety of others. 'Not, I hope, appearing to be unkindly in these remarks or unfair, my impressions are that the residents of' this hostel 'are a community ranging between alcoholics (meths drinkers, etc.) and very elderly wayfarers. The latter, by a competent person, may even be classified as geriatrics and it is with these impressions in mind' that he suggested preventive steps like proper patrol, alarm system, fire drill, etc. 'Failing these provisions, the paradoxical situation may occur whereby "a soul may be saved at the cost of a life".'

Within a week, fire safety was greatly improved in the hostel which thus gave a lead to others.

Bluff and persuasion worked in individual cases, but the overall outlook was still bleak. Hotels kept burning, and the message was lost on the law-makers. A Brighton blaze which killed seven people and severely damaged a seafront hotel in November 1968, was a typical example of the prevailing attitude. Because eventually its cause turned out to be arson committed by a member of the staff, it was disregarded as a potential trail-blazer for legislation. This easy way out helped to overlook the hazards exposed by the case—hazards that existed irrespective of the cause. Three years before the fire the fire brigade had recommended the installation of additional escape facilities serving staff bedrooms in the attic. It took two years, but it was done. Five years before the fire, a public health inspector had recommended the installation of fire alarms. This was not done. On the night of the fire, the porter who noticed the flames had to telephone the fire brigade and then race upstairs to wake up guests and staff.

To most people, arson seems to be a magic word that is capable of taking all responsibility for deaths in fire. Even authorities are frequent victims of this illusion. The security chief of an American hotel chain exclaimed: 'What do you expect? You want me to put an armed guard on every guest, every waiter and every passer-by? If a crazy torch wants to burn us out of business, he'll burn us out of business. We can do nothing.' Which may be true about the prevention of arson—but not the prevention of deaths. For to us, hotel guests, it makes no difference whatsoever what caused the fire and what made the flames spread fast. All that matters is: how do we have quick warning and how do we get out? Accident or incendiarism—we should not be required to display ingenuity, a talent for knotting sheets or the courage to jump.

In May 1971, fire broke out in London's Hills Hotel. A fierce blast of heat shot through the building killing residents in their beds. Seven people died there and another ten were seriously injured. A girl leaped from a second-floor window and was impaled on spiked railings. She died in hospital with some spikes, cut off by firemen, still inside her. A thorough investigation followed and questions of safety were raised. The forensic experts, detectives and fire investigators found some evidence of incendiarism: the fire had been started deliberately and its fast spread had been engineered. The word *arson* crept into the headlines and everything else was forgotten. A few weeks before the fire, a public health inspector had visited the hotel. His impression was that the fire precautions might not be entirely satisfactory. So other officials checked the hotel in this respect only a week before the tragedy, and found that 'as far as the regulations were concerned, things were in order', reported the *Daily Telegraph* on May 13, 1971. Yet 'things' were not in order with the regulations which ought to require the installation of a series of fire-doors to prevent—or at least slow down—the rush of killer heat and smoke in hotels irrespective of what might cause a fire.

The long list of problems concerning safety only begins with the fact that nobody in Britain knows how many hotels there are. If the hotelier does not want to sell alcoholic drinks, he needs no licence or registration. In London, inspectors who try desperately to check fire safety must first find the hotels from small ads in the papers, by a great deal of legwork, and with the aid of their colleagues, the public health inspectors, who build up their own hotel lists with similarly haphazard methods. In July 1971, the existence of 1,306 hotels was known to the Greater London Council. Only a quarter of these had been surveyed by the ten inspectors and none was passed as satisfactory without some work to comply with basic requirements. It was estimated that at least another thirty men were needed by the GLC—and that even then it would probably take two generations of inspectors to complete the initial surveys.

The Fire Protection Association made a special study of Fire Dangers in Hotels and published its report in August 1969. Case after case after case, all between 1964 and 1968, reflected the need to design and construct all hotels in a way that minimizes the fire spread and facilitates quick escape from all parts of a building. Perhaps the most astonishing conclusion was that in the fatal hotel fires there were inexcusably long delays in warning the staff and residents because there were no automatic detector and alarm systems. In many cases, the 'planned' warning arrangements were appalling: in one hotel (three deaths), a porter sent a chambermaid to the reception desk to raise the alarm—the receptionist telephoned the manager and then began to call the rooms one by one. Only one of the fifteen guests and forty employees answered.

In another hotel, employees decided not to warn anyone about a fire—they wanted to deal with it themselves. They tried to use fire extinguishers which had never been in their hands before but these did not work because they operated them incorrectly. Then they tried to connect a fire hose to a hydrant but failed because the cover cap on the outlet had been painted over and was jammed completely.

Two control switches and a single bell made up the fire alarm system of the Stornoway, Lewis, hotel where five women died in a fire in October 1966. The bell was not audible throughout the building.

Most hotels do not bother to display printed fire notices in the rooms because, they claim, the majority of guests never read them anyway until there is a fire . . . when it is too late to work out what to do and where to find exits. In a Shropshire hotel (at Church Stretton—five deaths), a bedroom notice advised: 'In case of fire shout FIRE.' This instruction was for an L-shaped building that measured 160 by 128 feet, and parts of which were four storeys high.

In a Belfast hotel, the resident who discovered a fire used an original method to raise the alarm: he banged two metal trays together which woke up the manager who roused the other occupants. Three people died. Sending runners from door to door to wake up residents is the standard method of fire alarm in many hotels. It is not a particularly effective system. In October 1970, Britain's Minister for Transport Industries stayed at a hotel near Windermere. Someone banged on the door at about half past five in the morning. When he opened it no one was there, so he went back to bed for three quarters of an hour. There was a fire. Later he was evacuated with his wife and the other sixty guests.*

The British Hotels and Restaurants Association denied that many hotels were dangerous fire risks and called the F.P.A. report 'unnecessarily alarmist'. Yet only six weeks later, in October 1969, the hotel association appointed a very experienced retired fire chief to act as fire consultant for its members. Considering that the association has some 12,000 full and affiliated members, this appeared to be a tremendous task for a single-handed operation. In 1971, a brief telephone conversation, however, went like this:

'You must be about the busiest man in Britain.'

'Not really. Most hotels that will need a lot of attention are still waiting for the new law. To see what will be required from them. Fire protection is expensive and must be tailored according to circumstances. Once the Act is passed, there might be many requests for advice.'

The F.P.A. study gave various checklists as an aid for hotel managers (maintenance and building, staff training and fire procedure checks) and called special attention to the increasing use of television sets not only in public lounges but also in bedrooms. It referred to several fires which had been caused in this way and advised that a member of the staff should always check that sets were properly disconnected, preferably unplugged, for the night. Was this warning unduly alarmist?

Only four months after its publication, guests had a quiet

* *Sunday Telegraph*, October 25, 1970.

Christmas celebration at the Rose and Crown hotel, a historic
Tudor coaching inn at Saffron Walden, Essex. There were no
parties, no drinking bouts, people stayed at their separate
tables, and went to bed early—unfortunately. Nobody was
awake when fire broke out in the oak-panelled television room.
An alarm bell was sounded but hardly any of the guests heard
it because soon the wiring burnt through. The drama that
developed was all too familiar. Screaming people in the windows,
escapes down knotted blankets, desperate leaps from the roof.
Three people got within three feet of a locked fire-door. Next
to the door, in a glass box, hung the key. Two of the group were
driven back by smoke. The third collapsed almost within reach
of safety. The glass on the box remained unbroken.

The investigation found that the TV set was the most likely
culprit. The manager recalled quite clearly at the inquest that
he himself had switched off the television both at the set and
at the wall socket. A lengthy argument between electrical
experts followed. Perhaps the fire had started *before* the set was
switched off. Perhaps there was over-heating which became
self-sustained, burning outwards until it reached the air and
burst into flames. Eleven people died, several were injured. To
them it made no difference who was right.

The Rose and Crown was owned by Trust Houses, a company which had been first to appoint a full-time fire officer and
had always provided fire protection in excess of that demanded
by regulations. Good regulations would have probably demanded protection in excess of that provided. After this fire, the
Warwickshire fire brigade invited 200 hotel managers for a
seminar on fire precautions. Only seven accepted the invitation.

In 1970, fire brigades up and down the country estimated that
between fifty and eighty per cent of the hotels and hostels might
be serious fire risks in most areas. Nobody knew exactly because
inspection was only by invitation—and from many hotels, the
invitation never came for twenty years. As most of Britain's
hotels are old, built without the benefit of modern ideas for fire
protection through design and construction, and because the
oldest hotels were often most exposed to disaster, there were
calls that historic inns should be phased out or their accom-
modation capacity should be drastically reduced. But then there
was a fire in Redcar. Modern fire-doors helped to contain the

7

blaze, but four out of twenty-four guests died, seventeen people were carried to safety by firemen from upper-floor windows, there were knotted-sheets escapes, and the building was completely destroyed. This hotel was two years old.

Many people engaged in fire prevention prayed for a Conservative victory in the General Election of 1970. 'Not because the Tories proved themselves particularly helpful when they were in power,' said a civil servant who would normally submit himself to torture rather than to discussing party politics, 'but because Tory victory seemed unlikely and so they were rather unprepared with properly drafted Bills ready for Parliament.' Those prayers were answered, the Conservatives won, and they did need time fillers to show vigorous activity by putting through new legislation.

It was a true but not insignificant coincidence that the new comprehensive Fire Precautions Bill was introduced in Parliament four days after the French dance hall disaster at Saint Laurent-du-Pont where 146 people were killed. The second reading followed three weeks later, and speakers on the subject stood in their shining armour as if wisdom and courageous foresight instead of calamity and a decade of negligence had prompted legislation. The Minister of State, Home Office, admitted that there had been tragic warnings, but claimed credit by saying that 'All too often in the past, before action has been taken, it has needed some major catastrophe to focus attention on some weakness or other in our provision for the safety of life in the event of fire'. This thought would have commanded more admiration in 1961, before or right after the Bolton club fire.

The Opposition spokesman on Home Office matters emphasized that this was one of the most important Bills to come before the House. It is a pity that this was not recognized just after the 1964 election, well before many deaths in hotels. Everybody was quick to cash in on the good cause and so nobody opposed the Fire Precautions Act which—after many more blasts of hot air in the House of Lords—received the Royal Assent by the end of May 1971.

Factories and offices were already covered at least in law. The new Act was to ensure safety of lives almost everywhere else except private homes, places of worship (many of which would be called potential death-traps were their good names not safeguarded by blinding hypocrisy), and so-called multiple occupancies. That the latter comes under no protective legislation is perhaps the greatest disgrace of all.

'Multiple occupancies' are the perilously overcrowded buildings which were originally meant to be one-family residences. Thousands of these are put to lucrative hostel-style use. In London, due to the ever-increasing housing shortage, it is not at all unusual to find twenty or thirty people crammed into what is essentially a large house for a family of four. 'All the risks in the book, oil heaters, rubbish, crude wiring, loads of inflammable materials and not even elementary precautions'—this is how a prevention officer described a building where four people died. The prospect? 'All the survivors are back there and new tenants are already moving in. The hall and staircase are virtually blocked: you have to climb over furniture and sacks of clothes to get in or out. The best I managed to do was to persuade them to keep a bucket of water on each of the three landings—two buckets were stolen within twelve hours. I have no right to enter or inspect the premises, let alone demand any precautions. What can you do? The law won't help. These are classed as private dwellings and we must respect the freedom of the individual to choose his own manner of death.'

With the new Fire Precautions Act, theatres, cinemas, dance, bingo and exhibition halls, hotels, hostels, boarding houses, certain blocks of flats and high-rise buildings, schools, training establishments, hospitals, homes for children and old people, and other types of buildings with mass fire risks were to be brought under control—in principle. In practice, it is not so simple. Fire authorities will have the duty to inspect, and the right to oppose the use of, these buildings until satisfactory improvements are carried out. Penalties will be increased to give the law more bite. But: the law will not be back-dated and so it will apply itself solely to new buildings. It will be only gradually, by special orders, that particular types of existing buildings like hotels will be brought into the new certification procedure. The main reason for the delay is that an estimated 450,000 buildings will have to be controlled by the fire authorities, which are still greatly under-strength and often burdened by the tremendous backlog of office inspections.

Well-trained officers for prevention duties are at a premium
—except that nobody is willing to pay that premium. It is
thought that another four hundred such officers will be needed
and the cost may be about a million pounds a year. What
nobody knows or even tries to guess at is how much it will cost
to bring about the necessary improvements in existing hotels
and how long it will take.

Haggling over the bare safety minimum for the future started
in 1969 when a working party of Home Office experts, fire
officers and hotel industry representatives was set up to hammer
out a voluntary code of practice for fire prevention. Two years
of hard work resulted in a compromise which embodies the
virtue of viability as well as the meek far-from-ideal-though-
perhaps-acceptable characteristic of all such bargaining. The
tragedy is that the value of lives cannot be accurately measured
against the cost-consciousness particularly of the struggling
small boarding-house owner even though this is what the
bargain is all about.

Fire officers, quite rightly, tend to take the view that people
must be able to trust the bus driver and his vehicle, and even
more trusted must be the hotelier and his premises where
people sleep and are, therefore, deprived of their initial self-
defence in the crucial first moments of extreme peril. Ideally,
prevention experts would want to see automatic fire detection
in hotels, automatic alarms throughout the building, possibly
sprinkler protection at least in key areas, fire-doors to protect
enclosed staircases and compartmentalize corridors, alternative
escape routes, and life-boat-type fire drills for staff and guests. It
is equally understandable that hoteliers seek the cheapest
acceptable solution, that structural alterations, sprinklers or the
installation of automatic smoke detectors and alarm systems may
be prohibitively expensive to many smaller establishments and
even to some richer hotel chains, and that hotel managers like
to cause the least inconvenience to their guests. (Some hoteliers
argue that fires should be dealt with by the staff if possible without the help of the fire brigade, and that alarm bells as well as
life-boat-type practice are 'unduly upsetting over-reactions'.)
Such highly controversial matters had to be brought to a
mutually satisfactory—or mutually unsatisfactory?—compromise when the working party produced the voluntary code

of practice which is to serve as a guide in the implementation of the new law. This leaves us with at least two disturbing questions.

(1) Is it right that, when the new legislation is put into practice, the enforcing fire authorities should have to start 'bargaining' with individual hoteliers from a position of weakness—that is, to try and reach a compromise based on the initial compromise of the code?

(2) Is the 'live and let live' principle more applicable to hoteliers than to their guests?

Nobody would argue against the noble intention of keeping legislative interference with individual liberty to a minimum. Nobody would want to force the small boarding house or seaside family hotel owner out of business by the demand of crippling capital investment for fire precautions. But who will state publicly, what politician will include it in his programme, that the inn-keeper's livelihood should be safeguarded at the expense of public safety? And what champion of individual liberty will defend the morality of the already existing dual safety standards—one for the rich and one for the poor? For this is what we have: if you can afford to stay in a new, luxurious and often ridiculously expensive hotel, usually you get not only more comfort, bigger bed, better picture on the wall, wider choice in temperature, breakfast and piped music, but also a better chance of survival in fire.

A comparison with some other practices may start an intriguing train of thought. The fact that people slip in bath-tubs and break their arms, heads or necks, does not result in a ban on manufacturing baths. Only warnings are issued. Other people make a habit of electrocuting themselves or creating hazards by faulty wirings. Yet we still have electrical appliances and can buy wire in any quantity—with the suitable warnings attached. The same has happened with cigarettes. Following the American example, every packet of cigarettes sold in Britain must carry the warning of health hazard: this will not curtail the manufacturer's liberty of selling his dangerous wares, and it will not deprive the citizen of his freedom of slowly cutting his own throat, but the seller will have to warn the buyer that gradual throat-slitting may not be as pleasant as at first sight it may appear to be.

Why cannot a similar system be applied to hotels? Fair
enough, let the small hotelier live, let him get away with less
investment and somewhat barer than bare minimum of safety,
but make him warn his guests—right at the entrance—that his
hotel has satisfied the basic requirements of the licensing
authority, but that it lacks certain safety features. No doubt,
this would be bad for business. But it may promote safety as one
of the attractions offered by a hotel. Or else, a positive approach
could be adopted: the stars awarded to certain hotels and
restaurants for good service or food have promoted the general
awareness of the fact that better dishes than a plate of cold chips
are available at some establishments. Why not stars for better
fire prevention in hotels? The classification could range from
the plain licence for the not-quite-a-death-trap level to the
five-star standard of using 'safety luxuries' such as flame-proof
curtains and upholstery.

Unfortunately, as if the past decades have not given us time
to foresee and forestall the practical, financial, moral and
legislative problems, a major improvement in all-round hotel
safety is expected to be a long, long process everywhere—
particularly in countries where serious thinking has not yet even
begun. It appears therefore, that for many years to come, the
traveller will be well advised to bear the thought of fire hazard
in mind wherever he goes, on holiday or business, in Europe,
the United States, Australia, Africa or the Far East. Although
it may be rather limited what a guest can actually do for fire
safety in a hotel, he can achieve quite a lot in creating a safety-
conscious atmosphere by making himself a troublesome
customer.

He can certainly read fire notices in his room or elsewhere in
the building—or ask questions about fire drill and escape
arrangements if they are not displayed. The third or fourth
curious guest may make the manager edgy, but he may do
something about it. When moving into the hotel, a guest can
take a look at escape routes and fire exits, and check if these are
clearly signposted. If not, more questions can be asked. (Probably we all notice fire exit signs anyway, except that we pay no
attention to them and so forget where they are.) If exit routes
are obstructed by, say, big baskets of linen, it is a godsent
opportunity to achieve more unpopularity at the reception desk.

A fussy traveller who wants to survive his holiday may unplug his own TV set for the night and do the same in the lounge if he is around at switch-off time. He may pull portable fires away from the draught and the reach of the dancing curtain. He may stop smoking in bed and demand more and bigger ashtrays everywhere. (Many hotel fires are started by night-smokers whose sleepy carelessness is aided by the scarcity and miniature size of ashtrays provided by obvious non-smokers.) He may call attention to fire-doors which have been wedged open permanently to give a free run for the staff—or he may simply remove the wedge and see what happens. Many guests never use the telephone in hotels, so it may be a good idea to check how to get the operator.

If there is a fire, it is always dangerous to start wandering around in a strange hotel. Unless it is quite certain that guests can get out *beneath* the level of fire (both fumes and flames spread upwards) it is often best to stay put in the room, shut the door first, seal the crack with a rug or towels, and call the operator or open the window and shout and shout for help. Those who already know where an alternative, perhaps external fire escape is, should consider that they may have to reach it via an unprotected smoke-logged corridor. And a final word from a fire investigator of bitter experience: 'Even the most fire-conscious troublesome traveller should not consider himself a fireman. However small that fire is, call assistance and give warning first before trying to fight the outbreak.'

If hotels can afford to remain death-traps and still attract the paying public on whose goodwill they rely entirely, perhaps it comes as a lesser surprise that a vast number of *hospitals* all over the world are in a similarly shocking condition. The most disgusting aspect of it all is that the very old and the mentally ill, people who are the least capable of self-defence and flight, are left the most exposed to disaster. To become a 'troublesome customer' will not help them: the sick, the old and the feeble are almost expected to be in that category. Frequently, these are the people with the worst faculty of convincing complaint and logical argument, and even if they are paying guests, they are usually tied to their doctors and hospitals by choice, convenience or their families' wishes.

Is there nobody who really cares for them? Oh yes, gradually, some improvements are being brought about everywhere. But how gradual can the 'gradual' be?

The problems are very similar to those in hotels. Old buildings, non-fire resistant construction, lack of proper fire drill for staff, lack of automatic alarm and fire-fighting systems, overcrowding, underpaid and overworked nurses, misused firedoors, insufficient escape facilities, and so on. In many countries, sprinkler protection for hospitals is still unheard of. New Zealand hospitals are probably the only exception with fairly common use of sprinklers. Suggestions to introduce them in the United States had a rather cool reception.

The American public seem to be totally unstirred by the fact that the chance of a fire occurring in a hospital is statistically one hundred times greater than in any other building in New York. At the 38th Annual Eastern Regional Safety Convention, on March 26, 1969, it was stated that electrical equipment was the major cause of fires in hospitals, with careless use of matches and cigarettes a close second.

A survey in the same year called attention to another modern hazard which is usually overlooked in most countries. It is the fast accumulation of rubbish and its not so fast disposal. It was estimated that in the average American office building each hundred square feet of floor space generates about two pounds of waste paper a day—several tons a week for the building. In hospitals, the situation is even worse: waste material for disposal averages eight pounds per bed a day—with offices, and laboratories about four tons in a thousand-bed hospital each day. Rubbish is highly inflammable and can rapidly spread and intensify a small fire to dangerous proportions. The American Hartford Hospital fire, for instance, began in the rubbish disposal chute and although it was a comparatively modern building of fire-resistant construction, the large volume of fumes killed seven patients, four employees and five visitors.

Nursing homes for old people, with due respect to the exceptions, have such a reputation that in the film *Where's Poppa?* a father on his death-bed warned his sons: 'You can dress like a gorilla, you can frighten her and kill her, but never put your mother in a home.' *Time Magazine* (December 28, 1970) commented: 'Momma may be far better off sharing an apartment with a homicidal son than in many of the nation's twenty-four thousand nursing homes' that provide care 'to at least one million of the twenty million Americans over the age of 65'.

The problem is at least as old as the oldest of these 'homes'. The disastrous warnings come every year but even the greatest massacres are quickly forgotten. Who remembers the wooden building that burnt down in Florida in 1953, killing thirty-three old people while an employee had to drive almost five miles to raise the alarm? Or the one in Missouri: seventy-two people died in the nursing home fire that could be seen for thirty miles in 1957. In Norwalk, Ohio, fire swept through a home which was only ten years old. The owner took precautions to make it fire-proof: 'Everything was in concrete blocks, the floors were four feet thick.' But only twenty-one of the inmates were able to walk. Sixty-three old people met their deaths.

375 people fared better when their seven-storey hotel for the elderly was completely destroyed by fire in Philadelphia on January 9, 1968. Only twenty-two old folk were seriously injured, the rest got away with a chill when fleeing into sub-zero weather. The fire was supposedly started by a seventy-seven-year-old man who was only trying to light a cigarette. Luckily, the rescue arrangements were better here than in most places.

When, in 1970, the Senate 'Special Committee on Aging' examined the problem and Senator Frank Moss, a Utah Democrat, sought the establishment of a corps of federal inspectors to raise the standard of homes for the old, Ralph Nader's research team submitted a devastating report for consideration. The director of the Maryland Health Facilities Association was quick to call this report 'clandestine, superficial and haphazard'. Apart from the shortcomings in medical care, the team examined the fire problems and found that many nursing homes were unsafe. For example, it referred to the investigation of an inferno in Marietta, Ohio: the building failed to meet some safety standards; personnel had received no emergency training; thirty-two people died.

The danger to life in old people's homes is far from being an American peculiarity. One can easily pick an international sample of cases from any single year. Take 1970: in January, four inmates died and thirteen were seriously injured when fire destroyed a West Berlin home; before the month was over, seven women died when a home with twenty-six occupants at Driebergen, near Utrecht in Holland, had a blaze; in February, five patients died and several were seriously injured in a fire in the geriatric ward of Exeter's City Hospital; in November, it was a dog's barking that woke the owner of a home at Pointe aux Trembles, a Montreal suburb, when a fire at dawn broke out, killing seventeen of the thirty-four inmates, even though the modern three-storey building had been thoroughly inspected by fire authorities only three months earlier. It is a far from complete list for the year. This Canadian fire followed closely the trail blazed by a three-storey home, a former school built of wood just before the turn of the century, in Notre Dame du Lac, Quebec, where thirty-eight of the sixty-nine inmates died.

In 1971, four of Britain's leading consultant geriatricians examined hospital services for the elderly.* Their report reflected the great deal of 'good work done by devoted people' who 'are, however, too few in number' and often forced to 'work under conditions more appropriate to the 1870s than to the 1970s'. It was found that a third of the hospitals examined were more than a hundred years old, and the squalid Dickensian buildings were rightly described as 'perfect examples of human warehouses' (many, in fact, used to be actual workhouses) which had retained their dreaded stigma for the aged. Many wards were grossly overcrowded and this situation, aggravated by serious staff shortage, added to the fire hazard. Bensted House, Faversham, built in 1832 as a workhouse, is a high fire risk. Evacuation in fire would be particularly hampered in Brook Hospital, Woolwich, where geriatric wards are upstairs but there are no lifts. St. Mary's Hospital, near Folkestone, has almost two hundred elderly patients—but no fire alarm system. Although general conditions and fire precautions are constantly improved by increasing investment, progress is offset by the growing demand for places, and unless drastic development is achieved within a few years, the longer average lifespan may create insurmountable problems by the end of the century when Britain will have some eight million seventy-year-olds.

When devastating fires occur in ordinary hospitals, tragedy

---

* 'Development of Services for the Elderly and Elderly Confused', a report prepared for the South-East Metropolitan Regional Hospital Board by Prof. J. C. Brocklehurst, Dr. W. E. R. Budd, Dr. A. N. G. Clark and Dr. R. E. Irvine.

is often averted by the fact that a high proportion of the patients
—unlike in geriatric wards—can walk and, with the right instructions, can save themselves or even assist in the evacuation
of the bed-bound. These relative advantages are, however,
tremendously frail, and they are shattered by the hospital fires
that frequently expose the disaster potentials in the unpreparedness that verges on criminal negligence. Reports from several
countries showed, for instance, that in a number of cases nurses
did not know how to work the 'break glass' type of alarms: they
broke the glass and pressed the button behind it anxiously to
sound the alarm, being ignorant of the principle of this automatic system that would have worked if the button, released by
the broken glass, had been allowed to jump out.

After the Exeter City Hospital fire (February 1970) it was
found that the foam rubber mattresses contributed a great deal
to the severity of the blaze and so to the five fatalities. It was
immediately understood that this was not the only hospital with
similarly stuffed and covered mattresses, and an inquiry was
initiated to advise hospital managements. Yet barely a year
later, after the Exe Vale mental hospital fire that had killed
four patients, the coroner had to express concern about the risk
created by these mattresses once again, because the inquest
indicated that 'there have now been two fires in the [Exeter]
area directly connected with foam rubber mattresses'.

After another British hospital disaster, the Department of
Health and Social Security gave useful advice for fire precautions in a Hospitals Technical Memorandum (No. 16, May
1969). Although it put ample emphasis on the importance of
staff training, it still showed considerable reliance on concise fire
notices 'at conspicuous positions' and more detailed printed instructions in staff rooms and notice boards. Experience in many
hospital fires shows that it is too late to start reading even a most
concise list of 'action to be taken' when flames and fumes
already begin to envelop a ward.

At the time of this Memorandum, most hospitals were inadequately equipped to deal with fire, according to the *British
Hospital Journal*. Why was it ever permitted to come to the point
where a hundred hospitals in the Sheffield region alone were
without any fire alarms? Ringing of hand-bells and shouting
'fire' were their standard methods of warning. A survey in

eighty-six Lancashire hospitals showed serious deficiencies in
fire-fighting, alarm and escape systems, and eleven hospitals
were regarded as dangerous fire risks.* Fortunately, the
hospital inquiries seem to be continuing in general with growing particular emphasis on fire precautions. It is a pity that
staff shortage, noted by the *Annual Report of National Health
Service Hospital Advisory Service* (May 1971), is not quite recognized as a fire hazard in the situation where wards of fifty or
more patients are often cared for by only one or two staff in each
shift. The same report welcomed the fact that staff generally
were well aware of the fire risks, particularly in old buildings,
but it also made the disturbing rediscovery that in some hospitals
actual fire drills were still not undertaken, and it called attention to the great difference between knowing fire drill in theory
and putting it into practice.

This general outcry against lack of safety, and anxious self-
examination by the authorities began in earnest after the public
inquiry 'into the circumstances leading to a fire at Shelton
Hospital, Shrewsbury, on the night of the 25–26th February,
1968, and to the deaths of twenty-four patients' in Beech Ward.
The gravity of this case was particularly emphasized by the
heavy toll representing more than half the number of patients in
that ward.

The inquiry disclosed a whole series of failures. There were
long, vital delays in raising the alarm. Some nurses never
had any fire drill, many others had received no evacuation
training for a great number of years. The emergency procedure
was slow and complicated, and the night porter had to telephone a hospital fire officer before calling the fire brigade. The
fire was started most probably by a cigarette end left in an easy
chair where it 'ignited the upholstery and caused it to smoulder
very slowly at first, producing a steadily increasing volume of
smoke for about one and a half to two hours before the general
conflagration' and discovery.

Shelton, being a large *psychiatric hospital* built in the 1840's,
called attention once again to the tremendous hazards that are
peculiar to mental homes, many of which are very old. Thirty-
two months after Shelton, and nineteen months after Nar-
borough (a mental hospital fire with four deaths near Leicester),

* *Sheffield Morning Telegraph*, May 10, 1969.

Christopher Mayhew, Chairman of the National Association for Mental Health, had to warn the government that unless more was spent to raise the standards in old mental hospitals 'there would be further scandals such as had shocked the nation last year'.*

Another special problem is security: in order to prevent inmates from escaping, doors have to be locked, windows are barred. When, in March 1971, fire swept through a three-storey psychiatric clinic in Zurich, Switzerland, most of the sixty patients and male nurses were trapped behind barred doors and windows. Firemen mounted a desperate rescue operation but thirty patients died. In December 1970, a Ghent lawyer called Belgium's only male mental home a 'snake pit'. He revealed overcrowding (1,350 people in sixteen filthy wards, and dormitories, designed for thirty beds, holding 110 patients each), lack of staff (only one doctor, five psychiatrists, and 360 male nurses of whom less than a third were fully qualified), and potential fire traps because the packed and lightly controlled dormitories were locked for the night.

A third, probably the greatest, problem with the safety of mental hospitals is the inmates themselves. Most of them are much less capable of saving themselves from fire than people in homes for the elderly; many of them have a complete lack of understanding of events and the world around them; some will start fires in feeble negligence while others, with a marked destructive tendency and a record of breaking windows, etc., will start fires deliberately. Without good witnesses or material proof, investigators must rely on circumstantial evidence.

In the Shelton case, incendiarism was ruled out as a possible cause of the disaster but the difficulties of inquiry were well demonstrated. Patient No. 27, a girl, dropped a letter when she died: '. . . Dad, I hope the Nurses and the Girls go on a blazing hot fire, Dad.' There were rumours that a survivor, Patient No. 23, had started the fire. She had been in the same hospital for thirty years. On three separate occasions, when a Sister questioned her, this patient admitted with a happy grin that yes, she started the fire, and once she even added that she had fetched some polishing wax for the purpose. She suffered from

* Speech at nurses' meeting at Cane Hill Hospital, Coulsdon, Surrey, October 24, 1970.

schizophrenia accompanied by echolalia, a mental condition in which the patient will agree with anything that is suggested to her.

Incendiarism, however, must be given careful consideration every time there is a mental home fire. Holland suffered two disasters of this kind within ten weeks of each other. One was at Wagenborgen, a village in the north, where eleven women died and eighteen were injured, ten seriously, when their ward was gutted in October 1970. The second fire came on February 2, 1971. In a home for the mentally retarded at Rolde, in the north-east, fourteen people died. The ward where the fire began was the home of thirty patients whose ages ranged from ten to fifty years. After both these fires, there were 'strong suspicions' of incendiarism. Yet even if this was the case, mental patients cannot be made responsible for the deaths. Blame, if any, must be borne by the sane who failed to prevent a small fire from becoming a holocaust and whose evacuation arrangements were not good enough for any eventuality—including a case of arson.

CHAPTER TWELVE

THE PERFECT CRIME?

A PIGEON-GREY Chicago granny, who controlled a large ring of *torches* (professional arsonists), always took great care of her charges—both her grandchildren and her detonators. In many ways, she was an evil genius. One of the very, very few women who have ever broken into this vile, all-male domain of crime, she escaped conviction for major offences even when her gang was smashed. She had the reputation of being an equally gifted expert on infernal machines and coconut cookies. She dreamed up weird flame-producing contraptions which were as logical and ingenious as a Heath Robinson apparatus, but she also had the good sense to recognize that a box of matches can give the police a much bigger headache than the unburnt remains of a timing device which, if discovered, would at once dry up her source of income: insurance money.

The timing device, illustrated, was allegedly inspired by her, but her gang never used it. She knew it would leave too much evidence on the scene of the fire. The man who pinched the patent and tried to take advantage of it was caught in Canada: he made three copies, forgot to synchronize the three alarm clocks involved, and one fire was still due to start when the other two in the building were already under the control of firemen.

On the right, the mausoleum-like inflammable structure serves as a rail for a strip of sandpaper. On the top, a 'pillory' holds a number of match-sticks. When the matches are suppressed, the heads rest firmly on the sandpaper. On the left, thin thread ties the sandpaper to a wooden column—on the right, a heavy piece of flat-iron hangs exerting a considerable pull on the strip. The vital component of the contrivance is an alarm clock from which the bells at the top have been removed.

The hammer is left in its place, but a razor blade is attached to it and the thread on the left rests on that. When, at the pre-arranged time, the alarm mechanism is activated, the hammer begins to wiggle, the razor cuts the thread, the flat-iron is freed to fall, pulling the sandpaper which ignites the match-heads and so sets fire to some oily rags, piled on top, at a time when the arsonist is already far away busy establishing his cast-iron alibi.

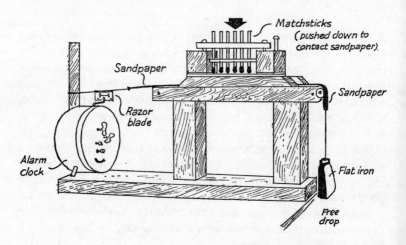

The arsonist, whose mistake left an intact working model for crime museums, was caught because he had the motive (he was to benefit from the insurance on the factory), the opportunity (only he had access to relevant parts of the building and had been seen near the place on a Saturday night when he had no business to be there), and the know-how (several experimental models were found in his home). He finally broke down and confessed when he was told that a vagrant child who, unknown to the arsonist, slept in a shed next door, was badly injured in the fire. The defence emphasized that the accused was certain that 'human life would not be endangered by his regrettable act' (he got away with the light sentence of a year's imprisonment), but this old conscience-salving excuse is a delusion at its best. Experience shows that every arsonist is a potential killer.

The firebug who crumples a single sheet of newspaper and 'lights it, handles a murder weapon as dangerous as a gun and a weapon that is inherently capable of far greater damage than any single firearm. A murderer with a gun is almost clean compared to the furtive firesetter whose match turns the dark night into a hell of smoke and flames,' said John E. Stuerwald, Assistant Manager of the Fraud and Arson Bureau of the American Insurance Association.

In the last ten years or so, there was a tremendous increase in this crime. In the early 1950's, the British police knew about an annual average of 580 cases of incendiarism. In 1969, the number grew to almost 2,300. American estimates reveal a similar trend: between 1956 and 1966, the number of known and suspected arson cases doubled. These were responsible for some of the most devastating fires with several billion dollars of annual damage. The situation is no better in other countries. Australian statistics show that almost five per cent of all fires have been started by a malicious act.

Yet the statistics are absolutely meaningless. Investigators, firemen, insurance and other fire specialists are totally—and justifiably—convinced that at least twelve per cent of all ignition causes, and perhaps as much as thirty per cent of all fire damage, must be attributed to arson. 'The reason for the grave discrepancy between realistic estimates and pipedreaming statistics is,' a Marseilles fire officer explained, 'that arson is still perhaps the most inexpertly and inefficiently investigated crime.'

As an experiment, exceptionally intensified fire investigation was conducted in several areas of the United States, reported the *Fire and Arson Investigator* (Volume XI, No. 2). The result indicated that between a *fifth and a quarter of all fires were of incendiary origin*. The Marseilles officer's opinion is fully supported by John E. Stuerwald who claims that 'the number of possible arson cases when compared to the number of persons actually arrested for arson also presents a disproportionate picture', and that apart from the obvious difficulties in arson detection, statistics cannot be relied on because, in many areas, the arduous job of fire cause classification is the duty of 'untrained and inexperienced personnel with a heavy workload'.

This is a major problem everywhere and, as we have seen, it has a fatally detrimental effect on the compilation of accurate statistics, on the identification of frequent sources of ignition, and so on the all-out effort to eliminate particular hazards. But there the similarities end because arson has a peculiarity that distinguishes it from all other types of fire risks: *preventive and punitive laws, however severe, can do little about it.*

When some other menace, like a faulty electrical appliance or a wedged-open fire-door, is recognized, strictly enforced legislation can help to minimize the risk. With arson, the politicians' optimism about and the authorities' faith in the only solution known to them—the firmness of the courts—has all too often been proved unjustifiable. In September 1968, Britain's Parliamentary Under-Secretary of State at the Home Office expressed hope 'that the new increased maximum fines will act as a deterrent . . .' At that time, only a third of the recognized incendiary offences led to actual convictions. Since then, there has been a slight increase in annual convictions, but the number is now only a quarter of the offences known to the police.

This 'quite terrifying' increase was recognized by Lord Justice Davies in March 1971 when he was hearing an appeal for reduction of sentence from five to three years on a Peterborough man who started five fires for excitement. The judge emphasized that 'arson is becoming a prevalent offence' even among people with no criminal record who start fires out of boredom or 'just for kicks'. He upheld the sentence of five years imprisonment. The two-year difference is unlikely to be a really impressive discouragement to those who still regard incendiarism as the safest crime, because even if against all odds it is detected, the evidence is mostly too weak to carry a conviction. Unfortunately, this comforting thought comes easily to those who start fires, driven by greed, grudge, revenge, protest or an emotional outburst, who use an inferno to cover up some other, often minor, crime, and who must see flames to satisfy the urge of a momentarily or permanently unbalanced mind.

Insurance fraud is perhaps the most tempting motive for arson. It seems so simple. It is easy to succumb when the growing noise of an airport or compulsory purchase suddenly devalues a house and makes it, in a sense, over-insured, when a firm is nearing bankruptcy or when a dress manufacturer stands to suffer crippling financial losses because his warehouse is full of last season's models which are valuable on paper but totally unwanted by the shops. The latter was probably the case when a workshop and store were reported burning near Düsseldorf, in the late 1960's.

The German police investigator,* who arrived at the scene while the fire was still raging, found many suspicious clues. There were at least five clearly separate seats of fires. One outbreak was between rows of sewing machines where nothing would have sustained an accidental fire had there not been a great deal of textiles piled up at this unlikely spot. Some remains were soaked in petrol. In the warehouse, the fire undoubtedly progressed from top to bottom. Once again, there were traces of accelerants. Next door, a small office was completely untouched by the flames. But beyond that, unknown to the first firemen at the scene, a separate outbreak was gaining hold on a room that adjoined the far end of the office. There was no path for the flames to travel except through the undamaged office. And there was an important clue for the investigator in that room:

Smoke was first seen coming out of the warehouse at two o'clock in the morning; firemen got there within four minutes and fought the warehouse blaze trying to prevent any spread of the flames; fire in the room at the far end was discovered only some twenty minutes later; yet in that room, an electric clock on the wall, near a window, had stopped at two minutes past two; the clock itself had suffered only heat damage which was insufficient to stop the mechanism; but the electric wire for the clock, nailed to the surface of the wall, was burnt through at a point, several yards away from the clock, where the evidence showed the seat of a separate fire.

There was no sign of any break-in. If it was arson, it had to be an inside job. Who had the motive?

The dice were soon loaded heavily against the owner. The building was dilapidated. The company was to move to new premises. The machinery was old, not worth the cost of transport. The firm was in perilous financial straits. On the last payday, it had to borrow from the bank, giving unsellable stock and machinery as security at face-value. Borrowing on assets turned out to be a regular practice: on some Fridays, the firm obtained loans from two banks at the same time to pay the staff.

* At the investigator's request, the locale and several other details of the case have been disidentified.

When the owner was found and questioned, she made several contradictory statements. She had no alibi except that a few weeks after the fire she recalled she had been treated by a doctor in Hamburg for VD on that evening. The doctor remembered seeing her but could not verify the date or the time. The owner was known to have some associates with a criminal record. There was no evidence against these people. She had to be released from custody. The insurance company paid up.

A police arson investigator commented: 'Frustration is part of my job. But usually there is "another time". Once they succeed, the temptation is too great to resist trying the same get-rich-quick-trick again. Then we get them.'

In cases of fraud the strongest weapon against the arsonist is that even if the police cannot produce sufficient evidence for a conviction by the courts, the loss assessors, private investigators of the insurers, can frequently find enough reason to prevent the claims from being made. Fortunately, the gain motive for incendiarism is written usually all over the remains of the blaze, and some of the essential elements of this crime—like the sudden removal of valuables and insurance documents from their normal places of storage just before the 'accident'—help to arouse strong suspicions. In order to make a profit, the arsonist must often forge documents to prove his alleged losses. Insurance companies' records can also help detection: one arsonist was caught when he tried to claim compensation for paintings which he had just lost for the third time in the third fire in a third country.

'To some extent an increase in incendiarism out of greed is predictable,' said New York Chief Fire Marshal Vincent Canty. 'Whenever we had a serious economic setback, not to mention real crises, we had a marked increase in both suspicious cases and proved arson. The worst situation arose, of course, at the time of the big slump in the 1930's. We sometimes say that fires go up as the Dow Jones goes down.'

This is the thought that induces several specialists today to forecast more suspicious outbreaks to come soon in Britain. The small man, should he be a trader, manufacturer or shopkeeper, can reach the brink of bankruptcy rapidly, a veteran loss adjuster said in Manchester. 'Once he's got to that stage, he is a desperate man. He is about to become the bread-loser of the family. A box of matches may be all he can afford. And if you look at the present fast-growing list of bankruptcies, you'll understand why I must cast a particularly wary eye on any claim.'

Apart from the protection rackets (at present, it is in Sydney that Italian gangs are busy burning each others' protected premises), insurance fraud offers the greatest attraction to *professional arsonists*. Some 'torches' work independently, others join large rings which enjoy the backing and know-how of organizers, inventors, informers and even financiers.

John Stuerwald and the Fraud and Arson Bureau fought one of their biggest battles against a Buffalo-based gang. 'Insurance and police reports indicated to us that there was a sudden increase of suspicious fires particularly in certain economically hard-hit areas. The destruction was usually near-complete because discovery of the fires came too late and several parts of the buildings seemed to go up in flames all at once . . . which indicated a professional touch. Investigation was difficult but we began to find clues that various liquid accelerants had been used.

'The police had a few likely suspects, but they all produced perfectly good alibis. We knew they would. At the scene of fires we began to find bits and pieces of metal which did not belong to the premises. They were part of a timing device. In the old days, when we had telephones with the bells on top of a little box on the wall, arsonists used the mechanism to their advantage: they fastened matches to the striker of the bell, lined its path with sandpaper, ran "trailers" (newspapers or oily rags) from there to various parts of the building where there was enough fuel to sustain the fire. With the "plant" (ignition device) fixed, the torch would travel hundreds of miles away and, while enjoying the protective company of respectable citizens, he would phone the number in the warehouse to be burned. The call would be "answered" by the first of the flames that might ultimately destroy the building, usually deserted over the week-end—the arsonist's favourite time.

'Our Buffalo ring used a radio with a clock for a timing device. We knew the system well, and soon we began to recognize the Buffalo gang's individual handwriting, too: their extremely sophisticated set-up involved jars of inflammables with fuses, excelsior in cardboard boxes, all plugged into the radio so that when the clock switched it on, the lot went off at once. They had trailers with a mixture of motor oil and gasoline (gasoline alone might have exploded) and laboratory tests began to show the exact mixture they used.

'But time was running out for us. We already had a dozen fires on our hands with insurance running into hundreds of thousands of dollars. They were smart guys, I grant them that, but like all others, they thought they had invented the perfect crime and just could not stop. A pattern began to emerge, but we had to catch them red-handed. Then, at last, we had the break we had been waiting for: a cab-driver overheard a conversation and reported it to us. There was a fat reward offered by that time and it seemed he'd earn every cent of it for he was a good witness. He took us to the place that had been surveyed from his cab by the torches, and gave us the time.

'We were ready when the show began. It was a risk, but we gave them time inside the building, so that when we went in, the whole set-up was there, ready to go up. Perfect evidence. We had everything, including an excellent witness in the cab-driver. But then he disappeared. He might have been bought out or killed. We never found out. The insurance claims were stopped, the ring was smashed, nevertheless its leaders got away with a "not guilty" verdict.

'I guess hard times are coming again. In the Northern, Middle Atlantic, some Southern and Mid-West states, there appear to be more rings around. They work in many ways. Some buy old buildings, slap on a coat of paint, insure some goods inside with false papers, and use a front-man as the "owner" who makes the claim. Others solicit assignments quite openly. They offer their services to business competitors—hold-ups in production or shipment—or they visit the owner of a house that has been up for sale for a long time and make him a straight proposition. They may make a fixed charge, but frequently they go for a percentage. Some also throw in a little blackmail after the fraud, but I can't say I'm sorry to see that happen.'

Trades in which trends, luck, fashion and other hardly calculable factors matter a great deal, are always the most likely to be hit by the desperate or professional arsonist. Rings follow the trail of economic depression. Philadelphia hotel torches moved to Florida. A ring that specialized in restaurant fires has recently found more demand for its services in Cleveland, Ohio. When Australian holiday habits showed a fairly sudden change, hoteliers experienced a drastic drop in business at, for instance, Dalesford, Victoria, and there was an immediate, correspondingly great increase in suspicious fires. In one case, a professional torch had to be let off the hook in order to make him turn Queen's evidence and so convict his partner and the hotelier who endangered all the guests' lives for a hundred-thousand dollar insurance claim.

Some American investigators use quite ingenious methods to *prevent* arson. If they hear about an ailing business or have reason to suspect that a building might go up in flames, they arrange a sudden increase of 'routine' inspections which often serve as a sufficient warning. Several anticipated hotel, restaurant and private home 'accidents' have been forestalled by an even gentler device: the fire department parked a fire engine in front of the building on several consecutive days whenever it was not needed elsewhere. What is to be gained from a fire that is not given time to burn?

If methodical prevention of fraudulent fires has only a very limited scope, the task becomes totally impossible when the arsonist's motive is other than profit.

Grudge is perhaps the best name for the largest mixed bag of motives, ranging from a sudden emotional outburst to a legitimate axe to grind by illegitimate means, from momentary frustration to deep-seated hatred, from rage to jealousy, from 'getting even' with an individual to taking revenge for real or imaginary grievances inflicted by a particular community or society in general.

It is in this group that we find the motives of thousands of *rural* incendiary fires: barns burn and neighbourly disputes get settled or hay-stacks go up in flames to mark the beginning of an endless vendetta. Frustrated *burglars* often burn the house that fails to come up to their expectations in yield for their efforts. They also apply the match if a promising safe turns out to contain nothing but some account books and company records. Some *tramps* pay for hospitality with arson: 'Why should

you have what I haven't got?' The force of their envy is matched
by their colleagues' fury. 'I was refused shelter, food or work,
so I fired the barn' is a comment heard frequently by the police
during interrogation of suspects.

French railway commuters burned out wagons after a steep
rise in fares. A rich Texan, whose horse lost a race, drove his
Rolls-Royce to the winning owner's stables and started a fire
that caused half a million dollars damage, in 1969. Many employees who were sacked took revenge by creating an inferno.
No matter how big or minute a personal problem or disaster
may be, it is a sense of impotence in face of adversity that gives
a tremendous impetus to a senseless act of incendiarism.

An English cabin boy, who felt he was treated by the crew of
his first ship 'like the lowest form of animal life', who was beaten
more frequently than fed, who was shut out of the messroom
while the rest of the crew ate, and who was lonely and desperate,
succumbed to an urge of immature revenge: he set fire twice
to the ship, jeopardizing the lives of forty-four people on board.
An eighteenth-century tale about press-gangs and all that? It
happened in 1970. He only wanted to see panicky fear in his
tormentors' eyes, he confessed.

A forty-six-year-old employee of Zurich's busiest telephone
exchange (Hottingen) heard, in February 1969, that he had
been passed over in his long-expected promotion to supervisor.
Rage was eating him for almost a month. Then he saw his
opportunity to hit back: armed with a sack of sawdust and a
fifteen-litre can of petrol, he waited for a weekend when he was
alone on duty, disconnected the alarm system, and struck a
match. The exchange burned fiercely. Pandemonium broke out
as some 30,000 telephone lines in the heart of this capital of
banking went dead. It was pure luck that the main banking
district was spared. Police patrol cars and radio cabs ran emergency services. The man gave himself up at the nearest police
station saying, 'Now they'll be sorry.' He did not know how
right he was. The immediate damage to the exchange amounted
to several million Swiss Francs and the lost business to hotels
and other firms was incalculably more.

One might perhaps sympathize with the cabin boy and the
telephone operator even if their over-reaction was wholly
unjustifiable. But to most people it is much more difficult to

follow the mental process of the man who set fire to a house in Rotherham, Yorkshire, in 1970. He always prided himself on his meticulous punctuality at work. One morning, both he and the woman with whom he lived there woke up late. He blamed her for it and accused her of oversleeping deliberately. In a 'cold fury', he ran out, bought a gallon of petrol, sprinkled the two ground floor rooms with it and started a fire. With over-sleeping as a motive for arson in mind one tends to be less surprised when American investigators readily recall a case that baffled them in 1954.

In St. Petersburg, Florida, a woman suffered two fires in five days. One burnt out her car, the other caused serious damage to her house. Eventually, the culprit was found. It was a friendly neighbour who started both fires because his wife had long accused him of adultery and nagged him to prove his fidelity by doing something against the woman next door whom she sus-pected of being his mistress. He told the court it would be a relief to him to spend three years in jail away from his wife's accusa-tions.

Few women regard incendiarism as a weapon. They represent no more than about four per cent of all convicted arsonists, and although champions of women's liberation movements may find it regrettable, practically all criminal fires started by women serve as outlets for suppressed emotions. Take, for instance, the series of fires that hit farms around Polln, an Austrian village, in 1970. Three farms were burnt down in a single week. The always handy profit motive had to be ruled out because one of the farms was not even insured. Panic spread in the village: who would be next? Then suspicion fell on a twenty-seven-year-old mother of two. As soon as she was questioned, she broke down and, sobbing bitterly, confessed. She had a good marriage until her husband began to spend all his evenings and many nights drinking and playing cards at the local inn. It was no good begging him to stop, so she reasoned that if his own farm were in danger, he would have to stay in and watch out for the firebug. She was right. After the third fire, her husband never left the house in the evening . . . until her arrest.

Jealousy is perhaps the most frequent cause of arson by women, but it can show many individual motivations. In 1966, a French girl started a series of fires because a fortune-teller had advised her that the flames would cast a love-spell over her hesitant boy friend. A seventy-one-year-old London house-keeper, who had faithfully looked after an old ailing man for twenty-five years, started fires in his house when she found out that despite his promises he left her nothing in his will. A German woman, who set up home with a younger man in Bavaria, worked for two years some twenty hours a day to redecorate a dilapidated farm building. At a housewarming party, her friend told her he would marry a younger girl. He wanted her to move out. The woman threatened to kill both of them, then set fire to the girl's home and, finally, she burned down her own house.

A strange variation on the jealousy theme evolved when three London church fires were scrutinized in 1962. Within five weeks, the fire brigade were summoned twice to outbreaks in a Batter-sea church. Nine days later, a box of provisions was found to be alight—at another church in Richmond. The only link between the two churches was the vicar who had just moved from Batter-sea to Richmond. It was his transfer that upset a keen social and church worker, a lonely middle-aged woman, so badly that she retreated from tension into a world of fantasy, and started the fires after she 'had a brain storm'.

Grudge against the church has led to many fires. In Canada, scores of Catholic churches were burned down by Frenchmen and Italians who had been disappointed in their religion or the priests. Church fires can be an expression of bitterness against the entire local community as shown by many American cases, or a demonstration of racialism like the burning of Jewish property in Germany. (In February 1970, vandals burned out a Jewish old people's home in Munich, causing seven deaths. Four months later, a synagogue was desecrated next door.)

Politically motivated arson is about as old as history, but in the 1960's, it reached an unprecedented scale. Incendiarism as part of demonstrations and rioting became more trendy, contagious and widespread than its contemporaries: the spectacular sky-jacking of aeroplanes and fashionable kidnapping of diplomats. Student and race riots anywhere, strife in Ulster, Pakistan or

Canada need no examples—they are on the front page of every newspaper all the time, and these all trigger off incendiarism as a natural by-product of hatred. And if black rioting in America echoes the cry 'burn, baby, burn', the whites often pay in kind. A most vicious, pertinent case was recorded by the New York-based International Association of Arson Investigators, Inc.

In Illinois, a small community jealously guarded its 'pure-white' character. A man who was not very popular among the neighbours, had three houses there—he lived in one and leased out the other two. He prepared to move to a city, but did not mention it to anyone. Some coloured friends from another state visited him one evening. Neighbours saw his visitors. The following day, everybody he met chided him about 'such friendships'. In return he told them all that he was going to sell his home to a coloured family. (In fact, he had already arranged to let the house to a white man.) His 'joke' spread rapidly in the neighbourhood and several people made a prompt decision: the house would have to be destroyed to avoid coloured infiltration and a potential threat to high property prices. Two days later they burned down the house using gasoline to accelerate the fire. When the fire department arrived, neighbours not only refused to help in opening a valve on the fire hydrant but also advised the firemen to let the house burn.

Once again, there is a tremendous variety in the ideologies arsonists try to support with their acts of destruction. In 1969, a young Londoner set fire to the Imperial War Museum in order to shield children from what he regarded as the glorification of the horrors of war exhibited there. (The damage was £200,000 —he was sentenced to four years' imprisonment.) The same year, when Governor Rockefeller of New York visited Buenos Aires, nineteen supermarkets of the 'Minimax' chain were burned down. The apparently well-synchronized terrorist campaign served a dual purpose: anti-American demonstration and a touch of personal dislike for the Governor whose family owns the company which financed the Minimax shops. And, also in the same year, Arab guerillas planted bombs and started fires in American, British, German and other European shops and stores in their misguided belief that arson, murder of the inno-cent, and an international expansion of the Arab-Israeli con-flict will win sympathizers to their cause everywhere. It was at

the end of 1969 that Paris began to burn . . . and 1970 became
the year of the firebomb.

The first Paris fire around Christmas was started probably by
anarchists. Perhaps it was the work of others. The fact was that,
within five months, there were more than four hundred cases
of bombing and arson. A peculiar modern problem is that as
with rioting, instant publicity serves as an appetizer and invitation to onlookers to join in the fun and games. This is what
happened once the recent American bombing had begun. This
is what happened when West Berlin was driven crazy with fear
as scores of explosions were intensified by rumours. This is
what happened when Arab guerilla organizations were vying
ferociously with one another for the credit of each successful act
of terrorism. And this is what happened in France, where
Maoists, Communist splinter groups, ideologically non-com-
mitted vandals, students, political agitators posing as students,
and right-wing organizations soon claimed a share of the glory.
They burned schools including the Antony Lycée in Paris,
destroyed petrol stations, electricity pylons, telephone lines,
lorries, part of the State-owned Evian mineral water plant,
offices of political parties, town halls, cars and houses of officials.
The scene was now set for groups with special grievances.
Businessmen and farm workers tried to burn down tax authority
buildings in several towns including Paris and Bordeaux. In
Lyons, eight tax offices were bombed on a single night. Small
shopkeepers of the Nicoud protest organization concentrated on
supermarkets and chain stores because they believe that these
are unfairly favoured by the tax laws and so threaten their
livelihood. As an exception to the rule, the French government
failed to over-react to the outrages, and for the time being, the
glamour of arson diminished and the hysteria petered out.

A special problem with politically motivated arson is that
even school-children know how to make bombs or blow themselves up and suffer horrible burns in the course of experiments.
Although the manufacture, sale and storage of explosives are
strictly controlled everywhere, any schoolboy with an elementary chemistry book and a week's bus-fares to spend may produce his own devastating, frequently suicidal, bangers. These
are then incorporated in crude but effective infernal machines.
The arsonist who tried to obliterate Macy's, New York's biggest

department store, planted five bombs on different floors just before closing time on a Saturday in October 1969. Four of them went off, starting fires which were extinguished by automatic sprinklers. The fifth was found intact: an empty cigarette box contained incendiary material, and a miniature battery wired to a cheap wristwatch acted as a timing device. Similar contraptions, many with small alarm clocks and packed explosives, have been used thousands of times all over the world. In West Berlin alone, two dozen explosions were triggered off in this way between November 1969 and February 1970, and many more of these devices were found undetonated.

The tremendous advantage the politically-motivated arsonist enjoys over his commercially-minded colleague is that the noise of explosion and the obvious cause of the fire do not matter to him—what may ruin the most carefully planned insurance fraud will only serve him as a source of pride and publicity. Infernal machines have, however, some disadvantages to hit-and-run political bombers. One is that these devices need a great deal of expertise to guarantee success. Another is that assembly, planting and the avoidance of premature discovery need meticulous planning and plenty of time. This is why the various 'cocktails' became so popular in riots, violent demonstrations and revolutions.

The most extensively used version is the petrol bomb or 'Molotov cocktail'—an easily breakable container filled with an inflammable liquid and topped with some crude wick, it is a formidable weapon (more against tanks and troops than buildings) although over-filling may prevent the bottle from breaking and under-filling may merely scatter petrol on the surface that needs a high temperature and thus sustained burning to ignite. Several specialists claim that Molotov cocktails have maimed more experimenters than intended victims.

For longer sustained fire, an advanced version, the 'rag cocktail' was invented by professional rioters: a long strip of rags, stuffed into the bottle and soaked in petrol may wrap itself round combustible objects, but will even on its own burn for several minutes. Its main drawback is that it takes time to push rags through the neck of a bottle, the bomb must be prepared well before use, and transport in its ready-made form involves the risk of accidents and discovery.

The latest and most dangerous American weapon of this kind is the 'soap cocktail'. In place of the strips of rag, it uses a granulated non-detergent soap—made of animal and vegetable oils—as a filling soaked in gasoline. The wick first ignites the gasoline which, having reached the temperature of approximately 375° Fahrenheit, will in turn ignite the soap. Its advantage is that sustained burning will set fire to almost any surface— its disadvantage is that its manufacture requires considerable expertise. The would-be arsonist must know how full the bottle should be and what kind of soaps will not extinguish themselves rapidly. Many Americans, including children, a German university professor's son, a French grocer and others have already injured or killed themselves when experimenting with this device.

Political or a less definite kind of grudge against society or an individual may be a strong motive for *arson by juveniles*, but it is only one of many. A twelve-year-old Austrian girl, in her insane anxiety about a bad school report in 1969, started fires in her classroom. She hoped in vain that the report would be burnt. She was taken suffering from shock to a Viennese hospital. Perhaps a little more attention to the child in time would have saved her from being driven to committing arson, a memory she might suffer from for life.

School fires are fairly frequent in most Western countries with the notable exception of Germany where, as a Munich policeman said, 'the sight of a burning school is as uncommon as that of a lion walking down Leopoldstrasse'. (With an afterthought, he then added that 'lion' was perhaps an unfortunate choice because 'most youths with their long bushy mane and animalistic ferocity' are now 'worse than a lion let loose on a city'. He was probably suffering from the hysteria that turned 'every long-haired intellectual' into a natural suspect at the time of the Berlin bomb-campaign.)

In most cases of school fires and outbreaks of juvenile vandalism, a considerable responsibility of parents and teachers is clearly indicated. A conference at Purdue University, which found that in some American areas juvenile arson had become the number two cause of all fires, also blamed witnesses and members of the public who often refuse to cooperate with arson investigators, and officials who tend to ignore the magnitude of the problem. They ought to have added many judges to this list, and the lawyers who, even in defence, condemn the 'scandalous and reckless' behaviour of youths without saying a single harsh word against family background and social circumstances that have instilled frustration, insecurity, and a senseless, escapist urge of destruction in these wretched culprit-victims. When in Clarksburg, West Virginia, two boys were caught robbing and setting fire to a flower shop, the police described them as 'real hardened criminals'. The boys were aged seven and ten.

In a staggering multitude of case histories, arsonist children admit that sheer boredom was the ultimate motive for vandalism. Reports show scores of fires started by children in industrial plants in one metropolis or another as revenge, because the management or some minor dictator has forbidden them to play in the factory yard or in some quiet backstreet adjoining the premises even though these are the only open spaces within a radius of several miles.

When young men are brought to court for arson, it is not the best line of defence—but that is why it has an amplified ring of truth—that 'there was just nothing, nothing to do'. Nobody could think of anything. Then somebody thought of fire. Suddenly there were flames and excitement to watch. Priceless paintings, buildings, barns were destroyed like that. Three young workers of the British Ford factory, Dagenham, roamed about together during their breaks in the night shift. In their aimless wanderings, they started fires. They put a match to rubbish or lit a roll of cardboard and threw it through a window. In December 1970, each was sent to prison for three years for malicious incendiarism. They claimed there was no malice in them: 'we were only skylarking. We had no intention of hurting anyone.' They blamed the 'unutterable boredom' of the assembly line. One had tried his hardest to rid himself of his feeling of tedium and had unsuccessfully applied to join the police.

It is no excuse, but it is not much of a life when the only fun is to strike a match.

Next to this desperate striving after excitement is another motive for arson: the dream of becoming a *hero*. This motive knows no age limit. The word 'hero' does not necessarily imply world-wide recognition. A tragic example occurred in Memphis, Tennessee. Six girls between the ages of twelve and fifteen, all of Fairview Junior High School, read about 'Teen-Age Gangs' in a magazine. They decided to organize their own gang and call it 'Corpus Debs' Club. The idea was to admit only heroes— hero meaning anybody who could create a big sensation. For their own act of heroism, they chose to burn down the Cattle Exhibit Building on the fair grounds near the school, because they felt this would 'create more of a sensation than anything else they could do'. The fire in 1955 caused a loss of $109,000.

The most usual victims of this thwarted hero complex are night watchmen who try to earn praise or even a reward for alertness and prompt reaction to the discovery of the fire, and firemen, particularly former or volunteer firemen, who hope to show off their fire-fighting prowess in public. In August 1969, when the liner *Queen Elizabeth* was berthed at Fort Everglades, Florida, as a floating tourist centre, a fire guard started three fires on board so that he could claim credit for discovering them. Firemen who become fire raisers often admit in an upsurge of shameless exhibitionism that 'I wanted to get the nozzle in my hand with everybody looking on and worrying about me' and that 'I wanted to perform heroic acts' particularly in the neighbourhood where girl friends or pals live. Young men who apply unsuccessfully to join the brigade, sometimes try to demonstrate that, say, bad eyesight should not have excluded them: they start a fire, raise the alarm, and risk their lives to put out the flames by the time the fire engines arrive. But perhaps the most tragi-comic fire was, in a way, caused by *good* fire prevention.

A twenty-four-year-old man took a job as works fireman at the Rolls-Royce factory near Glasgow, in 1965, because he thought it would be a glamorous and dangerous career. Instead he soon found himself bored and laughed at for sitting about dressed for a fire which never happened. So, on one of his tedious inspection rounds, he lit a fire in a refuse bin, returned to discover it a moment later, and put out the flames efficiently, with a show of heroic aplomb. A month later, he repeated the exercise. Yet another month later he set alight to some waste paper and continued his rounds intending to return and spot the flames within a few minutes. But this time he was delayed. The fire got out of hand and almost completely destroyed a building, packed with valuable equipment, causing an estimated damage of £1,225,000. He was gaoled for a year.

Arson may also be merely the by-product of some other crime. The motive then is *destruction of evidence*. It is used by many petty thieves, robbers, murderers and embezzlers. (In an English boarding school a teacher started two fires to divert attention from his homosexual activities—eleven indecent assaults on boys in the dormitory—and to give himself an aura of heroism by 'distinguishing himself in the face of an emergency'.)

All these criminals have one misapprehension in common: they believe that fire will always obliterate the traces of crime. Fortunately, they are often proved wrong. Ultra-violet photography of ashes, for instance, can reveal the secrets of books and papers which were burnt to hide forgeries or falsified accounts. This, however, presumes that the ashes will be subjected to specialist examination every time. But this is not usually the case. The fight against arson often falters at the detection level, particularly when the arsonist is successful in concealing his tracks and achieves complete devastation.

In countries where the initial investigation of fires does not necessarily involve the police—and this category includes some American states—the relationship between fire brigades and police forces leaves much to be desired. In Britain and Australia, firemen never hear about the outcome of most suspicious cases. The British Home Office circulates some information about police results in arson investigation, but most fire officers do not know and do not particularly care whether their initial suspicions were justified. In Germany, the fireman is automatically excluded: investigation is none of his business.

Los Angeles has one of the oldest American Arson Squads: it is part of the Fire Department, staffed by twenty-one specialists whose fearsome reputation is known to keep 'torches' away from their territory. But experience cannot quite make up for lack of time. In 1969, they handled 3,360 suspicious, undetermined and incendiary investigations. Considering that the section commander and his assistant must control the entire operation, the number of cases implies that each man had less than two days for a fire even if they all worked every day including Sundays and Christmas, nobody ever fell ill or took his annual holidays. The result? The arrest of 179 adults and 100 juveniles—but the

8

evidence was insufficient to get a conviction in every case. Assistant Section Commander Captain William McDaniel is convinced that extra manpower could drastically reduce arson by 'making insurance fraud an even less attractive proposition to hard-up individuals and professional criminals'.

The Australian state of Victoria has a population approaching the four million mark. The Victoria Police Department has an Arson Squad staffed by four detectives. They receive no specialist training apart from the general instructions given to all detectives, and they are expected to 'get the experience as they go'—except that they are usually transferred to other duties by the time they have got the knack of it. These men help out only in cases which baffle the local general detectives. When a former chief of this squad once gave a lecture, he admitted that his experience in 'the technical side of fires' was 'somewhat limited'. About the work-load he revealed figures showing that each of his men had to handle an average of two hundred suspicious cases a year, supplying the expert knowledge the local detective in charge lacked.

The investigation of arson is not essentially different from any other fire investigation—the good fire detective approaches each outbreak as a potential case of incendiarism. Apart from looking for his number one suspect—more than one seat of fire— he examines the entire scene to discover all suspicious circumstances. How 'efficient' was the destruction? Who discovered and reported the fire? How did he see it? Why was he there? Was it possibly in anybody's interest to incur these particular losses? Have there been previous fires in the same place? If the cause seems to be spontaneous combustion, was there really such a risk there? Was there a substantial increase in insurance cover before the fire? Were stocks suddenly disposed of? Were valuables removed or animals released before the outbreak? Were account books and other documents destroyed? Was there any sign of forced entry? (A memorable example, leading to the owner's conviction, was the fire in a factory, where there was no clue to suggest a break-in, but the owner claimed that all doors had been bolted by him personally. One door bolt appeared to be discoloured by smoke evenly—in the open position. When it was moved to 'closed' position, a clean centre portion became visible proving that the metal staple in the middle had protected it from smoke during the blaze throughout which the bolt had been open.) Were the fire-doors tied open? Were the alarms or sprinklers turned off?

This is, of course, far from being a full initial questionnaire for the investigator, who then turns his attention to more specific clues. Looking constantly for the possibility of several unconnected fires that started simultaneously, and searching for evidence like materials and containers (for instance a petrol can) which are not normally kept in the building, he now must make a full appraisal of the fire: could it have been accidental? The colour of the flames, an unusual smell, witnesses, the first firemen at the scene will help him. Considering the natural hazards at the premises and the normal propagation of flames, did the fire spread with an unnatural speed and was the pattern of the fire from origin to inflammable contents a bit too ideal for complete destruction? The really clever arsonist who uses only an untraceable match and the cunning re-arrangement of only that fuel which belongs to the building, often gives himself away by being too clever and by having all the facilities of the 'perfect' crime—plenty of time, a good knowledge of the premises, the opportunity, the easy concealment of entry, etc.

The fire detective then tries to put himself in the role of the arsonist and follows his mental process. He knows the two essential requirements of the crime: (1) the means of starting the fire in a way which can be trusted more than a thrown-away match and which will build up heat surreptitiously (so that discovery will come too late); and (2) the means of spreading the flames fast all over the place, ensuring ignition of all in-flammables in the premises—an accelerant, which multiplies the first deadly triangle.

Devices in the armoury of the arsonist vary a great deal. Only amateurs would make the mistake of the man who died in a recent fire in France: the case is still *sub judice*, but it appears that the aim of the fire was a large insurance claim; after the building had been soaked in petrol, the man entered and, using some rolled newspapers as a torch, he set light to it; the house 'went up like a bomb' and the man 'went with it'.

When a fire has to look like an accident, arsonists avoid the use of explosives, because they are noisy and leave too many obvious clues for the forensic scientist. The only exception is perhaps when even the explosion can be made to look like an accident. A favourite trick is to pile up paper around a drum of liquid fuel, like paint thinner, and light the paper. The heat will burst the well-filled drum, spray fuel on the fire and make the flames unextinguishable for quite a long time. The vapours inside the drum may bring the rupture about with a large explosion but if the arsonist is already away, and if the drum of fuel was legitimately in the building anyway, the investigators will have to rely on other clues to solve the crime.

Most arsonists are, however, in a hurry. The thrown-away cigarette is not a reliable source of ignition, but many criminals have made use of it with varying success, by attaching match-heads or two layers of paper-matches to it. Its delayed action gives the firebug up to ten minutes to escape. If the ignition is successful, it is difficult to trace the source although in some cases, ashes have been retrieved to give away the trick.

Candles are about the most commonly used timing device. The arsonist can even calculate how long the candle will take to burn down to the level where straw or other inflammable materials, including a celluloid tray full of liquid fuel, is waiting for the little flame (usually the bottle that held the candle, traces of wax and chemicals are the evidence for arson). A Canadian destructive genius placed several candles in a line like stairs and connected them with one another so that a fifteen-hour delay in the ignition of a building was achieved.*
In some other cases, the candle was placed on one dish of a pair of balanced scales: as the flame burned up the grease the dish rose gently, reaching, eventually, the fuel arranged above.

We have already seen two examples of the alarm-clock-triggered device, but there are many other methods, too. Army and wartime sabotage training have already been responsible for the expertise of numerous arsonists. Some secret agents' favourite method—pellet of percussion explosive fixed to hammer of alarm clock to start fire at preset time—has already spread to civilian use. Similarly, electricity is now used increasingly to produce the initial ignition. Sometimes it is the hand of a watch that eventually transmits current through a wire that heats the fuel nearby to ignition point.

---

* H. Rethoret: *Fire Investigations*, Recording & Statistical Corporation Limited, Toronto, 1945.

Many arsonists have tried to produce the essential spark through pre-arranged short circuits so that the innocent man who switches on the light or starts a machine will, in fact, start the fire; but the system was more ingenious than reliable, and aroused suspicions by the many traces it had left behind. In July 1956, there was a fire in a furniture factory at Perth Amboy, New Jersey. After a considerable amount of newspapers and excelsior had been found in the 'crawl space' of the attic, and a man behaved in a very suspicious manner (he tried to prevent firemen from chopping holes in the roof just over these piled-up inflammables), an executive confessed to having set the fire by using a five-inch yellow candle. Further examination of the seat of the fire produced no evidence of wax or wick, but a small pull chain switch for some fluorescent lights came under scrutiny: it was then discovered that the switch setting had been altered so that in the 'off' position two wires were automatically short-circuited starting a fire in the attic. More than fifty thousand dollars' insurance was at stake. The executive was sentenced to imprisonment but was placed on probation for two years and fined two thousand dollars.

Light-bulbs have caused many accidental fires and therefore investigators may have a difficult task when the arsonist chooses one of these as his source of ignition. Even a twenty-five or forty watt bulb can cause a fire, but fortunately, only in circumstances that leave tell-tale marks behind. The bulb must be wrapped in cheese-cloth or tissue paper and buried in material such as sawdust. Heat begins to build up immediately the lamp is switched on and the length of ignition time depends on the thickness of the wrapping which must nevertheless allow for sufficient ventilation. Swollen, misshapen bulbs, heavily stained glass fragments, and some electrical clues for the detectives make this an unpopular method.

To the trained chemist—and the competent arsonist—chemicals and their endless range of combinations are an inexhaustible fund of inflammable ideas. Most of these have the drawback that the recognition of arson and identification of the residues will help to achieve conviction and forestall insurance claims—whenever, or rather *if*, a properly thorough and expert investigation is conducted.

Some chemicals, like sodium, potassium, calcium and

sulphuric acid, react with water. Others like phosphorus, zinc ethyl and zinc methyl ignite on contact with air. In a Melbourne case, investigated by Inspector De Vere, such a chemical was immersed in water in a deep tray. A few small holes in the container let the water drip away gradually. When the chemical was eventually exposed to air, it flared up, igniting the fuel suspended within reach of the flames. A similar method, involving sticks of yellow phosphorus in a pin-holed balloon filled with water, has been used successfully in practically every country.

Perhaps the greatest ingenuity is displayed by arsonists in the use of various chemical combinations. Particularly in premises where the presence of chemicals is justified by normal industrial application, 'torches' suspend acid in a metallic container above a chemical mixture in a tray. Depending on how thick the bottom of the container is, the acid eats through the metal after a varying period of time, then flows into the mixture below and starts a fire with a tremendous heat output. The combination of a chlorate and icing sugar was used in a bowl below a telephone: sulphuric acid was placed in a small balloon in the path of the hammer of a telephone bell—when the call was made, the hammer burst the balloon, and the acid dropped into the bowl. A third variety was employed by the arsonist who filled a container with two chemicals that create auto-ignition on contact. To delay this reaction, he separated the two parts by an animal membrane which was slowly eaten away by one of the chemicals until contact and ignition became possible.

If the arsonist is clever, his choice of ignition method will also depend on the special circumstances, his knowledge of the premises, the available natural fuel and the most likely natural propagation of flames, the route of spread, in a given building. These factors, and his specialist feel for the behaviour of fire, will influence him in making the decision *where* to start the conflagration. His three main objectives are to *mislead the investigators* (to set the fire in the vicinity of everyday hazards like heaters, trash accumulations or electrical installations has obvious advantages in providing clues to allay suspicions and so camouflage the real cause); *to prevent discovery of the fire before enough heat has been produced to engulf the building* (wardrobes, for instance, with all their readily available fuel contents—not woollen clothes, of course—are attractive spots although their 'hide-out' qualities may be offset by the need for opening the doors to ensure proper ventilation) ; *and to assist the natural upward trend of spreading flames* (basements, with their rubbish, wiring and often unprotected walls are a favourite of arsonists partly because these have the entire building for fuel above the flames, and partly because deserted basements offer facilities also to the other two objectives, whereas attics will be the amateur's choice due to inexperience in kindling fires and perhaps easier access).

With the kindling of the first, perhaps delayed, flame at a well-chosen spot the arsonist's problems are not yet solved—he must now tackle the second essential attribute of success, the *rapid expansion* of the initial fire triangle. Although an abundance of inflammable materials, furniture, wooden structures and goods may be available as fuel everywhere around him, the arsonist knows that even paper, particularly the glossy heavy kind, may be very difficult to ignite and a closed book may long resist the fiercest flames. In order to reduce this resistance and speed up the destruction, he will start several fires and use *boosters or accelerants*—both of which expose him perhaps more than anything else to personal injuries and ultimate detection.

The best known booster is *thermit,* a mixture of aluminium and iron oxide, which can produce such an intense heat that many metals will melt and most other materials will burn in its path. (It also brings about chemical changes that leave an unmistakable residue for laboratory examination.)

The most commonly used accelerant is petrol because it is easy to get hold of in large quantities without arousing suspicion, and because it is very effective : in a recent American arson case, two quarts of it were enough to engulf totally a two-storey building in flames in ten minutes. The arsonist may sprinkle much of the goods and structures with inflammable liquid accelerants like kerosene, wood or grain alcohol, some duplicator fluids (in offices) and paint thinners (in factories), just to mention a few ; or he will run 'trailers' like a length of tinder, hemp rope soaked in saltpetre, a train of newspapers or oily rags from his ignition device to the spot where most of his intended fuel is in its normal position.

Trapped gases, samples of the debris, soil and floor, the fire pattern, the rapidity of spread are, on the other hand, the investigators' weapons—if he chooses to make full use of them. Forensic laboratories can help him in many ways. Traces of petrol might have disappeared in the fire and fire-fighting, but the charred wood that contains petrol residue turns red when it is painted with a reagent. Spectrographic analysis can also reveal traces of petroleum products but the method is not yet used widely enough. Vapours are identified by gas-liquid chromatography. The 'explosimeter', a portable gas and fume detector, now helps some of the most advanced American arson squads to spot traces of accelerants in the debris, but this useful gadget is still virtually unknown to the majority of fire detectives elsewhere.

Accelerants, particularly if they are volatile like petrol, create explosions rather rapidly, and lean or rich mixtures—an excess or shortage of air added to vaporous fuel—leave clearly identifiable 'foot prints'. (If the mixture is rich, for instance, the explosion will be less destructive, there will be more soot deposits and heat, leading to fire due to surplus fuel.)

On the whole, one can understand the French firebug who exclaimed during criminal court proceedings in 1968: 'Everybody [presumably, in the underworld] envies me . . . They all think that arson is easy, that all you do is put a match to a house and throw in some petrol for good measure . . . They're wrong! This is a profession! You must know what you're doing or you're the first to burn.'

It would be so satisfying to add a note of reassurance to the public and declare sternly, 'Arsonists beware! Fire detectives will surely catch all of you!'—but people would only be driven to the security of a fool's paradise, and arsonists would be driven to laughter. They know what the study on behalf of the British Home Office has now confirmed and what is painfully true in every country—that the *initial decision* about a possibly suspicious fire is left entirely to experienced but scientifically untrained investigators. Although scientific assistance is generally known to be essential, this help is not available readily enough. 'The outcome of this is that the more subtle forms of incendiarism may go undetected,' and many arson cases are mistaken for accidental fires or are recorded as 'cause unknown'. And even if not every positively identified arson case can lead to successful prosecution, full knowledge of the case would reveal the fire-bug's 'handwriting' to the investigator, a clue which can be more essential than fingerprints in tracking down the profes-sional 'torch'—and the pyromaniac.

CHAPTER THIRTEEN

THE URGE TO BURN

'OH, MAMA, burn, burn! Burn, it feels so good I can hardly stand it!' The well-dressed, middle-aged man who mumbled these words during a recent Chicago warehouse fire, gradually worked himself into a frenzy. When the flames broke through the roof roaring as they soared, until they seemed to singe the clouds, the man began to moan in ecstasy.

Onlookers warned the Fire Chief in charge who called the police. The man was arrested on suspicious behaviour. Answering the first question, he readily admitted that he had started this fire—and another fourteen. For several months, the police tried to verify his stories of incendiarism: many of these wretched characters like to boast about their exploits. This man could prove only nine of his 'successes'. He claimed that he had first set a few fires when he was a teenager and girls ignored him because of his pimpled face and slight stutter which became much worse when he felt excited or embarrassed. In his late forties, he became impotent. He started fires to vent his frustration and found that 'a good hot blaze not only made me a man once again but gave me the sexual power to go on and on with women like a male nymphomaniac'.

He was committed to a mental institution where he confided to a psychiatrist that his mother had died in their burning home while rescuing him from his cot. Although he was only a toddler at the time, he could give very vivid descriptions of the scene. This, again, might have been a lie: it was verified that he had lost his mother very early, but the circumstances of her death were not clearly established and the fire might have been his delusion.

A similar fantasy haunts a seventeen-year-old girl who will eventually inherit several million dollars. The money will be put in trust for her while she must remain in a private mental home—probably for life. She is in constant mourning for her mother who is alive and well and comes to visit her in San Francisco every week. The psychiatrist in charge of the home obtained permission from the parents for this author to meet the girl.

This pleasant, slim blonde, her hair cropped to an almost short-back-and-sides, and her cheap, black, self-sewn mini-skirt and jacket of some rough denim, brutally contrasted with the luxury of the home, the softness of the leather arm-chairs and couch in the consulting room, the elaborate hair-do of some nursing staff, and the genuine baroque furniture of her own choice in her room.

She chose an uncomfortable stool in the consulting room, and perched on its edge throughout the interview with her psychiatrist. At first she appeared perfectly normal. She chatted about food, complained about the quality of the lobster she had for lunch, paid no attention to the little flame as the psychiatrist lit his pipe, and began to talk about the school which she had to leave as she could not keep up with the rest of the class. (She was slightly retarded as a child, but it was hoped that through care and private tuition she would catch up with her generation.)

'My mother, God bless her, if only she stayed alive . . . She still comes to see me in my dream. She always tells me I'm O.K. Nothing wrong, my baby. It's only that she doesn't come when I call her.'

She paused and the psychiatrist lit his pipe once again. She now watched the lighter and seemed to emanate a touch of sorrow when the lighter clicked shut and the flame disappeared. 'I just called her and called her, and then Rock came. He was good to me.'

'Rock' was her nickname for the twenty-six-year-old man who watched—possibly started—the fire in a house where she was holidaying in Italy and from where she fled, chased by the flames, to the adjoining bushes. He caught her there and raped her. She was twelve years old. She claims quite adamantly that everything happened with her consent, but it is on record that she was found wandering, screaming hysterically, some eight miles away in the morning.

'I called Mother but Rock came,' she repeated. 'The flames

made his face electric. He burned so beautifully.' Slowly, without the slightest inhibition, her hand slid up her knee and disappeared between her thighs under the skirt. From then on, she masturbated throughout the conversation, apparently without reaching an orgasm. Her monotonous voice and stony face remained totally unaffected.

She and the psychiatrist pieced together her story almost as though they were doing a routine double-act. They must have been through it many times before. Her occasional incoherence showed lapses in her memory and sense of time.

According to the parents, Rock abducted her. She insists she went with him of her own free will because only he loved her now that her 'mother was dead'. The parents were desperate to keep her name out of the press.* They employed scores of private detectives who searched in vain for the girl in fourteen countries for three years.

'We travelled by foot or by car. Rock had so many cars. Every time we went somewhere we had a different car. But he didn't want to kiss me. He told me to play with myself if I needed sex. So did he. Only when we sat at that log-fire did he love me again. Then he rushed home and said I must go with him. A big, big, big house was burning. And the fire engines came. That beautiful noise. And all those electric men all red and glowing. And Rock climbed down through a window into a cellar and helped me down and the lights danced on the walls all around us and the warmth came in and water trickled down from all those hoses and Rock loved me again and he didn't tell me to play with myself and he put those hot flames right inside me . . .'

She paused for about ten minutes with an expressionless face like a mask in a Chinese opera. She pushed her body forward every now and again to assist her hand. 'I loved Germany. People smiled at me,' she added suddenly. 'And the forests are warm and red and Rock told me I should sing "Oyveh es brennt" [Oh, it's burning] to the tune of the sirens.'

The route they took from country to country and town to town has never been precisely traced. Nor is it known how they managed to cross frontiers. But wherever they stayed, they

* For the sake of all those involved, and in agreement with the psychiatrist, several details of this case history had to be omitted or concealed in order to avoid identification.

started fires, although it is impossible to tell with any accuracy if this was only his doing or if she assisted him. In the mental home she has never made any determined attempt to set fire to anything. As a precaution, all her clothes, furniture and personal belongings are specially impregnated to increase flame-resistance. She is never left alone for any appreciable time during the day, and at night, a nurse keeps an eye on her with the aid of a two-way mirror.

In the last few months of their wanderings, the couple developed a set routine. They would take a room in a small hotel or boarding house and spend their days sizing up a building opposite their window. Then they would start a fire there, watch the flames and fire-fighting from their room with a grandstand view—'Rock is so good to me . . . He always comes to me from behind so that I can watch everything with him.'

It is not known where or how they obtained money. The probable explanation is that he was a burglar who stole everything they needed just as he took cars for single journeys.

The end of their rampage came at a small fishing village. It was winter and they moved into a deserted holiday villa. He prepared to burn the church just across the road. But he forgot it was Christmas: all the villagers seemed to be in the church for the midnight mass. 'Rock was angry. He likes people. He never harms anybody, never. But he was angry and I wanted him. We started just a little fire in our room. It was lovely. And hot. And we danced around with a burning cross which was on the wall because it was Christmas. It was so good.'

She started another sentence but interrupted herself saying: 'I must go. Rock always says we must not stay long,' and she walked out.

The psychiatrist finished her story. Apparently, they started at least eight fires in the room. She sometimes says that they made love in the circle of flames, but her recollections are very vague. She does not know how she got out of the burning house. She was found at dawn well outside the village, perched on a stone, dazed. She had a few small burns on her body but not on her clothes, which suggests that she suffered her injuries in the nude. 'Rock' was found naked and dead in the smouldering ruins of the house. He was burnt beyond identification. A local paper reported 'Vagrant Punished by Flames'.

Sexual stimulation is, of course, not the sole motivation of pathological fire-setting. About the various categories of mental illness of which incendiarism is a symptom, and about the pathological classification of individual patients, there is a great deal of controversy among psychiatrists. Some even argue that there is no such disease as 'pyromania'. Without trying to participate in their dispute or adding to the semantic confusion about words like 'firebug' and 'pyromaniac', one can venture to state that pathological fire-setters hardly ever fall clearly into one category or another; and that some of them are insane, completely out of touch with reality (the girl in San Francisco was basically termed a paranoid schizophrenic), while others are psychoneurotics or psychopaths hovering on or just about crossing the vaguely drawn border-line between sanity and insanity.*

Real pyromania is part of the psychoneurotic group (functional nervous or mental disorders) which is usually divided under three headings—neurasthenia, hysteria and psychasthenia. It is the latter to which a great variety of manias and phobias belong. Some of them are quite harmless, many of them are tremendously widespread, most of them are not regarded as insanity because the sufferers usually know what they are doing, that what they are doing is wrong, but do it just the same to escape from inexplicable fear, panic, pent-up anxiety or unnerving impulses.

Compulsive hand-washers, picture-straighteners, ashtray-cleaners, door-knob polishers are the mildest forms in the mania range. Others like kleptomania, the urge to steal without a purpose, dipsomania, the periodic craving for alcohol, nymphomania, an insatiable sexual desire in women, are much more dangerous and approach the other end of the scale where homicidal mania, the urge to kill, can be found. Among the phobias the best-known are claustrophobia, the dread of confined spaces like a room or aeroplane, hydrophobia, the uncontrollable fear of pools, ponds, rivers and the sea, and xenophobia, a morbid fear of strangers.

Pyromania belongs in this notorious company. Its victims can relieve their anxieties and neurosis only by yielding to their

---

* We shall adhere to the apparently standard terms for the various groups, but there is no universal consistency in their usage.

impulses for incendiarism. Their motivation can be as varied as their background and the pressures under which they initially cracked. Some policemen and fire investigators seem to believe that 'all pyromaniacs are also masturbators' (as if the latter was a crime), which is, of course, sheer nonsense. It is true that many pyromaniacs are sexually stimulated by fires, and to some a blaze is a straight substitute for the sexual act; but to the majority the sexual experience is, if anything, only a fringe benefit. Imprisonment does not cure them, psychiatric treatment might. The real motivation of the fire-setter, like the cause of many mental illnesses, is buried somewhere deep in his past and circumstances.

Take the man who burned Catholic churches and surgeries. Psychiatrists found he bore a vicious hatred of his father who was a doctor and a Catholic and had left the family for another woman. Or the man who was abandoned by his parents at the age of six: he became a firebug when his wife left him. Many cannot explain why they have the urge to burn something. Some just 'want to see the flames', others merely 'want to hear the fire engines', and there have been a few who confessed, 'I simply must start a fire whenever I see notices like "Highly Inflammable" or "Avoid Naked Light"—it's a sort of come-on to me.'

Are they truly insane? The main difference between them and those like the Swiss telephone operator cited in the previous chapter, who set fires in revenge, may be revealed by no more than the symptomatic regularity and frequency of incendiarism.

In 1969, the British police caught a thirty-five-year-old man suspected of arson. He was taken to the police station and it was there that he had the first real meal in his life. Until then, his mother had kept him on tins of baby food alone. As a child he suffered from a stomach complaint. His mother, now seventy-eight years old, found it safer not to change his diet later on. After his father's death, his sole purpose in life seemed to be to stay at home and look after her. In her over-zealous protective compulsion she warned him that he would be dismissed from home if she found him drinking, smoking or getting involved in sexual activity. Mother wanted to give him a strictly religious sheltered life, controlled their money and sent him out shopping with a precise list and the exact amount necessary to buy what

she needed. Between March and October 1968, he started
eleven fires about which he made entries in his diary. He was
put on probation for three years on condition that he submitted
to psychiatric hospital treatment for twelve months.

Few women are pyromaniacs. A strange exception was the
American girl who started fires in deserted buildings in the
Texan area where her boy friend served as a volunteer fireman.
She saw his fire-fighting, the nozzle spurting water over the
flames, as a natural extension of his sexual prowess. A police
investigator became suspicious of her when he spotted her in the
crowd of onlookers as she was going through a bump-and-grind
routine of go-go girls. She was found guilty of starting several
fires and remanded for psychiatric treatment. It then emerged
that she had a recurring erotic dream of her boy friend mastur-
bating over her and semen flowing like water from the fire hose.

Sometimes a man's hero complex, the desire to be seen as a
courageous fire-fighter, is coupled with pyromania. In 1957, a
twenty-two-year-old volunteer fireman was arrested in Montgomery County, Pennsylvania and charged with arson. He
confessed to having started three large dairy barn fires involving a combined damage of $90,000. With a little more care
he could have been prevented from committing these crimes: it
was known to the police that he had been setting fires from the
age of five when he had burnt down his parents' home; in 1948,
at the age of thirteen, he started two large fires, with $100,000
damage, in a children's home occupied by more than a hundred
people, in Yonkers; he was then caught and sent to a school for
juvenile delinquents; later he spent seven years in a State
mental hospital where he started two fires; and just before he
was accepted as a fireman, he was confined to another mental
hospital for a short time.

Many pyromaniacs suffer from ultimately self-destroying
impulses to obtain mental relief. Perhaps the best example of
this was the twenty-year-old American who was caught in 1954
at the end of a long and painstaking investigation. He started
scores of fires and committed at least thirty burglaries in Bucks
County, Pennsylvania. He lived in an attic where police found
several hundred boxes containing items later identified as
stolen. Nothing was missing, he never used or sold what he had
'collected'. Each box was numbered and this code was shown

with a list of contents against an entry of origin (name and address of each house he had burgled) in a meticulously kept looseleaf-type book. He readily admitted all burglaries and fires. For his kleptomania he could offer no explanation. About his pyromania he confessed that fire had fascinated him from a very early age. He was an excellent student, never associated with girls, and lived out his sexual fantasies with the aid of his collection of several hundred books, magazines and pamphlets on sex. At about the age of seventeen, he discovered that the sight of flames and the sound of fire engines gave him sexual stimulation and occasional satisfaction. His favourite pastime was to look through the boxes and remember fires and burglaries.

In the same year, another young American, student son of a university professor, was discovered to be a kleptomaniac, pyromaniac (he burned down the chapel at Beloit College, Wisconsin, causing a quarter of a million dollars damage), and possessed by additional homicidal and suicidal tendencies (he slept with a large knife under his pillow and he contemplated burying it in his father's back). Once again, his case proved that pyromania is not tied in any way to low intelligence—suggested by some fire investigators—because his I.Q. was two hundred, higher than Einstein's.

It is often argued that sexual motivations in pyromania are due to a connection between fires and early sexual experiences in childhood. This was borne out by a Columbia University research project which involved the study of 1,145 American case histories (all males over the age of fifteen), and by the examples of hundreds of pyromaniacs elsewhere. In Germany, for instance, a thirty-four-year-old man has recently been arrested for setting small grass fires along a busy *autobahn*. The case is still under investigation, but it is alleged that he has been starting fires ever since the age of twelve when he witnessed his mother having intercourse with an American soldier in front of an open stove.

Many people become pyromaniacs when their grudge, frustration and real or imaginary grievance grows into a pathological hatred of certain sections of society. The woman who hates and burns prams because she cannot have children is a well-known type to be found all over the world. For similar reasons, others start fires in houses where children live. Some men have burnt prams and nurseries because they became jealous of their own babies with whom they had to share the love of their wives. Fifty-seven families at an Islington, London, housing estate, were terrorized by a series of fires for sixteen months. Their ordeal, including the discovery of disinfectant in the drinking water tank, ended in 1963 with the capture of a thirty-two-year-old arsonist who confessed that he 'only wanted to upset them' when he became envious of the happily married couples after his own marriage had broken up. Some pyromaniacs who burn only churches and religious objects, and others who 'hate all wealthy people' including owners of cars, simple gadgets or cheap equipment as ordinary even as a garden hose, also come into this category.

When courts, advised by psychiatrists, have to rule about the sanity or insanity of fire-raisers, the problems involved can be so complicated that many discrepancies result. There are several cases on record in which the same psychiatrist gave contradictory advice about the same arsonist in two court cases within a few months—first finding him insane and next pronouncing him mentally normal. Distinct from the pyromaniacs in this psycho-neurotic group, the recognition of subnormal behaviour is easier if the accused is *mentally defective* (idiot, imbecile, moron, feeble-minded and their variants), and the mental age of a baby, toddler or child is governing his actions. The same is true if the firebug belongs to the psychosis group, the truly insane, which includes the various types of schizophrenics, paranoiacs and others.

Most of these suffer from delusions and hallucinations, many live a horrible nightmare twenty-four hours a day, suffer from persecution complexes and start fires in imaginary self-defence after letters to the government and complaints to the police have failed to stop 'The Enemy' poisoning their food and gaining control of their minds by secret rays deflected into them from Venus. Paranoiacs, often successful in everyday life because they are capable of meticulous planning, conduct terror campaigns with ruthless precision (the 'mad bomber' of New York was an example) and often suffer delusions of power and grandeur. People in the final stages of syphilis may become arsonists when, believing themselves to be kings, Napoleon or a financial magnate, they start fires to demonstrate their infinite power. Alcoholics who have reached the state of delirium are also known to have burned down buildings deliberately in order to 'kill the snakes and mice crawling out of the walls'.

Finally, another difficult problem group, containing many fire-raisers, is that of the *psychopaths* who are emotionally unstable to a degree approaching the pathological but with no specific mental disorder. Many of the occasional arsonists, like the heroic fireman or the jealous wife, may come under this heading, and the fire-raiser with a psychopathic personality sometimes also turns out to be a victim of sexual deviations, for example bestiality or necrophilia.

From experience, a top-notch American investigator goes on to suggest that with 'sex firebugs' who obtain sexual excitement and satisfaction from watching fire 'you will *usually* find that they are also deviated in some other way'.* He also refers to the fact that a comparatively high percentage of homosexuals and lesbians have been found guilty of incendiarism, and that the records of the American Insurance Association revealed fire as a favourite weapon of homosexual revenge against both male and female partners, probably because of a frequent abhorrence of personal violence and a fear of personal injuries in direct attack. But, surely, the claim that, in looking for an arsonist, 'if you can round up the queers, the degenerates that might live in or near the area, you may get your man', is utter nonsense. This is an excellent method for finding scapegoats but not for protecting society from the mentally sick.

Tracking down the pyromaniac and the insane arsonist is a particularly complex and arduous exercise. It is disastrous that too many investigators lack the training for understanding these unfortunate people, not only because they have little or no compassion for the culprits but also because this is reflected by their high failure rate of detection.

One of the investigator's main difficulties is that the motive of fire-raising is missing. The pyromaniac may burn *anything*, *anywhere*, *any time*. But usually at least one of these three elements is fairly constant. Some may burn only cars or hay-stacks, others may start fires only in certain areas or buildings. The gradual emergence of a pattern may become visible to the careful

* *The Fire and Arson Investigator*, Vol. XIX, No. 2.

observer who, at the end, may be able to predict the next blaze.

The phases of the moon have long been suspected of having a bearing on the periodic frequency of incendiary fires. Britain's Fire Research Station compiled what could be called a 'statisti-kit' picture of the average fire-raiser for kicks. In 1968, on the basis of available records, the embodiment of the type appeared to be a male teenager who is most likely to strike on the seventh day after the new moon, most probably somewhere along the centre line stretching from Dorset to Yorkshire. The statistics show fairly consistently that the third day after the new moon is much less troublesome to the fire brigades than the seventh when they are kept exceptionally busy with burning hay-stacks and the like. It would certainly help investigators if this research project was repeated internationally because the figures from a much larger than merely British sample would then help to increase accuracy—or dismiss entirely the idea of any lunar connection with fires.

At least in one American case, the investigator's suspicion that an arsonist may be a 'lunatic' did help to solve a long mysterious series of fires. There was one fire after another in and around the peaceful Springfield Township, Pennsylvania, in 1955. One day two fires were started in a similar fashion, and another day there were five outbreaks. In all, there were twenty-two cases and it occurred to the investigators that the majority of them fell within the full-moon cycle. During the next full moon, special surveillance was arranged throughout the night, and a man was caught in the act of setting a fire. He was a twenty-four-year-old volunteer fireman who admitted being responsible for all the car, school, barn and field fires. His sanity was carefully evaluated. Despite the fact that while he served with the U.S. Army Signal Corps in Korea he suffered serious head injuries in a truck accident that killed four soldiers, he was found sane and sentenced to twenty years in the State Penitentiary.

In a recent French case, a brilliant piece of detective work has led to the arrest of an arsonist. It was observed that in a Paris suburb there were numerous fires for about a month— then the series came to an abrupt end. A week later, another series began in another suburb. Apparently, the arsonist moved on and on followed by a trail of destruction. A pattern began to emerge: all fires were started at dawn with some burning object thrown through a window, and in several cases a man hailed a cab nearby and was driven to a certain approximately square-mile area in town. Then for a couple of years his tracks were lost. Whether he stopped or followed a different pattern was not known. And then another series of outbreaks began. A watch was maintained from midnight to daylight and taxi drivers were warned. One morning a driver reported that he had taken a fare—a man in his pyjamas—from the vicinity of a fire to an address where the police duly found the suspect. When he was questioned, he immediately admitted, almost with relief, that yes, he did start all those fires because he could not resist the temptation, and the sight of the flames so aroused him erotically that, almost invariably, he had to visit his girl friend at once.

Whatever the pattern of these fires may be, one factor is common in all cases: the pyromaniac or the insane always stays on the spot to watch the flames. This is, after all, the motive of the act. Some of them are given away by their particular excitement, some by their trembling zeal to help man the fire hoses, some by their urge to rub against boys or girls or expose their genitals while enjoying the spectacle, while others have been caught because of their noticeably regular presence among onlookers at fires. This happened, for instance, when the Australian *Daily Mirror* carried the picture of a woman being rescued by firemen—in the background crowd a reader recognized a man who had been seen at various fires before, and police investigation led to the arrest of the arsonist.

In the early 1960's, the Melbourne Arson Squad investigated several small fires in the St. Kilda district. Most of these were in dark lanes where garden sheds and weatherboard houses were burnt. They could have been the work of several people. As there were more and more outbreaks, people in the area began to worry. But the area covered at least ten square miles and the Squad could not possibly patrol it all day and night.

Then some lodging houses were set alight. In most cases, the fires were started in wardrobes, using rubbish and bedclothes available on the spot for fuel. Often people were sleeping only a few feet away from the arsonist who had sneaked in and prepared the fire quickly, efficiently, and with increasing expertise.

There was no particular identifiable 'handwriting'. The firebug must have carried only matches—he used no accelerants. Yet the Squad suspected that as the fires had all been started in this manner and within that area, a single culprit could be responsible for the more than a hundred outbreaks of 'doubtful origin' which they now had on record.

There was no quick solution. All the cases were examined. Then a large wall map of the area was prepared, and on this the place and time of all fires were marked. Marking more blazes and more destruction was the painful duty of the investigators for another seven months. By that time they had more than two hundred cases on their hands and one of the fires had killed a sleeping child.

The first pattern to evolve concerned the timing of the fires: most of them were started between half past seven and eight o'clock in the evening with some outbreaks as late as nine o'clock. Then an investigator observed another pattern: most fires were started on Mondays. This promising discovery was, however, confused by a few fires (same area, same manner, same timing) discovered on other weekdays, breaking the 'after-Sunday' pattern. It was then that the patient observation paid off. An investigator noticed that these other weekdays followed public holidays in every case!

The final clue was in the frequency of the fires: it appeared that if the arsonist started one fire, he would start at least one other within an hour and possibly a third also nearby. The Arson Squad now ventured to predict the next day when fires would burn in St. Kilda. Following a public holiday, the Squad was reinforced by many extra policemen, and the ten square miles were patrolled closely although they had to keep out of sight so as not to frighten away their prey.

At 7.40 that evening, the control room for the operation was notified about a fire. The investigator, who reached the spot within minutes, confirmed that it might have been the work of the arsonist they were after. Thirty minutes later, there was a second outbreak about a mile away. The man slipped through the net once again but the Squad-men now saw the direction of his movement from the first fire. The net was tightened.

Only twenty minutes later, two miles away from the first fire, there was a third outbreak. As soon as the flames went up, the police closed in. A man was seen hurrying away. He had only three boxes of matches on him—but his fingerprints were found in the last building where the flames had had no time to obliterate the evidence.

He was a pitiful little man, a French migrant, quite intelligent with reasonably good English, who had made no friends in Australia, had an empty, isolated life, and a grudge against society due to his own misery rather than any particular grievance. Flames both frightened and fascinated him. He confessed to having started more than forty fires, but denied responsibility for the one in which the child was killed. The police had no evidence to convict in that case. As soon as he was arrested, the long series of outbreaks ended. Only one question remained : why did he go on his usual rampage always the day after a holiday? The explanation was simple, he gave it himself : on weekdays, at work, people were friendly to him, he had hopes that his life had perhaps reached a turning point ; then came a lonely Sunday or, worse, a long holiday, without speaking a word to anyone, just brooding alone with all his pent-up anxieties and fire-fantasies of revenge. Is this insanity? Was he alone responsible?

CHAPTER FOURTEEN

BLACK FRIDAY: THE EARTH ALIGHT

KIM NOVAK rushed home from the film studio, dressed for the occasion—slacks, boots, a shirt, no bra—and grabbed a garden hose to soak down her $200,000 home, but the strenuous effort did not prevent her from sparing a few smiles for the gathering photographers. Yet the scene was not part of some well-planned gigantic Hollywood stunt. The dollar-paved hills around Los Angeles were burning. The devastating brush fire disregarded the exclusiveness of Bel Air and Brentwood, and the world came to learn how black the smoke of burning mink is.

Stars like Joan Fontaine and Cliff Robertson were already homeless. Burt Lancaster stared at a mailbox, an exercise bicycle and a set of smouldering barbells—all that was left of his $500,000 house—and swore that 'no fire, nothing will drive me away. I'm going to rebuild it brick by brick'. Zsa Zsa Gabor searched frantically for the ashes of her Picasso, four Toulouse-Lautrecs, and Ming china. And a man—presumably with somewhat limited experience of fires, wars and other disasters—declared:

'I have seen trouble all over the world, but nothing like this.'

His name was Richard Nixon. Then a former Vice President, he rescued from his threatened rented villa only the manuscript of his memoirs and a taped account of his Moscow 'kitchen-debate' with Khrushchev. His house was spared by the flames, but 447 treasure-packed mansions (rock bottom price $50,000 at the time) went up in smoke, leaving behind insurance claims amounting to twenty-four million dollars and a star-studded cast of refugees.

This happened in 1961. It was a disaster, no doubt, but it was soon forgotten: tragic, merciless brush fires are an almost annual

event in Southern California. Most of them are caused by carelessness, some by arson and others by negligence. In this case,
for instance, several law-suits were filed against Los Angeles
City Council alleging that the city was negligent in allowing a
rotten tree to fall and cut a power line, thus starting a fire. (This
is how Aldous Huxley's widow was awarded $48,000 in an out-
of-court settlement eight years after the fire for the destruction
of her home valued at $160,000.)

The menace to individuals and the damage to countries from
the most fire-prone areas is tremendous. Forest and brush fires
cost the United States alone in excess of a thousand million
dollars a year, and Southern California in particular has a
climate that invites disaster with its long rainless spells, dust-dry
countryside, low humidity and fast winds. One can pick almost
any year for examples. Take 1959 : on January 2, after no rain
for three months and only half an inch in July, the wind raced
a fire at fifty miles per hour in Topanga Canyon, in the Santa
Monica mountains, destroying a hundred houses, while another fire, in the Benedict Canyon, burnt eighty houses causing
the evacuation of 4,000 people; the two fires scorched 11,000
acres. In March 1964, brush fires attacked Los Angeles on a
twelve-mile front. In August 1969, some desert towns had a
record temperature of 118° Fahrenheit (almost 48° Centigrade)
and fires blackened 45,000 acres of brush and grassland in a
single day.

1970 was a particularly bad year in Southern California. Late
in September dozens of fires got out of hand and ravaged the
area for more than a week. Within a couple of days, some
60,000 people had to be evacuated. There had been no significant rain for two hundred days. One major fire was probably
started by careless trash-burning near the glamorous Malibu
Beach. A firebug, allegedly seen starting five separate fires, was
sought by the authorities who were quick to arrest several
hippies fleeing from the worst-hit areas. Luxury homes were
burning once again. Part of Spahn's Movie Ranch, where
Charles Manson's killer tribe, the Satan's Slaves, used to live,
was partly destroyed. By the end of the week, eleven people
were dead and 350 were injured. 400 homes and 300 other
buildings were destroyed, and almost 600,000 acres of brush-
land were reduced to ashes. Two years earlier, unusually heavy

rains had nourished the undergrowth—now this powder-dry
fuel, some thirty tons per acre, generated the amount of heat
energy estimated to equal 12,500 Hiroshima bombs. In the Las
Virgenes Canyon, the flames spread across fifty acres in five
minutes. A 10,000-feet-high pall of smoke hung above Los
Angeles and nothing could stop the blaze in the hills until the
hot seasonal gale-force Santa Ana winds from the desert dropped
and slackened the pace of the inferno.

If the Californian 'paradise on earth', which attracts the
highest rate of annual immigration, can turn into a land of
horror overnight, what nightmarish imagery can even attempt
to describe the conditions when hell itself is let loose on the
Australian bush?

More than a million square miles of Australian countryside
are susceptible to bush fires. In an average summer, about a
million acres are laid waste with practically all life wiped out.
The state of Victoria, with its climate and vegetation, is probably
the *most dangerous area in the world*. Its eucalyptus forests contain
about 150 tons of fuel per acre—five times as much as the
land around Los Angeles. This is the continent where a strange
anomaly in human behaviour is best demonstrated: while it is
true that about ninety per cent of all bush-fires are caused by
people (with the rest brought about by lightning and spontaneous combustion), it is the highly responsible attitude of the
Australians that prevents more frequent and more tragic
disasters.

In the second half of the nineteenth century and the first
decades of the twentieth, the general prospect looked rather
bleak. Immigration was increasing fast, the lure of gold and
land populated forlorn bush-country with potential peripatetic
fire-risks. It often seemed that people were helpless when they
came face to face with the infernal force. Only their stubborn
determination made them build again and again upon the
ashen land. More people meant more fires, and more deaths in
each outbreak. That was the situation in Victoria when the
year 1939 began and January 13, a Friday, approached.

Numerous fires had been burning ever since December. After
a long drought, it was now a hot, dry summer. Around Christmas, the once rich plains lay bare and baking. The forests were
tinder at the foothills, at alpine heights, everywhere. The once

moist carpet of the forest floor crackled painfully underfoot.
Hot winds rose in January. Water reserves began to run low.
Creeks and springs stopped running. Riverbeds were exposed
and their slimy skins cracked into jigsaw puzzles.

A depressing sense of dreaded expectancy settled like a cloud
over the state. Hardly anybody was prepared to face the peril—
even fewer people knew what could be done. There were only a
few firemen, no fire-breaks or protective clearings, no water
conservation, no planned prevention, no policy, no policing of
the regulations such as existed. The law was 'so notoriously
unpopular, because it is unreasonable and inflexible, that there
is no public opinion to check an intending law breaker'.*
Children grew up with contempt for the unjust and wholly
inadequate legislation. The Forests Commission was regarded
generally as the fire warden. This was a misconception due to
the fact that, in certain danger periods of the year, its forest
officers had to grant permission to all who wanted to light fires.
Many settlers had never heard that they needed permission.
Others were much more experienced in the matter than these
officers who frequently refused permission only so as to shun
responsibility.

Many forest officers were young men without any particular
zeal for fire prevention, often seeking the friendship of people
whom they were supposed to control. There were clear examples
that sometimes their guesswork substituted for the experience
they lacked. An officer visited two saw-mills and was dissatisfied
with the state of prevention even by the insufficient standard of
requirements, but he only shrugged his shoulders because he
considered his district was safe and would not burn in the way
it did only a few days later.

So people went about their business as usual. Settlers burned
off for growth or clearing, graziers burned land to promote grass
growth, miners used fire to prepare ground for prospecting and
operations, campers cooked among the trees, tourists burnt
passages through the bush, sparks jumped freely from saw-mills,
engines, and locomotives with defective spark arresters. Many
small fires were fought until they were regarded as being under

* From the investigation Report of the Royal Commission, 1939, which, together
with various documents and eye-witness accounts, formed the basis of this harrowing tale.

control—when they were not. Others were just left alone. If
only they were more superstitious . . .

Friday, the 13th, brought a gale-force wind. It blew the small
fires together and the state was alight from end to end. The sun
came up and shade temperature in Melbourne reached 114°
Fahrenheit, but the sun could not be seen for long: by midday,
most places were in total darkness under a thick blanket of
smoke and floating ash. It could not be dispersed even by the
wind that sometimes struck with so great a force that it blew out
hundreds of giant trees, complete with their roots to which tons
of soil and massive rocks adhered as they lay exposed to the
flames.

The fire leapt from one mountain top to another. Farms and
townships were thus attacked from all sides at once and annihilated within seconds. Men groped about in the darkness with
hurricane lamps trying to find a safe spot for their families before
the approaching front line of fire reached them. But by then
everything was so hot that a single piece of burning bark carried
by the wind made brick buildings explode into a flaming
furnace only to collapse into yet another black *whiff*.

More and more people were trapped. Some had the good
sense to make a run for it: they jumped into cars and had a good
head-start on the fire. The heat caught up with them as they
raced along highways but there was no sign of the inferno.
Many reached the safety of towns outside the bush. Others
never knew exactly what happened to them: a barn-size
fireball would appear from nowhere—if it dropped, it incinerated them on the spot or at once roused an impenetrable
sea of flames all around. These fireballs—the gas product of
pyrolysis, the chemical process of burning—travelled with great
speed on the wings of wind and air-currents created by the
immense heat, soared higher on the back of some up-draught,
and dropped like bombs with devastating effect, often far ahead
of the main fire.

Black Friday, as the day is now remembered, produced an
inexhaustible fund of miracles, tragedies, inventive heroism,
senseless self-sacrifice, the craze of joy and desperation. Men
at a mill made last-minute efforts at clearing the inflammable
scrub all round. They were late. All but one were burned to
death while trying like moles to burrow in the sawdust heap. At

a settlement a man submerged himself in a huge tank that held several thousand gallons of water. His remains were found on the dried floor of the tank only a few hours later. Fine men died trying to save children, horses and dogs. One man lived by the same act: everybody else ran and died when the flaming trees of the forest fell and blocked their route; he tried to free the horses from their stalls but they stood trembling and would not run— then the animals began to fall and bury him so that he survived under their burning bodies.

A policeman arranged sandbags along the main street of a small settlement. He turned on the hydrant, and the trickling water saved some two hundred people lying in the gutter. Railway workers saw a village burst into flames. They filled a gravel truck with water, drove it into the village, broke into burning houses where families huddled together for hopeless shelter, hurled women and children into the water and drove dozens of them to safety.

At a timber-mill, thick, solid planks were stacked fifteen feet high. A sudden breath of the fire raging some fifty feet away reduced it all to a four-inch layer of ashes. The men, who saw machinery melt into a red-hot mass, filled every container with water and then joined their families who had already retreated into a wooden hut which was fortunately surrounded by a vegetable garden. To fight the hundred-foot tongues of the flames reaching towards the hut, they took it in turns to rush out, shielded by a piece of roof-iron, and pour water on the walls. One man made the mistake of dropping his hot shield: a heat wave hit him and, although he managed to stumble back to safety, a box of matches burst into flames in his pocket.

The moonless night at noon had already swallowed the small township of Noojee, in the Gippsland forest country. The single branch-line across the inferno was still open but the prospect was that Noojee would soon be cut off completely. A railway official telephoned through at two o'clock urging the guard of the local train not to wait for the usual departure time at 3.10 but to leave at once. A few open trucks were quickly assembled and twenty-one women and children set out to race against the flames.

The area with its fishing streams some ninety miles east of Melbourne is now a favourite beauty spot. On Black Friday it was as red and uninviting as the lips of a dragon. The streams were dry and fried fish lay everywhere. The small train climbed the steep mountain-side slowly. The passengers were scorched by the heat and deafened by the tremendous roar of the fire which blanked out their shouts and screams. Flaming trees fell on the line but, miraculously, always behind them. Any tree-trunk in front would have been a death sentence.

There were bridges to cross: spanning deep ravines and gullies, balancing on slim wooden legs high up in the black air, each had to be inspected for safety. As the train stopped at the last ravine between the burning forest and hot but intact open country, there was no time to be careful—hungry red waves rolled right behind them. Arthur Amstead, the guard, took a quick look. The bridge seemed to be safe. They had to take a chance. The passengers closed their eyes and prayed. When the shaky clatter stopped below them, they knew they had reached safety. They looked back anxiously towards the blazing forest that separated them from friends and families still in the village. This is how they saw the bridge for the last time: only a couple of minutes later, mammoth tongues of flames snatched at the wooden frame and licked the metal of the line until nothing was left.

The remaining inhabitants of Noojee, about a hundred frightened souls, gathered in the narrow main street. The wooden hut that housed the post office was their last link with the outside world. News of disasters came ceaselessly. Post-mistress Gladys McIntosh kept calling isolated homes in the bush to give more warning, say good-bye and wish them good luck.

Graziers and mill-hands brought in their wedding rings and small savings. Perhaps the safe would take care of them. The roar of the fire got nearer and the first houses in the street went up in flames. People began to run towards their only refuge: the Latrobe river. Under a shower of sparks, burning fragments and hot ashes, they submerged themselves in the warm water and hoped it would not begin to boil.

Gladys McIntosh saw the flames, slammed the door and sent out a last telegraphic message: 'I am about to close down now, as the flames are licking the building. I have locked the valuables in the safe, and I am going to the creek. If the worst comes to the worst, you will find the keys of the safe and the office strapped to my wrist.'

The words of this brave woman made headlines everywhere in the war-worried press even before anybody knew that she survived Black Friday to be awarded, eventually, the Order of the British Empire.

It was a miracle that so many survived and *only* seventy-one lives were lost. 'Miracle is the only word for it—we were so helpless,' said Robert Seaton, then a district forester, now deputy Chairman of the Country Fire Authority, in Malvern, Victoria. Like most people who remember the day, he spoke with an indelible respect for the fire. 'Green Hills and Blackwood were my area. I dropped off some crew of fire-fighters behind the fire, and then drove along the bush track in my canvas-covered utility. The fire caught up with me on both sides but I took not much notice of it for I knew that, as usual, all I had to do was dive through the flank out of trouble. But then I saw that there was a mile-wide sea of flames beyond that flank. Bit of a dive it would have been. That's it, I thought to myself. I had no choice but to keep going and hope for a miracle. I reached the main road. Men fighting the fire out there didn't believe their eyes that somebody had come out of the forest alive.'

Most people just stood around in agony watching as a lifetime's work was obliterated in a few minutes. Men from the brigades fought till they collapsed, but the struggle was mostly to no avail. During the night the temperature dropped a little and, at dawn on Saturday, the wind began to blow itself out. The black blanket above was gently penetrated by sunshine. The inferno began to subside. Rain fell on Sunday. It washed away the merciful cover from the sight of death.

Sixty-nine mills were burnt to the ground. Townships were wiped out. Millions of acres of rich land and fine forests were destroyed in Victoria, New South Wales and South Australia. The soil itself was burnt to such a depth that it took years to recover. Machinery, steel girders and railway lines were twisted as if they were fine wire. Only the metal collar remained of a chained dog. A man, presumably hit by a fireball, was charred to death in 'frozen' speed as he ran—like one of the men cast in lava at Pompeii. The land was littered with corpses of men, cattle, horses, wallabies, kangaroos and deer. Dead sheep still stood compressed in corners of fenced-off ground. The redness of horror was replaced by the lasting blackness of grief.

But at least Black Friday was not forgotten. After a full investigation, laws were updated, law enforcement was tightened, a tremendous and still continuing propaganda campaign was mounted to warn people and teach them how to prevent fires and protect their families and homes, and a uniquely vast organization effort led to the establishment of the world's proportionately largest single fire-fighting force that has today 115,000 registered personnel (including auxiliaries) with 1,200 fire-fighting vehicles to protect 64,000 square miles.

This determined effort did not stamp out the perennial peril. The losses are still staggering. On the island of Tasmania, 'just across the water' (some 120 miles) people were caught unawares in 1967 almost as the Victorians had been in 1939: a bush fire disaster took sixty-two lives, injured hundreds of people and made 4,000 homeless, in addition to causing horrible devastation of land, industry, communications, and livestock including 50,000 sheep, 1,400 cattle and 25,000 poultry. (110 fire origins were identified and of these only twenty-two could have been started accidentally—the rest were lit deliberately 'in reasonably good faith, with little or no thought that they could cause considerable damage and even loss of life'.)*

There were many potentially catastrophic outbreaks in Victoria, in the Blue Mountains of New South Wales, and in the dense, high grass of Queensland, but on the whole, the unpreparedness of Tasmania was rather the exception than the rule, and even days of extreme danger with 253 separate outbreaks of fire in a limited area did not lead to a repetition of Black Friday.† This was no miracle, not even a matter of luck. Perhaps because the peril is most acute in Victoria, that is where probably most has been done about it. If only the rest of the world took sufficient notice of the painfully acquired Australian

* A. G. McArthur, Forest Research School, Canberra: paper presented at the Second Australian National Conference on Fire, at the University of Sydney in August 1968.

† January 8, 1969, was the worst day in Victoria. There were 253 fires, twenty-one of these assuming major proportions, but all were quickly spotted and controlled on the same day before they had a chance to join forces with the aid of the wind. Twenty-one people lost their lives but then, with the much greater density of population, a Black Friday would have claimed hundreds of lives.

know-how, hundreds of people would still be alive and multi-million losses would have been avoided in other fire-prone areas like California, the French Riviera, and Brazil, where forest fires got out of control in Parana and the conflagration, fed at a frightening rate on the richest coffee plantations, killed some three hundred people and made homeless a thousand times more in September 1963.

The Australians have reached a comparatively high level of safety through victories on four fronts:

(1) The establishment and development of the Country Fire Authority to coordinate and control the entire battle against fire all the year round. The CFA works out legislation, strategy and tactics, has a large, well-equipped operations room to direct state-wide activities on days of danger, helps to keep the Victoria emergency plan (for police, fire, ambulance and auxiliary services) up to date, puts into practice the results of research into methods of improving fire protection and prevention, trains and controls fire brigades—in all, it puts order in place of panic and strife.

The CFA is also responsible for partial and *total fire bans* on days of increased hazards. On the basis of reports from everywhere, they use an ingenious Grassland Fire Danger Meter—three cardboard discs pinned on top of one another*—which sets, in turn, the degree of curing against the temperature, relative humidity, and prevalent wind velocity. After two discs have been adjusted, the user just reads off the danger index (low, moderate, high, very high and extreme) and it even gives the likely rate of fire spread, which is invaluable to the fire-fighter. It is cheap, simple and effective. When one of these meters was shown to a few French fire-fighters on the Riviera, they were duly impressed; they said it was excellent and a pity that they had never seen it before, but unfortunately they then shrugged their shoulders and the matter was closed.

(2) The realization of the fact that prevention of the major bush and forest fires is a community task, and the efforts of the specialists will be effective only if they are fully backed up by all individuals. Needless to say, people still remain the major factor in starting fires, but now they cause disasters by acts of folly,

* Designed by A. G. McArthur in 1965.

9

criminal negligence and plain carelessness rather than utterly thoughtless ignorance.

(3) The third victory brought improved techniques and much more meticulous execution of protective measures, the most important of which is probably the careful preparation and clearing of firebreaks (fuel-free zones) early in spring.

(4) The introduction of forthright, nothing's-too-sacred investigation into the circumstances of each outbreak followed also by a *post mortem*, their word for an operations analysis. These do not set out to reprimand people for mistakes, but to learn from every plan, every battle, every skirmish and every move against the lifelong enemy.

In the light of this national effort in Australia, the French practice shows signs—and scars—of criminal negligence.

The South of France, particularly the Côte d'Azur, is a notorious forest- and brush-fire zone. The annual outbreaks not only destroy thousands of acres of rich woodland, olive groves, vineyards and gardens, but also upset the balance of nature: the scorched earth creates more dryness and higher temperatures which, in turn, increase the likelihood of more fires.

Each summer, French reports declare that this is 'the worst fire for ten/twenty/fifty years' (delete whichever not applicable). Firemen risk their lives and put up a heroic struggle, while the authorities are quick to look for suspects: pyromaniacs, yes, it must be their work . . . arsonists, surely it's they who did it . . . a youth has already confessed . . . a man is being interrogated . . . political extremists . . . juveniles . . . idiots . . . With a scapegoat already in custody, the public get ample reassurance. By the time the suspected criminal/maniac/anarchist is released, nobody remembers the case or the fire.

In mid-July 1970, fires fanned by a fifty miles per hour *mistral*, the wind from the north-west, devastated some 35,000 acres of forest, heath and farmland. 25,000 campers had to be evacuated, often abandoning all their belongings. On scanty evidence, a psychology lecturer was quickly arrested. The magistrate claimed that he was jailed at least partly for his own protection from lynching. The case immediately stirred up a ferocious political storm. The accused claimed the charge was part of a political vendetta, denied everything, and declared, 'I don't see why I would have started fires where there were already so many.' People talked about a 'new minor Dreyfus affair'. The fire was already forgotten. Six months later, the case, too, was forgotten when it was dismissed by a court in Draguignan, and the lecturer was acquitted.

Between arrest and acquittal, however, to the grave disappointment of those who hoped that one scapegoat would be enough for the year, there were other serious fires. Corsica, as in most summers, was still burning. The fires at Marseilles and near the Spanish border, which were thought to be 'under control' by the time the lecturer had been provided with an alibi as impenetrable as the walls of his gaol, flared up again when whipped by strong winds. Perhaps those in charge ought to have asked the Australians how little the words 'bush-fire under control' may mean. Another 10,000 acres were ravaged.

August brought some more fires, but then the summer mercifully drew to an end. Came October—and it happened again. Now the Var *département*, the region between Cannes and Toulon, was the worst hit. Eleven people were killed and at least twenty were badly burned. 15,000 acres of forest and moor, almost a hundred villas, electricity and telephone lines, were on the list of losses. In less than twenty-four hours, the outbreak was said to be under control (three firemen were dead), and in less than thirty hours, a youth who confessed to having started at least one fire with criminal intent, and a minor aged fourteen, were already under arrest.

Dr. Alain Bombard, an environmental scientist, gave immediate warning that if the horrifying process was not halted, great tracts of forests and valuable land would turn into desert and unimaginably worse fires would soon follow. He called for 'revolutionary solutions' like those used in Canada, where Quebec authorities drench the vast Laurentides Forest with 'artificial rain' every Saturday throughout the summer. Others spoke about the need for more air assistance to fire-fighting on the ground. (France already uses the Canadian system of 'water-bombing' very successfully. The bomb bay of 'Canadair' aircraft, a flying boat based on the Catalina model, is filled with water from the sea or nearby lakes and the 'bomb' pours down as a fine spray on burning or threatened areas. Allowing for refuelling and flights from and to water supplies, one Canadair can drop about 100,000 gallons of water in a single day if the sea or lake is near enough.)

But the main, already well-tried methods of prevention and protection were hardly mentioned. When, during the October outbreak, André Bord, Secretary of State in the French Ministry of the Interior, flew over the blazing area, he declared that only the creation of firebreaks and the introduction of regular patrolling could give real protection against the annual ferocious fires in the Var and Alpes-Maritimes regions along the Riviera and in the mountains behind. He made these solutions sound like novel ideas, as if the date was 1930 and not 1970, and as if France had to wait for her own Black Thursday—the day when the eleven people were killed. Regular patrolling, in order to discover fires at the earliest possible moment, would of course be easier in this densely populated area than in the Australian outback, but the use of spotter planes, now successfully employed in bush-country—not to mention satellite photography experimented with in America, and the 'eye in the sky' airborne television system to assist Australian bush fire fighting tacticians —does not yet appear to have occurred to those who give more reassurance than protection to the Côte d'Azur.

France and Spain are among the most popular holiday countries in Europe. Both have extremely fire-prone areas which are flooded with tourists at the height of the fire season. Yet both countries do very little about warning and educating their own population—let alone the tourist. And it is often the unsuspecting holiday-maker who gets the blame for outbreaks. At a meeting of the U.N. Food and Agriculture Organization in Rome on September 9, 1970, R. de Rada, assistant Director of Spain's Forestry Department, complained that 'too many tourists' (twenty-three million in 1970) were attracted to his country with a population of thirty-three million. In 1969, Spain lost some 50,000 acres of her national forests through fires, and he blamed careless tourists and campers for most of them. J. A. Spencer of the British Forestry Commission disagreed, because people in a crowd would control one another but the lone visitor would feel free to do as he pleased. In 1969, for instance, a young woman on a lonely hike in the mountains of Tucson, Arizona, started a 'signal fire' to call for help when she lost her way: the signal burnt some two hundred acres of scrub and oak trees.

Whoever is the more dangerous, the camping crowd or the lonely tourist, has it never occurred to the French and Spanish authorities to warn their visitors and teach them how to prevent fires as well as how to behave in one? How many motorists, town-dwellers from Düsseldorf, Manchester or Stockholm, would know which is better when driving through a blazing forest—to drive fast, stop and stay in the car, or get out of the car and run?

In the October 1970 Riviera fire, five of the victims came from one American family which had settled in Tanneron, a mountain village, seven years earlier. It was claimed eventually that all the inhabitants were warned to lock themselves in their homes and seal doors and windows against smoke: a sensible instruction particularly if there was already a fuel-free zone round the house, if shrubs and trees were kept well away from the walls, if a garden hose was already fitted and water was available, if the roof was in good repair, and if all other necessary advice was given repeatedly and long before the actual outbreak, so that it all had ample time to 'sink in' and alter the natural instincts of everybody in the household.

As it happens, the mother of the family was frightened to stay and decided to flee. She packed her four children—aged between two and ten—into the car and drove out of the village, by now encircled by flames. Probably in a dense cloud of smoke, she lost control of the car and crashed into a 150-foot deep ravine.

In Australia, a constant massive propaganda effort serves to teach the motorist—it really ought to be part of the driving test there, along with the highway code—that it is dangerous to drive on through smoke and flames when a definite path of escape cannot be seen. One wonders if this American woman was ever warned to stop, park the car away from trees, dry grass and scrub, stay in the car, close tightly all doors and windows, crouch on the floor, cover all occupants completely with coats or blankets, turn off the ignition and keep the headlights on. Probably she and most other people had never heard this advice. Just as residents and foreign motorists who tour fire-prone forest areas have never heard that more grass, bush and forest fires have probably been caused by faulty silencers than by care-lessly discarded cigarettes. (Once again, the Australian example shows that although it is illegal there to drive a car with a faulty silencer or a tractor without a standard spark arrester, all motor-vehicles are a constant menace because on a hot day the dry grass does not need much encouragement to burst into flames.)

Since the horrors of Black Friday, the world has learned a great deal about the bush and forest fire hazards—even if these lessons are not yet taken quite seriously everywhere. A great deal more research is still needed so that the techniques of prevention, protection, investigation, education and meteoro-logical forecasting could be improved (many crack brigades of fire-fighters have been caught on the wrong foot by sudden unforeseen changes in wind direction with tragic results). But until some twenty-first-century solution can give us much greater safety in the perilous regions, perhaps even carefree Riviera tourists—and permanent residents—will accept the view of Arthur Pitfield, Chief Officer of the CFA:

'Total fire bans on days of extreme danger can go a long way towards safety. It is always a very hard decision to put out such a ban, particularly in borderline cases. We don't like to cry wolf too often. We also know that a total ban on lighting fires in the open may cause a great deal of inconvenience—after all, it stops burning off, barbecuing, welding, and in principle any-body in the city of Melbourne could be charged for lighting a cigarette or throwing away one in the street during the ban. The penalty is stiff: a fine of two thousand dollars or two years' jail or both for breaking a total fire ban! If the forecast is wrong, and we put out a ban which then proves to have been unneces-sary, a lot of people are understandably upset. But what's the choice?'

CHAPTER FIFTEEN

THE CAN CARRIERS

THREE MILLION pounds' worth of complicated, top-secret radar and signal equipment was threatened with destruction when fire broke out at the Royal Air Force Neatishead station, near Norwich, an important link in Britain's defence system. The flames swept swiftly through the underground offices and nerve centre. If anything was to be saved, the firemen had to act fast.

Officers entered the inferno to investigate and size up the situation. All but one returned. It was suspected that if he had collapsed somewhere inside, he would have no chance against the killer fumes from the burning electrical installation, but to be sure he had to be found. Search parties with protective clothes and breathing apparatus were sent in. Some returned empty-handed. Others brought out the missing Divisional Officer—dead. Two men from the rescue party were still due to come out. The fire roared freely. Search was becoming not only dangerous but well-nigh impossible.

The two men had already been inside for some twenty minutes. Their oxygen reserve would last for about another ten minutes. One of them had a long service record and a great deal of experience. That was on what colleagues outside pinned their hopes for both of them. The other man was to be married only a week later.

County fire chiefs cannot afford to run out to fires every five minutes. They must trust their men on the spot. But on this occasion, Norfolk Chief Officer Robert Pearson was already there to assist and take the responsibility for whatever was to happen. He never forgot that cold February day in 1966, when he himself also went down sixty feet below ground and passed out two or three times.

The thirty minutes were up. Then another ten minutes passed. Every limit of the men's breathing apparatus had surely been exceeded. Chief Officer Pearson knew that only too well: his painful first-hand experience had told him that nobody could live that long in such a furnace. He also knew that to stop that blaze he would have to flood the entire underground station.

Short of a miracle there was nothing to wait for. But they had to wait. Flooding meant a formal death sentence on the two men—at least the irrevocable admission that they were given up as dead. To send more men, however well equipped, in search of the two would have been an unjustifiable gamble amounting to murder.

An hour had gone by. The two men must have been dead for at least half an hour. But knowing that and admitting it are very different propositions. The conflagration was now entering a critical phase. Everybody knew the flooding would have to be carried out. But when? The burden of making the actual decision is squarely on the shoulders of the highest ranking man on the spot. The Chief took a calculated and reasonable gamble—and waited for another thirty minutes. Then quietly, he gave the order: 'Start flooding.'

The pumps pushed cool water down the throat of the monster below until it could take no more and began to retch back dirty hot liquid, testifying to the conditions in the gutted belly of the station.

Much of the installation was saved. Then the pumps worked ceaselessly to get the water out. It took them two days. As soon as it was possible, firemen entered to recover the bodies. Apparently, the two, already dazed and confused, had groped around and entered a small telephone exchange room. A self-closing door then shut tight behind them. One man must have collapsed in there. The room was extensively damaged by heat and smoke. The other man must have found his way out somehow. He ran out of strength at the bottom of a staircase which, eventually, collapsed on top of him.

At Neatishead, it happened to be a county Chief who had to make the inevitable, nevertheless heartbreaking, decision. A man so high up the ladder now gets about £4,500 a year. Very often, similarly trying and character-testing decisions must be made by much lower ranking officers who are usually in charge of each outbreak at the beginning. These are the men who have to evaluate the peril, summon assistance if necessary, and deal with the most pressing critical problems that often present themselves in the early stages. These men are likely to earn less than £2,300 a year.

If these officers, their knowledge, experience, gallantry and judgement, are not worth more than a skilled craftsman or a foreman who is never asked to risk his life, then they should not be trusted with all the weight of making crucial decisions that affect life and death. Or else, if we have sufficient confidence in them to entrust them with our lives and wealth, they ought to be afforded the salary and status that kind of skill and responsibility call for. And this applies right across the board—from the youngest firemen to chief officers everywhere.

The problem of due recognition for firemen is as universal as fire itself. The main reward for the men who fight fires is the lip service we pay to their legendary heroism. They must be heroes so that they can carry the can for all our lack of foresight, carelessness or outright criminal negligence, for all our fire prevention deficiencies. Italian firemen, during a Rome demonstration for a better deal, used these internationally applicable slogans: 'Fewer medals and more bread!' and 'You can't live on glory alone!'

Yet we need heroes in the fire service: partly because few communities are willing to pay them in better currency than medals, and partly because, despite all the technical advancement, fire-fighting is still a very ancient skill. For apart from exceptional circumstances and some specific types of fires (like oil or magnesium) when various chemicals and foam must be used to combat the flames, the essentials of fire-fighting are still water and men who apply it from close quarters. The principle is simple: dry fuels burn readily; if the fuel is wet, the heat must evaporate the moisture before ignition becomes possible; if water can be applied at a faster rate than the heat can boil it away, the fire will be extinguished; finally, more water is added to cool the temperature at all surfaces and so make sure that there will be no re-ignition.

The increasing speed and efficiency of this exercise are served by more and more modern equipment—faster, better engines, pumps, ladder trucks, elevated platforms to manoeuvre men into the most advantageous position, special assistance from field communication and searchlight units, sophisticated electronic facilities for speed and full control, mask service vehicles and a vast range of protective clothes and life-saving paraphernalia— but the cost of these is often totally prohibitive particularly to smaller communities. Really effective standardization is there- fore difficult in every country, and the problem is perhaps the most acute in the United States where an admirably sustained determination to preserve local independence or 'home rule' also retains tremendous drawbacks in this respect. Only re- cently, for the $2\frac{1}{2}$-inch hose alone 155 different screw threads were in general use, with the result that brigades from neigh- bouring areas could not fit their couplings and help one another even if they wanted to. Some of the better-off American local authorities are keen to buy the latest, glittering pieces of hard- ware complete with built-in obsolescence, but they tend to forget that extra sophistication and rocketing costs are not always commensurate with the urgent need for substantially improved effectiveness. A disgruntled U.S. fire chief commented: ' . . . we appear to have huge and admittedly beautiful pieces of fire- fighting apparatus when actually all we need in a basic instance is a pumper, a vehicular fire hose carrier, an engine and wheels to get it to the fire location. As a matter of fact almost all fire- fighting equipment in our country is much too heavy and cumbersome.'*

Many American fire officers, however, would be more than happy with that glittering not-quite-worth-the-price machinery . . . as long as it worked. Some of the most dreadful examples of contrast can be found in New York. When Francis Smith was appointed President of the City Council, he toured fire depart- ments and was 'absolutely shocked' at the condition of some of the fire apparatus. Describing a visit to a station in Harlem, one of the busiest in New York, he said, 'I never thought I'd walk into a fire station in January 1969, and have the firemen tell me they always had to push an engine to get it started on a call.'

Several American specialists now want to see some Federal

* Quoted by U.S. Chief Donald Holbrook: 'Economics of the American Fire Service', a paper presented at the Institution of Fire Engineers' forty-fifth annual conference in October 1968.

control introduced, so that it is left not only to insurance company ratings to compel local authorities to invest more in fire defence. Yet nationally-enforced basic requirements for fire brigades cannot quite eliminate the perilously vast differences in standards: there will always be local authorities who hope to get away with the bare minimum. In Spain, for instance, many villages and holiday resorts have such a shortage of fire engines that, in 1970, a young Frenchman's idea paid off handsomely: he converted a van into a mobile water tank with a pump and drove it across the border where he found booming business for his private one-man fire brigade.

In Britain, a centrally controlled system ensures that each area has a fire brigade that satisfies the minimum requirements according to the grading of risk in each locality (it even specifies the number of minutes within which each fire call must be answered), and encourages and guides local authorities in providing more than the bare legally enforced minimum. About ninety-five per cent of the country benefits now from the 'dial 999' system which eliminates dangerous over-reliance on single little stations in godforsaken villages and creates centralized interdependence for the entire fire service. Yet 'blind spots' can still be found, particularly where volunteer or retained part-time firemen supplement (or substitute for) the local professional force.

One of these 'blind spots' was exposed, for instance, at Paignton, the popular family holiday resort in South Devon. Despite repeated warnings from the local branch of the Fire Brigade Union, a lone fireman was again on night duty at the station on September 8, 1969. A fifty-four-year-old man, with a quarter of a century of service behind him, took over at six o'clock in the evening when the day staff left. The following morning he was found dead. It meant that throughout the night, from the moment of his death, the station had been unmanned, and calls, including direct alarms from the local theatre, would have remained unanswered. By the time an emergency caller could have realized that the police or the Torquay fire station ought to be contacted, crucially valuable minutes would have been wasted, causing additional damage and possible loss of life.

On Wednesday, January 27, 1971, there was a warehouse fire in Hornsea, Yorkshire. The alarm was raised but nobody came

to fight the outbreak. Then, at last, the first firemen arrived—
in an ordinary saloon car. Meanwhile, at the local fire station,
an unusual battle was in progress: neither of the two fire
engines would start. The emergency call was then passed on to
another two stations which sent engines to the fire with understandable delay. The *Sheffield Morning Telegraph* quoted a fire
brigade spokesman: 'It is always a problem with heavy
machines when there is a bit of panic. The carburettor gets
flooded, and in this case a battery was flat. We can only assume
that something was left switched on when they had their drill
last Thursday . . .'

Although, in the 1970's, the days of the leather buckets, giant
syringe-like hand-squirts or horse-drawn fire engines may
largely be over, there is still plenty of the medieval about in
fire-fighting, particularly in remote areas even in the richest
countries.

In 1953, writing about pathological fire-setters in the *Journal
of Criminal Law, Criminology and Police Science*,* a psychiatrist
suggested that 'fire-fighting should be deglamorized and removed as far as possible from the category of the thrill and
spectacle. There should be less opportunity for the public to
participate in fires. *The days of volunteer fire fighting are behind
us*—we hope . . .' (Author's italics.)

Alas, those hopes were unfounded. In the 1970's, volunteers
are still part—often an essential part—of our fire defence
system and in an age of specialization such as ours, when firms
prefer even their junior filing clerks to be specialists, in say,
shipping, many people's survival and much of our precious
world are left in the hands of enthusiastic amateurs with shoddy
equipment. Some do it for the thrill, some for the glory, some
for the few coins they earn for a turn-out, some because they
care about the community, but—with the exception of those in
a few countries like Australia, where volunteers are mostly well-
trained and controlled by professionals—the majority of them
still fight fires as their ancestors did 300 years ago.

In some German villages, in the absence of men during the
day, the toll of the church bell calls women volunteers to the
shed where a small pump on wheels is kept. They hitch it to a
borrowed tractor—or pull it to the fire by hand. In Japan,

* Northwestern University School of Law, Nov.–Dec. issue.

Tokyo's scaffolding workers, who also serve as volunteer fire-men, keep up the old routine of doing acrobatics at the top of twenty-foot bamboo poles because they find this impressive circus act a good way to fight fires and even save lives if there are no ladders or only too short ones at hand.

In some villages in Scotland, part-time firemen are convinced that life was much easier a few hundred years ago: at least there were always horses around. Now they have to go begging people to let them borrow a lorry which could transport their pump to fires. A few years ago, men serving 150 square miles of country-side from the Kinloch Rannoch station (a wooden hut with a trailer pump) had a case that ran like the script of a Laurel and Hardy film. A fire was reported and while the men were getting together at 'base', the part-time fire-master phoned round for a lorry. The nearest he could locate was three miles away and the owner said 'come and get it'. So firemen got a taxi to pick up the lorry. On the way back, the lorry ran out of petrol. A second taxi had to be called to go and collect some. The delay: half an hour. The damage: £30,000—most of which could have been saved if they had had an old army-surplus jeep to pull the pump.

The volunteers' devotion has never been in doubt. It was per-haps best illustrated in Upton, Nottinghamshire (population 475), back in 1962. When a wooden building was demolished, a brick wall also had to come down and, behind it, a red cart was found. It then transpired that the building was a fire station. The local volunteer brigade was very active towards the end of the last century: in 1899, they bought a fair length of hose for £26, then added an axe and an oil lamp to the equip-ment, invested £5 in a cart which they painted red in 1904, and built their very own station in 1910. Times began to change with two world wars, but the station remained. Then a unit at Southwell, only a mile away, began to serve Upton, too, and eventually the red cart was bricked up. But the last survivors of the old brigade still considered themselves to be on call. One of them, an eighty-year-old resident, said in 1962: 'We did put out a stack fire or two in the olden days, but things have been a bit peaceful lately.'

In the United States pathetic situations like this result in multi-million-dollar losses. The country has approximately 25,000

fire departments (new ones come into being at a rate of about
300 a year) and, of these, only 3,000 are fully paid, really
professional ones. There are about 2,000 departments where
the key personnel are full-time firemen and they are backed up
by volunteers or 'on call' men. The remaining 20,000 departments are staffed only by volunteers. The choice among these
three types of fire service is purely a local matter. It is foreseen
that, for many years to come, the system of using volunteers will
remain an economic necessity because many local authorities
have insufficient funds or conviction regarding the enormity of
the hazard. Many of the volunteer departments, serving urban
and rural regions, are like social clubs: officers are democratically elected by members each year, and the equipment may be
owned by the municipality or the members. Some local authorities finance the necessary apparatus, while others only contribute towards the cost through a special tax assessment of the
population. Many volunteer brigades must rely entirely, however, on fund-raising activities—like holding fairs or organizing
card parties.

In addition to the more than 100,000 full-time professionals,
there are about a million volunteer firemen in the United States.
Half of the latter receive no compensation for their services.
About a quarter of the volunteers get a small token payment
for each hour spent at a fire or training session. And in some
of the 'clubs' firemen pay an annual fee for their member-
ship. These conditions explain not only why in many communities even the essential fire-fighting equipment is missing, but
also why so little can be demanded from the volunteers: all men
own cars and that gives them freedom of movement, but because they often work up to fifty miles from their fire stations
and cannot get through traffic jams in the same way as fire
engines can, they sometimes miss the show altogether. 'Thus
the daytime availability of volunteers in many communities,
especially in rural areas, is at a frighteningly low point. The
same condition exists when they reach out beyond the home
base for entertainment and social contacts.'*

Yet the worst relic of the past is probably the collection of
'protection money' for some American brigades. The system
comes right out of seventeenth-century England. It was after

* D. Holbrook, op. cit.

the Great Fire of London in 1666 that insurance companies came into being, and these had their own fire brigades. Eventually, each firm had its *fire mark* fixed to properties insured by it. When a brigade arrived at a fire, the chief looked for the mark: if the building was theirs, the men fought the blaze; if it was another company's, they let the house burn and left without delay or stayed on to admire, perhaps ridicule, the rivals' efforts. Many firemen in Britain still believe that the system had great advantages at least in one respect: the people who insured buildings were the same as those who had to protect them from fire; therefore, it was in the insurance companies' direct interest to equip their brigades with the best available at the time, partly for efficiency and partly for the free publicity fire-fighting provided. (Today, firemen are often convinced that numerous buildings would not be insured or only at special premiums if the insurers had to pay for fire-fighting, and also that the brigades would then be much better paid and equipped.)

In North America, Peter Stuyvesant, the last Dutch governor of New Netherlands (now New York), organized the first volunteer fire brigades, in the 1650's. In the early eighteenth century, Benjamin Franklin followed in the steps of Stuyvesant and helped to set up the Union Fire Company, a volunteer brigade in Philadelphia, which served for some eighty years. At about the same time, insurance companies were established along the lines of their English models. The identifying fire marks became a similarly vital feature of the operation, although the American companies usually financed but did not own the brigades. Eventually, the open rivalry between the 'competitors' was replaced by mutual assistance and cooperation—but the spirit survived in areas where volunteer units depend entirely on 'protection money'.

In March 1968, an $18,000 family home caught fire in House Springs, Missouri. The local brigade arrived in due course, inspected the house, found the 'paid-up' tag missing—and watched the flames destroying the building. Firemen explained that the protection premium was their only revenue. Ten days later, another house nearby was burning. The brigade came, but, once again, the premium of seven dollars had not been paid. On this occasion, however, the firemen were not permitted to watch the spectacle: men of the neighbourhood, armed with clubs, guns and rifles, went to the owner's assistance and forced the firemen at gunpoint to put out the fire.*

Even if this case was not really typical, it was far from being unique. And there are many staunch supporters of the belligerent factions in the firemen's unions everywhere who firmly believe that 'ultimately, only something like this blackmailing madness can solve our problems in the regular fire service, too'.

Today, and for several decades past, one of the most pressing problems of professional fire services in most countries is that the brigades are seriously under-staffed: *they have more vacancies* (with sufficient funds to fill them) *than applicants*. The reason is simple: the jobs are not attractive enough to compete with industry for good men. This lack of attraction is, in turn, the result of two factors, one of which is the level of wages, and the other the social status that goes with the job.

We have already referred to the first. With the exception of a very few countries like Germany where the pay is comparable to that in industry, most nations grossly under-pay their firemen. The struggle for a better deal—more money, shorter hours, better conditions—is constant and international, but firemen, like doctors and nurses, suffer the disadvantage of being practically unable to strike. The few who did try to resort to that weapon lost public sympathy overnight. In August 1969, American firemen went on strike in Gary, Indiana, and their six-day industrial action ended with mass-suspension of staff, although even these strikers had specified that they would let unoccupied buildings burn (a $300,000 lumber-yard fire led to scuffles with the police and out-of-town firemen), but would be ready to go into action as soon as lives were threatened.

Firemen therefore had to invent token forms of strikes which were, of course, much less effective. In 1971, a thousand French firemen from all over the country staged a sit-down in the Rue de Rivoli, Paris, to support their claim for better pay and working conditions. In December 1970, two thousand Italian firemen gathered in Rome to take part in a demonstration march, followed by the occupation of fire stations, and a hunger strike. They resorted to this original idea under great moral pressure from the public which they tried to counter-balance with the statement that they would continue to provide emergency

* *Daily Telegraph*, March 28, 1968.

services 'as long as our physical condition permits'. The most effective part of their nation-wide four-day strike was that all airports were paralysed, at least until air force fire crews were brought in to provide a stand-by service on the runways. (In countries where airport firemen belong to an entirely different organization, this weapon is not available to brigades unless solidarity is strong between the services. In Britain, for instance, airport firemen earn almost twice as much as their colleagues elsewhere.)

In the United States and Britain, firemen's strikes are usually restricted to affect only routine chores (like cleaning duties), drills and inspections, so that their main work, answering emergency calls, is continued without interruption. Although these so-called strikes are an almost annual event, British firemen's pay rose by an average of three per cent a year throughout the 1960's—which was, of course, far below the wage increases awarded to industry. (In 1970, they were offered a rise of less than half what was given to dustmen—who were out on strike.) And even when the new American and British pay agreements remedy the most obvious grievances, people tend to forget tha firemen are required to provide continuous gallantry for forty-eight or often fifty-six hours a week.

The other way in which they are left behind by the times is in their current social status. Although children may still run with glittering eyes after fire engines, fewer and fewer youngsters would ever dream about becoming a fireman. In some ways, perhaps, the fire brigades themselves are to blame. While university trained people everywhere are specially invited and lured to all kinds of trades, while in the United States specialist universities train young men aspiring for the top jobs in fire-fighting, in Britain, for instance, the brigades insist that all men must start 'on top of the ladder' and work their way up—even if they wish to end up as top administrators. But the main reason is that the public have subconsciously degraded the job, forgotten about its importance (at least between outbreaks), and come to notice the skill, effort and heroism less than the sweat and dirt that go inevitably with them.

There may be yet another factor. Perhaps the social degradation of firemanship starts right at the top in each country. At times when leaders had the clarity of mind to notice the fire peril, there were Stuyvesants and Franklins to look into the problems of fire defence. At times when fire-fighting was a novelty and in the vogue, it was a hobby, a social event, to participate in the battle and so, incidentally, add glamour to the fireman's chore. (In the nineteenth century, when London's fire brigade was taking shape and growing fast, fire chiefs were much-liked and respected society figures; the Prince of Wales, later King Edward VII, and many aristocrats went to fight fires regularly and they had their own uniforms, helmets and axes at fire stations where they sometimes spent full evenings playing billiards and hoping for a fire call.) All this rubbed off stardust on every ordinary fireman and helped to give them due recognition. Today, kings, queens, presidents and many other dignitaries still like to parade in uniforms—but instead of a fireman's outfit, they choose to appear as fliers, sailors or tank commanders. Do *they* feel that adding some status personally to their fire-fighting troops would perhaps degrade them?

'We're the lowest of the low in the eyes of many, I can tell you that,' an embittered Manchester fireman complained in a sudden outburst. 'And I tell you something else. Considering what bloody shambles this whole fire prevention and fire protection lark is, it's just short of a fucking miracle that we don't lose more men and more buildings through our own doing. But perhaps they just wouldn't care if we did. As long as we carry the can.'

CHAPTER SIXTEEN

THE FLAMING BLUNDER

WHAT CAN be done?

What can authorities and fire specialists do for the public? What can people do for themselves? Judging from the disconsolate results of the past, the futile efforts and the ever-mounting losses, it is obvious that there is no easy, complete and immediate answer.

This book perhaps reflects some of the strain that has been brought on by the ardent attempt at remaining objective in face of bitter and subjective prejudice—the prejudice against senseless killings, injuries and losses, against apathy, acquiescence, stupidity and negligence. Initially, looking at some aspects of the fire peril, and sensing some of the heat of drama and the cool breeze of statistics, the observer becomes puzzled. Then anger takes over as one looks beyond all that. Three years of research and world-wide consultation with authorities inescapably arouse a feeling of outrage. This is, of course, the reaction of the outsider, the layman. The specialist might have experienced the same very early on in his career. Since then, he is bound to have grown accustomed to it: he can now see the brighter sides of the problem, value the minute victories of the day-to-day battle, and, above all, he has learned to respect (even fear and revere?) the enormity of the seemingly insurmountable hurdles. He knows he must and can live with it all.

This book, therefore, aims to be a lay appraisal of the waste and slaughter by flames—a stirring alarm sounded by care. It is not for us outsiders and likely victims to teach specialists their job, but it is for us to call for action when our lives and wealth are threatened.

So what is there to be done?

First of all, it would appear to be vital to introduce a new element of common sense and compassion as a driving force behind the professional effort. Next, we must forget the old folly that it is enough just to warn people, that the long-prescribed panacea of 'educating the public' and 'changing human attitudes to fire' can come out of the odd newspaper article, horror poster, wall-chart, and the pushing of leaflets through letter-boxes. When 'men, women and children' are stubbornly named as the three main causes of fire, when the 'stupid public' gets repeatedly blamed for holocausts and minor disasters, it is the specialist with his educational propaganda programme who gets himself certified as a failure.

An abundance of advice, so full of undoubted goodwill, distributed freely and untiringly by a multitude of fire brigades, accident prevention and fire protection organizations, makes perfectly good sense. It is only that it fails to get through to people. Fund-consuming campaigns, annual fire prevention weeks with maximum publicity exposure, focus some attention on the problem, but the message fails to sink in. It is beyond the scope of this work to analyse why and where the method cannot achieve the desired impact. It may be the short duration of the campaigns. (No advertiser can hope to 'sell the message'—and his product—to everybody, young and old, in a country through a sales drive that can be sustained financially for no more than a week a year.) It may be some special reluctance in people to take advice on a *minor, old and familiar theme* like fire. It may even be due to the suspicion of and resistance to the media. Whatever is the cause of this abysmal failure, it is a fact that the campaigns do not make any visible dent on the fire monster.

A particularly thorough experimental project with telling results was carried out in Britain at the end of 1967. A specially devised, extraordinarily expensive and intensive propaganda campaign with a barrage of maximum publicity was directed at all citizens of Leicester. A market research organization conducted two large-scale series of interviews before and after the experiment. The random sample showed a slight increase in general awareness of the fire peril, and parents appeared to be slightly more concerned as a result. On the other hand, the level of careless behaviour remained unchanged, there was a fractional *decrease* in the proportion of people claiming to have taken special precautions against fire, and the answers to the request 'pick out the four commonest causes of fire' from a list of ten were somewhat *less* accurate at the end of the campaign than before. There was hardly any improvement in practical matters related to dealing with actual outbreaks. People continued to give answers classified in the interviews as 'wholly silly' (like 'if an oil heater flared up or a frying-pan caught fire, you should pick them up and carry them outside the house'—which is the surest way to suffer injuries and cause big fires). People learned more about the services provided by fire brigades from the campaign. Although the propaganda made it clear that the fire brigade would give *free advice* on what fire extinguisher would be best for a particular purpose, there was a marked increase in the number of people who came to believe that the brigade would give them *free fire extinguishers*. The campaign was a non-event. It was its non-effect rather than a detrimental effect that was reflected in the actually negative results.

The regularity of fire prevention weeks may even increase people's resistance to repetitive advice, creating a feeling that 'it's old hat', in the mistaken belief that they *know*, not only have heard, all that before anyway.

Special campaigns, however, with a clear-cut objective, limited to only some aspects of the fire problem, may have good results. One of the few comparative successes concerned the use of *fireworks*. The logical advice backed by wisdom and experience, repeated ad nauseam by firemen and others, failed year after year in all countries. A degree of effectiveness followed only when the truly outraged, desperate and compassionate lay campaigner took a hand. This is what happened in Britain— and, to a lesser extent, in the United States.

Guy Fawkes night, commemorating the anniversary of the Gunpowder Plot, has grown into a meaningless annual jamboree supposedly providing pleasure in the shape of splendid fireworks but, in fact, taking a horrible toll mainly among the children of Britain. When recording of firework accidents began in 1962, the number of serious injuries was close to the one thousand mark. By 1968, this number had fallen to 392, and, in the year after that, there was another forty per cent drop to 250. These figures ignore the fact, of course, that even in 1969, another 2,500 people received hospital treatment, and an additional 10,000—more than half of them under the age of thirteen—were treated for minor burns by their local doctors.

Many of the campaigners were branded as 'killjoys' at first, but even the most devoted fireworks enthusiasts found it difficult to argue with facts and views like those of Harold Taylor, Secretary of Booth Hall Hospital, Manchester, the country's largest burns unit for children, who said: 'It seems extraordinary to me that we can teach our children not to play with fire for three hundred and sixty-four days of the year, and put explosives into their hands on the three hundred and sixty-fifth.' He, among many, accepted the accusation of being a killjoy because, he claimed, 'I'd rather kill joy than children.' (It is, of course, just a 'side-product' of the fireworks that they cause extra fires. In 1970, when Guy Fawkes night coincided with the London dustmen's strike and the streets were covered with litter and piles of rubbish, firemen had their busiest night since the war. Instead of the usual seven or eight hundred outbreaks on that one night, London firemen had to answer 1,500 fire calls stretching their resources to the limit.)

The significance of the successful campaign in Britain may have benefits reaching well beyond the field of fireworks. What factors have contributed to this success? Propaganda and really bitter publicity—sometimes scorned for being 'scandal-mongering' when it is only a benevolent exposure of a true scandal—were one. Another was intensified warnings in schools. A third was the increasingly responsible attitude of the manufacturers: they not only improved the safety of their products, but they also financed a massive campaign to arouse all parents and children against the danger of potential misuse, and other hazards. The fourth factor was that some shops simply stopped selling fireworks; and the fifth was new legislation which banned the direct sale of fireworks to small children. The result was a reduction in sales and an even greater reduction in accidents.

The role schools must play cannot be over-emphasized. Attempts by schoolchildren to make fireworks and other explosives cause dozens of injuries each year. Her Majesty's Inspectors of Explosives believe that many cases of illegal manufacture of explosives are never reported, but often the offenders have learnt the mixtures during chemistry lessons in school without the teachers warning them about the hazards. These lessons are supplemented subsequently by the children's ingenuity. Bernard Levin once recalled in his *Times* column a school incident when an innocent game with fire resulted in the Christmas paper chains going up in flames: somebody discovered that filling a cracked ping-pong ball with methylated spirit would make 'a charming firework'; Levin's own invention led to further improvement—the introduction of lighter-fuel created an 'even more charming firework'—and a few nasty moments for the participants. But, while Levin only progressed from there to becoming a self-confessed flame-fancier ('a forest fire is a thing of terrible beauty'), many others graduated to less innocent pastimes. It was purely fortuitous that merely five weeks after his article had been published in Britain, ping-pong ball firebombs were planted in eight supermarkets in New York's East Harlem and Lower East Side in a single Sunday night in August 1971. It is quite feasible that those bombers, too, learned their basic idea in school: they packed paper containers with ping-pong balls; injected a common inflammable fuel into some of the balls and filled the rest with acid; when the acid ate its way to the fuel, the fires began.

Some Americans have turned similarly basic knowledge of chemistry into a very profitable business—illegal manufacture of fireworks for the traditional July 4 displays. Firework-bootleggers are quick to cash in on the persistent demand that has survived the introduction of legislation which has all but banned fireworks for private use. Roadside stands spring up in New York in June, street vendors sell their contraband wares, a lorry-load of fireworks (usually stolen from manufacturers licensed to produce them for community displays) may reach an inflated street-value of $130,000—and each year about ten thousand people are injured with two or three children dead as a result. Clearly, in this case, good legislation has failed to win the full support of a strong, popular, special campaign.

In contrast, there are the countries where only the usual banal lip-service is being paid to the cause of greater fireworks safety. Sometimes even authorities fail to take the necessary precautions. In March 1971, two people were killed and almost two hundred were injured when, in the Spanish town of Valencia, at the pre-spring Fiesta of Fire, powerful sky-rockets went off with a tremendous bang; but, instead of shooting high to give the usual spectacular fireworks, some exploded in the crowd of onlookers while others rose barely overhead only to fall like mortar bombs back into the square packed tight with people.

Italians like to greet the New Year with gay big bangs and fireworks. It seems to escape their notice that the thousands of merrymakers who get injured each New Year's Eve fail to see the hilarity of the joke. Some half-hearted campaigns are launched periodically against the jolly massacres, but without public backing they do not get far. Legislation fails even to prevent amateur manufacturers from blowing themselves up (each year several families are wiped out when their temporary cellar workshops explode) and from marketing their shoddy goods. Almost a thousand workshops are licensed to manufacture officially tested types of fireworks and bangers, but these cannot satisfy the demand. Southerners augment their income every winter by setting up clandestine workshops in and around Naples where some 30,000 amateurs work with explosives, although, since 1964, nearly 10,000 people have been arrested and charged with this offence. Once again, it is easy to see what essential factors of a successful concentrated fire prevention campaign have been missing from the Italian effort, which is, consequently, still a long way from matching the British results in this field.

Another success came out of a special checklist campaign for Australian householders at the beginning of the bush-fire season ('you should be able to answer "yes" to each question regarding the following precautions . . .'), while the British Insurance Association's similar checklist campaign in 1967 had a very poor response from industry. (Some trade associations expressed no interest in the subject, one refused to deal with it at all because this was 'a matter for the individual firms', and of about 40,000 managing directors who received the lists only 2,000 or five per cent bothered to report on the results—many of these admitted that the lists had no effect on furthering precautions and, presumably, the majority who did not answer paid even less attention to the fire problem.)

Despite the failures, the costly propaganda and education effort continues. As D. I. Lawson said, it should not be abandoned 'because there is no alternative, but some studies will have to be made to see how it can be improved'. The ready-made alternatives may indeed be missing as yet, but certain areas, where desperately needed improvements have long been overdue, are already clearly defined. The first of these is the urgent overhaul of legislation and a thorough speed-up of law-making procedure to keep up with the changing facets of the fire peril. The introduction of more regulations may be wholly unwelcome because they are bound to curtail some rights of the individual, yet they may save lives: dead people have little use for civil liberties. Certain laws can also fight and restrain stupidity—madmen in a frenzy may dislike the strait-jacket but it helps to protect the wearer as well as society.

In other areas, much of the improvement depends on making additional funds available. Fire research and investigation, the evaluation of already functioning services, the development of better fire-fighting and prevention must all wait for more money. Many specialists tend to argue that it is impracticable to talk about finances because nobody is willing to pay more. They say the public does not care enough. They may be right. Perhaps the public, ignorant of the facts and the enormity of the menace, are reluctant to fork out more. But who, of those speaking in the name of 'the public', has gone to the national or local electorate with a straight proposition? What politician has spelled out all the relevant facts and asked if the public is prepared to pay for safety? With the need for detailed explanation of the danger, the vicious circle is closed once again: we are back to the essential requirement of propaganda and education—the two weapons that are the least effective. In this respect, however, major improvement could perhaps be made on three levels.

(1) At places of work, the *unions* ought to take a considerable share of responsibility. They could enforce a higher standard and stricter regularity of the fire drills, a more meticulous observation of precautions; check and demand proper maintenance of means of escape and fire-fighting facilities; and— helping both their own members and management—ensure that no place of work remains a potential fire-trap.

All this, of course, would require from union leaders a much greater interest in fire problems, and from shop stewards a better understanding that fire defence is very much a part of good working conditions and therefore deserves more attention and even militancy. It is no good fighting for more pay, shorter hours and longer holidays if the beneficiaries of a better deal remain exposed to death or maiming injuries by fire.

(2) In the *home* where all the propaganda efforts have so far failed—and there is no reason to expect greater success in the foreseeable future—a more attractive and therefore more widely used advisory service could make a considerable impact. As we have seen, even where fire brigades are ready to offer advice to householders, most people do not know that this help is available. A wide-scale publicity campaign and an ensuing up-surge in general demand from the public would only lead to an immediate and total collapse of the existing system—resources to meet a flood of requests are totally inadequate. If, on the other hand, a new self-supporting service was set up, it could grow with the demand without any further burden on the already overworked and under-strength brigades.

One possibility is to organize a *home advisory service* as an independent section of the fire brigades. Inspectors, specially trained for this service, should not be paid from the usual funds (rates, etc.): the section must be self-supporting with its own income from a fee payable for each visit, say, once every two or three years, by invitation only from the individual householder. Thus the entire system would be voluntary and the inspector's recommendations for simple precautions would not be com-pulsory except in a moral sense.

The charges could be kept low: each inspector could do six or eight visits a day, and apart from his salary, the fees would only have to cover some limited administrative expenses. Publicity could gradually convince people about the advantages of having their homes 'fire-tested'—as old cars are checked for safety. The fee may appear to be a stumbling block, but then it is usually found that booklets and services that are given away free are less appealing than those people must pay for. And, ultimately, the expense could be greatly reduced or even elimi-nated by an arrangement with the insurance companies: the house that has been fire-tested is less likely to burn if the recommendations have been carried out, and even if there is a fire, the damage will probably be less extensive than otherwise; this would reduce the risk the insurers have to take and so a premium reduction would be justified. If the discount equalled only half of the fee, the householder would recover the full cost on two years' premiums. Most probably, however, the reductions could also pay for the mostly inexpensive fire precautions recommended, thus leaving the householder with a safer home —and the insurers with fewer large claims to meet.

(3) Long-term improvement would have to rely on the *education of children*. The various methods of propaganda and re-education of the public at large have a common enemy: the reluctance of people to listen, no matter what good sense the advice may make. The school is the last place where, short of draconian legislation, people must pay attention. It is also the last place where the recipients are conditioned not to be offended by receiving advice.

Today there are many signs of schools returning to the old Roman principle of *non scolae sed vitae discimus*—we do not learn for the school but for life. Schools teach small children the rules of the road. Some forward-looking schools, with the cooperation of police instructors, have made driving a voluntary part of the curriculum for school-leavers. Why not teach fire prevention and self-defence from fire on the same basis with a pass or a diploma as the prize for a successful examination?

Much is already done in schools with better fire prevention in mind. But most of this is rather haphazard, with the odd lecture which teenagers ignore even if they are bound to listen, with the usually rather dull and unimaginative wall-chart that fails to attract and even less hold the students' attention, with elementary games which children regard as no more than that, and with some specially drawn cartoon characters like the American 'Sparky the fire dog' and 'Smokey the bear' whose popularity is grossly over-estimated as a valuable impact of fire prevention and whose natural appeal to children is mistaken for effectiveness. Similar figures have now begun to appear in several countries where authorities claim solemnly that these 'instil in the minds of children and adults alike the meaning and importance of fire safety' and 'help symbolize and dramatize the fire prevention programme', but where, nevertheless, many children told this author that Dog, Bear & Co. are 'funny'. Why are they funny? 'Because they always burn houses and things.' This is not to dispute the fact that entertainment is a good short-cut to children's hearts and therefore a valuable teaching aid, but to emphasize that the message in the fun and games may easily get lost on the very children whom it aims to educate.

As for the older child, serious studies have one place, fun and games have another in the mind. With a recognized place in the curriculum, fire prevention and protection studies would command respect and attention without unduly taxing the already stretched timetable.

In Germany, schools put a great emphasis on teaching road safety—and the results are excellent—but they somewhat neglect the fire hazard. Most schools in English-speaking countries teach some 'fire safety in the home', but frequently, the myth of the cartoon character and the casual participation in the odd fire prevention campaign make teachers and fire experts complacent. As far as can be ascertained, what has been done in Lambeth, the London borough with a population of a third of a million people, is unique.

Instigated by the council's safety officers, Lambeth schools introduced regular fire training for students between the ages of fourteen and sixteen. The course, eight two-hour lectures, ends with an oral examination where students are required to answer any of three hundred standard questions. At first, the failure rate was ten per cent, but this was cut to only five per cent a year later, and most of these succeeded at the second try in winning the coveted certificate.

The course covers a wide range of subjects from essentials of first aid to simple repair jobs done safely, and from the right way of cleaning an oil heater to ways of spotting defects. An important part of the training is to prepare students for emergencies: those who understand what is actually happening in a fire are the least likely to panic, and the most likely to take the right course of action in saving themselves, others and property. The knowledge of what may happen increases caution—and gives self-confidence when something does happen. Students also gain some basic skill in fire-fighting, but the lectures strongly impress the 'no heroes, please!' principle. (In January 1966, a five-year-old London boy, left alone at home, fought a fire for an hour with cups of water. Miraculously, he succeeded, but neither he nor his parents who had taught him 'fire-fighting' understood what a risk he was exposed to by staying in the house and failing to call for help.)

If courses like this were held in every school in all countries, we would eventually live in a society where everybody is aware of the hazard and knows what is right to do when there is a fire. But the system would also have an immediate impact on parents—much more so than current methods of propaganda could ever hope to achieve. This beneficial side-effect was clearly shown in the Lambeth project, which aimed at just that from the start by instructing children to take their questionnaires home and ask parents to test their knowledge and answers to all the three hundred questions. Children were asked to check, with the help of their parents, their own homes for safety and prepare a list of faults they discovered. In Australia, an even more direct way of involving the older generation was devised: children had to ask their parents about the various dangers and fire prevention in their own homes. Undoubtedly, this has caused some embarrassment, but the gentle, well-meaning blackmail forced everyone in the household to pay attention to the problems, particularly when the first challenge was followed up by daily tasks for the children: each day instructions appeared on the blackboard, and pupils had to check how much unwanted rubbish was accumulating in and around the house, how open fires and electric heaters were guarded, how many boxes of matches were accessible to younger brothers and sisters, how mother would react to a fire in a frying-pan, and, among many other measures of fire prevention, how many people in the household knew the correct steps to take in case of a fire.

As one comes to think about the tremendous propaganda effort to educate people, the cost and energy it absorbs appears ridiculously disproportionate to the amount the public would be required to learn. It is all so obvious, so childishly simple, and yet when a very random sample poll (already referred to in Chapter VII) was conducted for this book, most people turned out to be completely ignorant of even elementary self-defence. The questions dealt with the most common situations, asking for instance, 'what would you do if someone's clothes were burning?' Seventy per cent of our sample would have run to fetch some water (thus leaving the victim and his unprotected head exposed to the flames) instead of rolling the human torch in a rug or blanket which would smother the fire.

Most people knew that if there was a fire in the room they

should *not* open the window. Yet one in every five would have opened the window ('to let out the smoke'), thus supplying the flames with fresh oxygen, and there were others who hesitated about what to do, close the window or open it—in a fire, this delay might have killed them.

If that last cigarette or an electric blanket set fire to the bed, what would you do? Almost everybody in the poll would rightly have tried to put out a small fire with water, *but* more than eighty per cent would have forgotten to unplug the electric blanket (also other electric appliances) before applying water; by this omission they might have electrocuted themselves. If the flames were persistent and the fire seemed to be getting out of hand, thirty per cent would have tried to carry the burning bed-clothes and mattress out of the house or throw it all out of the window—a likely way to spread the fire and invite disaster.

The use of doors in the house turned out to be perhaps the most hazardous gap in fire defence. One question in the poll was: if you had to escape out of the house and nobody was following you, would you shut the door behind you or would you leave it open so that others could get out easily? Only thirteen per cent gave the right answer (shut the door to avoid creating draught that would intensify the fire, sweep it up the stairs and trap others in the house), with the rest getting it all wrong (thirty per cent), or saying 'I don't know' or admitting 'I've never thought of it'.

Similarly, most people never thought of shutting the door— and, if possible, the window—when they escape from a room where there is a fire. Even an ordinary panelled timber door may well contain a fire within a room for at least twenty minutes (killer smoke and heat much longer) but certainly long enough for everybody in the house to escape. This is why it is vital to keep all doors in the house shut throughout the night— yet in our sample only three per cent of those asked took this simple life-saving precaution. If you suspect that there is a fire in a room, would you go in to investigate? A third of those who answered were not sure what they would do, and more than a third would have opened the door to go in and investigate— an act that often has disastrous results because of the sudden gush of heat and smoke.

What if you were trapped upstairs with flames, heat and fumes completely cutting off the normal escape route? The right answer would have been to retreat to a room with a window—preferably a bathroom where there is also water—fill the gaps and cracks in the door with towels, rugs, anything handy, then open the window and shout for help, but jump out only in the very last resort. The wrong answers varied a great deal, but there were several common mistakes people would have made. Many would have tried to run through the inferno, disregarding what amounts to a hail of bullets with the presence of carbon monoxide. Others chose to run to a window, open it and shout for help without first closing the door—as if the perfect draught conditions they thus created would not act as an invitation to the fire.

The overwhelming majority in our poll did not make sure that all electrical appliances, including television sets, were unplugged for the night; and hardly anybody knew that if there was nowhere to retreat to and they had to choose between imminent death and a desperate escape attempt, they should crawl on their stomachs rather than run because even in really large fires there is almost always some breathable air within six inches of the floor.

Finally, we asked people about the basic code: if possible, shut the door of the room where the fire is, warn everybody in the house to escape, call the fire brigade. This correct sequence of action was chosen by less than a third of those interviewed in our poll—and many of even these admitted that they were only guessing.

Pathetic? Then what about the psychiatric test made for a recent British court case?* The victim of a road accident claimed to have suffered serious brain damage. In the course of medical examinations, psychiatrists asked him what he would do if he saw a fire in a cinema? The patient would receive no marks if the answer was 'I'd shout FIRE!'—but he would be given full marks for 'I'd go out and find an attendant and inform him of the fire'. The judge accepted that such tests might satisfy the psychiatrist, but he was not impressed because the assumption was that 'a fire will keep nice and low while an attendant is being sought . . .'

* Watt v. Burn, Queen's Bench Division, June 1970.

Yet, don't we all base our lives on a similarly cosy assumption that fire is something that will always happen to somebody else?

With our self-defence non-existent, with the state of our prevention and protection systems in such disarray that it amounts to an international scandal, you are still entitled to believe that the losses are on an acceptable level, that fire deaths are a natural wastage, that the current amount of suffering is inevitable, and that the problem does not yet deserve another thought. If so, sleep well, and rest assured—only a few hundred of us will be wasted tonight.

BIBLIOGRAPHICAL NOTE

Fire in general is such a vast subject that a brief bibliography, short of running to dozens of pages, could only do injustice to it. Lists of selected references (only the titles and authors of books, articles, research notes, regulations, etc.) fill a volume each year, and many of the several thousand entries note the publication of further, more detailed bibliographies related to the literature on some more specialized questions.

To the layman, interested in the subject, the following books are recommended for further reading in English:

Paul L. Kirk: *Fire Investigation*; John Wiley & Sons, Inc.; New York, London, Sydney, Toronto; 1969

H. Rethoret: *Fire Investigations*; Recording and Statistical Corporation, Ltd.; Montreal; 1945

J. Kennedy: *Fire and Arson Investigation*; Investigations Institute; Chicago; 1962

G. V. Blackstone: *A History of the British Fire Service*; Routledge & Kegan Paul; London; 1957

G. Stecher: *Fire Prevention and Protection Fundamentals*; The Spectator; Philadelphia, New York; 1953

B. Benzaquin: *Holocaust*; Pan Books Ltd.; London; 1962

ACKNOWLEDGMENTS

The following is only a short list of the organizations which gave the bulk of the assistance essential in assembling and selecting the vast material for this book. I am most grateful to them for giving me access to their confidential records and case histories, for permission to conduct time-consuming interviews with their officials and various specialists, and for all the guidance, advice and helpful criticism they rendered so patiently throughout the three years of research. I had to omit the names of individuals who helped me, partly because these are too numerous to list, and partly because many, whose cooperation was invaluable, preferred to remain anonymous for various reasons.

I am greatly indebted to many national fire protection associations (particularly those in Britain, the United States, Australia, France, Sweden and Holland);

to fire brigade officials (particularly in New York, San Francisco, Chicago, London HQ, City, Chelsea, Norfolk, Manchester, Sydney, Hamburg, Munich, Cologne, Frankfurt, Paris, Nice, Rheims, Milan, Naples, Brussels, Zurich and Stockholm);

to police officers and forensic scientists in eleven countries, and to the arson squads in New York, Los Angeles, Melbourne, Frankfurt and Munich;

to several airlines (particularly to Qantas, for the detailed account of Australian safety procedures and examples of incident investigation, also to BEA, BOAC, Lufthansa, and SWISSAIR for similar information);

and to numerous other organizations including Britain's Fire Research Station at Boreham Wood for interviews and permission to use their library; Australia's Country Fire Authority for interviews and case histories; Israel's London embassy for details of the Aqsa Mosque fire; the Fire Department of the Home Office with special gratitude to Inspectors of the Fire

Services,; the Fraud and Arson Bureau of the American Insurance Association; the Münchener Rückversicherungs-Gesellschaft; the Institution of Fire Engineers; H. M. Factory Inspectorate; Lloyd's fire insurers; several firms of loss adjusters; and the Vereinigung zur Förderung des Deutschen Brandschutzes.

I also wish to express my thanks to Percy Bugbee, former General Manager of the U.S. National Fire Protection Association and Dipl. Ing. Hans Brunswig, Oberbranddirektor i. R., a Hamburg consultant, for their helpful advice and correspondence; to the editors of numerous specialist journals (particularly the *F.P.A. Journal*, *The Institution of Fire Engineers Quarterly*, *Fire*, *Fire Protection Review*, *Fire News* of the U.S. NFPA, *Fire News* of the Australian FPA, *Canadian Fire Service News*, *American Fire and Arson Investigator*, *V.F.D.B. Zeitschrift*) for the useful guidance and the wealth of information on case histories; and to Maureen Everson, F.P.A. librarian, H. Mumford, London Fire Brigade librarian, for assistance in picture research, and Ann Garai for help in the preparation of the Index.

INDEX

The subjects discussed in this work offer an almost infinite variety of detailed index entries and cross references. Due to limitations of space, these had to be restricted to a system that may help readers with an interest only in certain aspects of the problem (e.g. examples of *School Fires*). For cross reference, there is a *Gazetteer* listing *Countries* and *Places* mentioned in the text.